Wave Propagation in a Turbulent Medium

WAVE PROPAGATION IN A TURBULENT MEDIUM

by V. I. Tatarski
INSTITUTE OF ATMOSPHERIC PHYSICS
ACADEMY OF SCIENCES OF THE USSR

TRANSLATED FROM THE RUSSIAN
by R. A. Silverman

DOVER PUBLICATIONS, INC.
NEW YORK

Published in Canada by General Publishing Company, Ltd., 30 Lesmill Road, Don Mills, Toronto, Ontario.
Published in the United Kingdom by Constable and Company, Ltd., 10 Orange Street, London WC 2.

This Dover edition, first published in 1967, is an unabridged republication of the English translation originally published in 1961 by the McGraw-Hill Book Company, Inc.

Library of Congress Catalog Card Number: 67-26484

Manufactured in the United States of America
Dover Publications, Inc.
180 Varick Street
New York, N. Y. 10014

TRANSLATOR'S PREFACE

This book is a translation of V.I. Tatarski's **"Теория Флуктуационных Явлений При Распространении Волн В Турбулентной Атмосфере"**, literally "The Theory of Fluctuation Phenomena in Propagation of Waves in a Turbulent Atmosphere". It is hoped that Tatarski's book, together with the translation of L.A. Chernov's "Wave Propagation in a Random Medium" (McGraw-Hill Book Co., 1960) will furnish a comprehensive and authoritative survey of the present state of research in the field of wave propagation in turbulent media, with special emphasis on important Russian contributions.

For typographical convenience, the numerous footnotes appearing in the Russian original have been collated in the Notes and Remarks section at the end of the book; I have taken the liberty of adding some remarks of my own, all identified by the symbol T in parentheses. The Russian original has also been supplemented in two other ways: 1) Dr. R.H. Kraichnan has written an Appendix qualifying the material in Chapter 5; 2) In the References section, I have cited some readily available English and German translations of Russian papers. (The origin of one reference, No. 61, was not clear to me.)

The time has come to thank the team of Jacqueline Ellis and Maureen Kelly for their expert performance in preparing the masters for both this book and the Chernov translation. I also take this occasion to thank my wife for her painstaking proofreading of both books.

AUTHOR'S PREFACE

In contemporary radiophysics, atmospheric optics and acoustics, one often studies the propagation of electromagnetic and acoustic waves in the atmosphere; in doing so, it is increasingly often necessary to take into account the turbulent state of the atmosphere, a state which produces fluctuations in the refractive index of the air. In some cases the turbulence manifests itself as atmospheric "noise", causing fluctuations in the parameters of waves propagating through the atmosphere; in other cases the atmospheric turbulence behaves like a source of inhomogeneities which produce scattering. This latter phenomenon has attracted the attention of numerous investigators, since it is connected with the long distance propagation of V.H.F. and U.H.F. radio waves by scattering in the ionosphere and in the troposphere. Thus the problem of "waves and turbulence" is at present one of the important problems of radiophysics, atmospheric optics and acoustics.

In the last decade, a large number of papers pertaining to this problem have been published. These papers are reviewed in the special monograph by D.M. Vysokovski, entitled "Some Topics in the Long Range Tropospheric Propagation of U.H.F. Radio Waves" (Izdat. Akad. Nauk SSSR, Moscow, 1958); this monograph is chiefly concerned with papers by foreign authors. Recently there has also appeared a monograph by L.A. Chernov entitled "Wave Propagation in a Medium with Random Inhomogeneities" (Izdat. Akad. Nauk SSSR, Moscow, 1958).* However, the present monograph differs from those cited in that the author has tried to make more complete and consistent use of the results of turbulence theory.

In recent years the study of turbulence (in particular, atmospheric turbulence) has advanced considerably. In this regard, a large role has been played by the work of Soviet scientists [e.g. 8,9,11-15,17,21,22,30]. However, the results of turbulence theory are often not used in solving problems related to wave propagation in a turbulent atmosphere. In a considerable number of radiophysics and astronomy papers devoted to radio scattering, the twinkling and

---

* Translated by R.A. Silverman as "Wave Propagation in a Random Medium", McGraw-Hill Book Co., New York, 1960. (T)

quivering of stellar images in telescopes, etc., only crude models, which do not correspond to reality, are used to describe the atmospheric inhomogeneities. Naturally, the results obtained in such papers can only be a very rough and purely qualitative description of the properties of wave propagation in the atmosphere.

In the present monograph we try to give a general treatment of the theory of scattering of electromagnetic and acoustic waves and of the theory of parameter fluctuations of short waves propagating in a turbulent atmosphere. We take as our starting point the Kolmogorov theory of locally isotropic turbulence, which gives a sufficiently good description of the turbulent atmosphere. In Part I we give a brief exposition of some topics from the theory of random fields and turbulence theory which are necessary to understand what follows. There we give special attention to the representation of random fields by using generalized spectral expansions. Spectral representations are very appropriate both for formally solving many problems in the theory of wave propagation in a turbulent medium and for interpreting these problems physically.

Part II is devoted to the scattering of electromagnetic waves (Chapter 4) and acoustic waves (Chapter 5) by turbulent atmospheric inhomogeneities. The radio scattering theories of Booker and Gordon, Villars and Weisskopf, and Silverman are studied from a general point of view, as being different special cases which follow from a general formula. In Part III we consider amplitude and phase fluctuations of short waves propagating in a turbulent atmosphere, first fluctuations of a plane wave (Chapters 6 and 7), then amplitude and phase fluctuations of a plane wave in a medium with a smoothly varying "intensity" of turbulence (Chapter 8), and finally fluctuations of a spherical wave (Chapter 9). In Part IV we present some results of experimental studies of atmospheric turbulence (Chapter 10) and the results of experiments on the propagation of sound and light in the layer of the atmosphere near the earth. The results of observations of twinkling and quivering of stellar images in telescopes and the interpretation of these results are given in Chapter 13. In presenting experimental material we give the corresponding theoretical considerations.

Some problems which have much in common with the foregoing have not been considered in this book. Foremost among these is the question of radio scattering by the turbulent ionosphere, despite the fact that the mechanism for this effect has very much in common with that for radio scattering in the troposphere. We did not think it possible to go into the specific details which would have to be considered in studying this phenomenon. We have also not included in this monograph the interesting problem of radiation of sound by a turbulent flow, considered in the papers of Lighthill.

I wish to express my deep gratitude to A.M. Obukhov and A.M. Yaglom for the help they gave me while I was writing this book.

CONTENTS

Part I

SOME TOPICS FROM THE THEORY OF RANDOM FIELDS AND TURBULENCE THEORY

Part II

SCATTERING OF ELECTROMAGNETIC AND ACOUSTIC WAVES IN THE TURBULENT ATMOSPHERE

Part III

PARAMETER FLUCTUATIONS OF ELECTROMAGNETIC AND ACOUSTIC WAVES PROPAGATING IN A TURBULENT ATMOSPHERE

Wave Propagation in a Turbulent Medium

Part I

SOME TOPICS FROM THE THEORY OF RANDOM FIELDS AND TURBULENCE THEORY

Introductory Remarks

The index of refraction of the atmosphere for electromagnetic waves is a function of the temperature and humidity of the air. Similarly, the velocity of sound in the atmosphere is a function of the temperature, wind velocity and humidity. Therefore, in studying microfluctuations of the refractive index of electromagnetic and acoustic waves in the atmosphere, we must first of all explain the basic laws governing the structure of meteorological fields like the temperature, humidity and wind velocity fields.

For us the most important fact about the atmosphere is that it is usually in a state of turbulent motion. The values of the wind velocity at every point of space undergo irregular fluctuations; similarly, the values of the wind velocity taken at different spatial points at the same instant of time also differ from one another in a random fashion. What has been said

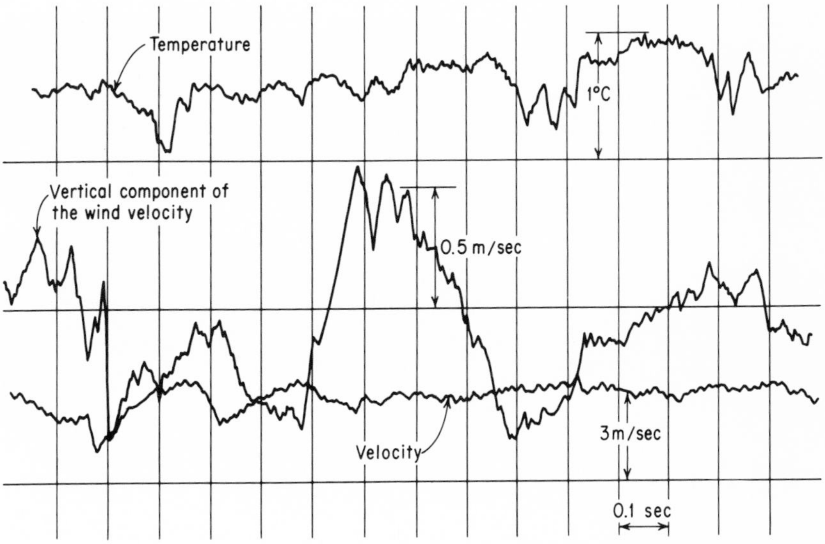

Fig. 1 Simultaneous record of temperature and wind velocity.

applies as well to all other meteorological quantities, in particular to temperature and humidity. In Fig. 1 we give as an example a sample of the record of the instantaneous values of the wind velocity and the temperature at one point, obtained by using a low inertia measuring device. We see that both of these quantities undergo irregular oscillations, which differ in amplitude and frequency and are superimposed in a random manner. It is natural that statistical methods are used to describe the laws characterizing the structure of such fluctuating quantities.

Chapter 1

METHODS FOR STATISTICAL DESCRIPTION OF CONTINUOUS RANDOM FIELDS [a]

1.1 Stationary random functions

The curves shown in Fig. 1 serve as examples of realizations of random functions. The value of any such function $f(t)$ at a fixed instant of time is a random variable, i.e. can assume a set of different values, where there exists a definite probability $F(t,f_1)$ that $f(t) < f_1$. But to completely specify the random function $f(t)$ it is not enough to know only the probability $F(t,f_1)$; one must also know all possible multidimensional probability distributions, i.e. all the probabilities

$$F(t_1,t_2,\ldots,t_N;f_1,f_2,\ldots,f_N) = \tag{1.1}$$

$$= P\left[f(t_1) < f_1, f(t_2) < f_2,\ldots,f(t_N) < f_N\right]$$

that the inequalities $f(t_1) < f_1$, $f(t_2) < f_2,\ldots,f(t_N) < f_N$ hold simultaneously for all possible N and $t_1,t_2,\ldots,t_N$, $f_1,f_2,\ldots,f_N$. However, in the applications it is usually difficult to determine all the functions (1.1). Therefore in practice, instead of the distribution function (1.1), one ordinarily uses much more "meager" (but much simpler) characteristics of the random field. Of these statistical characteristics of the random function $f(t)$, which are widely used in practice, the most important and simplest is the mean value $\overline{f(t)}$ [b]. The next simplest and very important characteristic of the function is its correlation function $B_f(t_1,t_2)$ [c].

$$B_f(t_1,t_2) = \overline{\left[f(t_1) - \overline{f(t_1)}\right]\left[f^*(t_2) - \overline{f^*(t_2)}\right]}. \tag{1.2}$$

It is clear that the relation $B(t_1,t_2) = B(t_2,t_1)$ holds for real functions f. The correlation function vanishes when the quantities $f(t_1) - \overline{f(t_1)}$ and $f(t_2) - \overline{f(t_2)}$ are statistically independent, i.e., when the fluctuations of the quantity $f(t)$ at the times t_1 and t_2 are not related to each other. In this case the mean value of the product in the right hand side of

(1.2) factors into the product of the quantities

$$\overline{f(t_1) - \overline{f(t_1)}} \quad , \quad \overline{f^*(t_2) - \overline{f^*(t_2)}} \, ,$$

each of which equals zero. Thus, the correlation function $B_f(t_1,t_2)$ characterizes the mutual relation between the fluctuations of the quantity $f(t)$ at different instants of time. In analogy to the correlation function $B_f(t_1,t_2)$, one can also construct more complicated characteristics of the random field $f(t)$, for example, the quantities

$$B_N = \overline{\left[f(t_1) - \overline{f(t_1)}\right]\left[f(t_2) - \overline{f(t_2)}\right]\cdots\left[f(t_N - \overline{f(t_N)}\right]}.$$

However, we shall use only the mean value $\overline{f(t)}$ and the correlation function $B_f(t_1,t_2)$.

The mean value of a function can be a constant or can change with time (for example, as the wind gradually increases, the mean value of the wind velocity $\overline{u(\vec{r},t)}$ at any point $\vec{r}$ increases). Similarly, the correlation function $B_f(t_1,t_2)$ can either depend only on the "distance" between the times t_1 and t_2 (in which case the statistical relation between the fluctuations of the quantity f at different instants of time does not change in the course of time) or else it can depend also on the positions of these points on the time axis. A random function $f(t)$ is called stationary [d] if its mean value $\overline{f(t)}$ does not depend on the time and if its correlation function $B_f(t_1,t_2)$ depends only on the difference $t_1 - t_2$, i.e. if

$$\overline{f(t)} = \text{const}, \; B_f(t_1,t_2) = B_f(t_1 - t_2) = B_f(t_2 - t_1). \tag{1.3}$$

It is easy to show that $B_f(\tau)$ satisfies the condition $|B_f(\tau)| \leq B_f(0)$. We shall always assume below that the mean value of a stationary random function $f(t)$ is zero [e].

For stationary random functions $f(t)$ there exist expansions similar to the expansions of non-random functions in Fourier integrals, namely a stationary random function can be represented in the form of a stochastic (random) Fourier-Stieltjes integral with random complex amplitudes $d\varphi(\omega)$ [1]:

$$f(t) = \int_{-\infty}^{\infty} e^{i\omega t} d\varphi(\omega). \tag{1.4}$$

Using the expansion (1.4) we can obtain an expansion of the correlation function $B_f(t_1 - t_2)$ of the stationary random function f(t) in the form of a Fourier integral. In fact, substituting the expansion (1.4) in the left hand side of (1.2), we obtain

$$B_f(t_1 - t_2) = \overline{f(t_1)f^*(t_2)} = \int\int_{-\infty}^{\infty} \exp[i(\omega_1 t_1 - \omega_2 t_2)] \overline{d\varphi(\omega_1)d\varphi^*(\omega_2)}.$$

Since in the stationary case the correlation function must depend only on the difference $t_1 - t_2$, the quantity $\overline{d\varphi(\omega_1)d\varphi^*(\omega_2)}$ must have the following form [f]:

$$\overline{d\varphi(\omega_1)d\varphi^*(\omega_2)} = \delta(\omega_1 - \omega_2)W(\omega_1)d\omega_1 d\omega_2, \tag{1.5}$$

where, obviously, $W(\omega) \geq 0$. From this it follows that [g]

$$B_f(t_1 - t_2) = \int_{-\infty}^{\infty} \exp[i\omega(t_1 - t_2)]\ W(\omega)d\omega, \tag{1.6}$$

i.e., the functions $B_f(\tau)$ and $W(\omega)$ are Fourier transforms of each other. Thus, the Fourier transform of a correlation function $B_f(\tau)$ must be nonnegative; if it is negative at even one point, this means that the function $B_f(\tau)$ cannot be the correlation function of any stationary random function f(t). Khinchin [6] showed that the converse assertion is also true: if the Fourier transform of the function $B_f(\tau)$ is nonnegative, then there exists a stationary random function f(t) with $B_f(\tau)$ as its correlation function. This fact, which we shall use below, makes it easy to construct examples of correlation functions. When the specified conditions are met, the non-random function $W(\omega)$ is called the spectral density of the stationary random function f(t).

We now explain the physical meaning of the spectral density. For example, let f(t) represent a current flowing through a unit resistance. Then $[f(t)]^2$ is the instantaneous power dissipated in this resistance, and the mean value of this power is $\overline{[f(t)]^2} = B_f(0)$. Using Eq. (1.6), we obtain

$$\overline{|f(t)|^2} = \int_{-\infty}^{\infty} W(\omega)d\omega.$$

Thus, in this case $W(\omega)$ represents the spectral density of the power, so that in the literature of radiophysics this function is often called the noise power spectrum. In the case where $f(t)$ is the magnitude of the velocity vector of a fluid, $W(\omega)$ represents the spectral density of the energy of a unit mass of fluid, so that in the literature of turbulence theory this function is often called the spectral density of the energy distribution.

We now give some examples of correlation functions and their spectral densities.

a) The correlation function

$$B(\tau) = a^2 \exp(-|\tau/\tau_o|) \tag{1.7}$$

is often used in the applications. The corresponding spectral density is easily found to be

$$W(\omega) = \frac{1}{2\pi} \int_{-\infty}^{\infty} e^{-i\omega\tau} a^2 \exp(-|\tau/\tau_o|)d\tau = \frac{a^2\tau_o}{\pi(1 + \omega^2\tau_o^2)} . \tag{1.8}$$

Here $W(\omega) > 0$, so that the function $a^2\exp(-|\tau/\tau_o|)$ can actually be the correlation function of a stationary random process.

b) The correlation function

$$B(\tau) = a^2 \exp\left[-a(\tau/\tau_o)^2\right] \tag{1.9}$$

corresponds to the spectral density

$$W(\omega) = \frac{a^2\tau_o}{2\sqrt{\pi}} \exp(-\frac{\omega^2}{4}\tau_o^2). \tag{1.10}$$

c) To the spectral density

$$W(\omega) = \frac{a^2\Gamma(\nu + \frac{1}{2})}{\sqrt{\pi}\,\Gamma(\nu)} \frac{\tau_o}{(1 + \omega^2\tau_o^2)^{\nu + \frac{1}{2}}} > 0 , \quad \nu > -\frac{1}{2} , \tag{1.11}$$

corresponds the correlation function

$$B(\tau) = \frac{a^2}{2^{\nu-1}\,\Gamma(\nu)} \left(\frac{\tau}{\tau_o}\right)^{\nu} K_\nu\left(\frac{\tau}{\tau_o}\right) , \quad \tau > 0, \quad \left(B(0) = a^2\right) , \tag{1.12}$$

where $K_\nu(x)$ is the Bessel function of the second kind of imaginary argument. This correlation function is also used in some applications.

In Fig. 2 we show how the correlation functions (1.7), (1.9) and (1.12) depend on τ/τ_o, and in Fig. 3 we show the corresponding spectral densities.

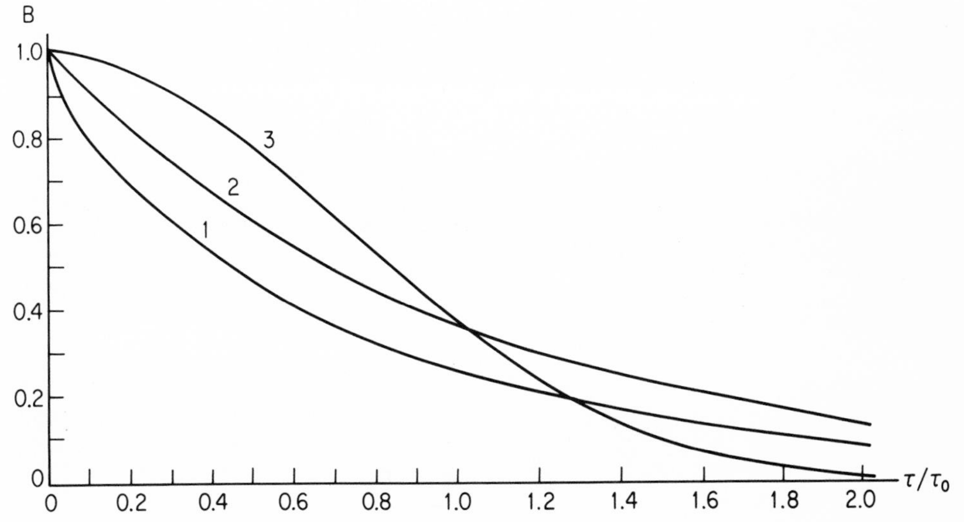

Fig. 2 The correlation functions

1) $\frac{2^{2/3}}{\Gamma(1/3)} \left(\frac{\tau}{\tau_o}\right)^{1/3} K_{1/3}(\tau/\tau_o)$;

2) $e^{-\tau/\tau_o}$; 3) $e^{-(\tau/\tau_o)^2}$.

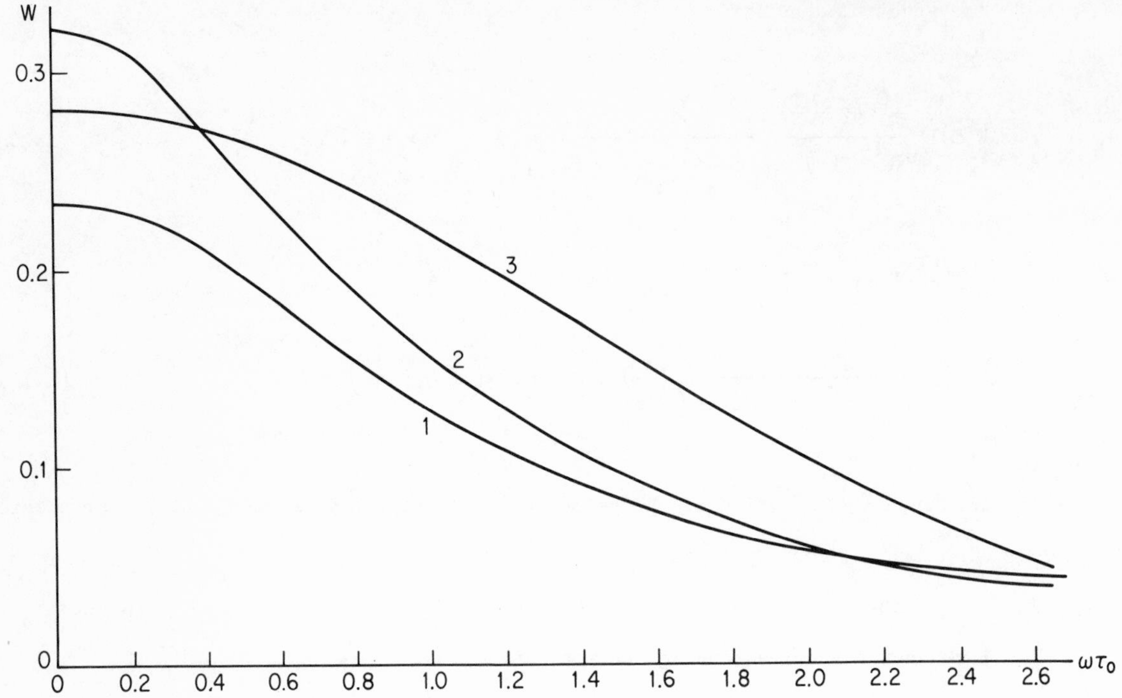

Fig. 3 The spectral densities of the correlation functions of Fig. 2.

The time τ_o required for an appreciable decrease in the correlation function, for example, the time in which $B(\tau)$ falls to 0.5 or 0.1 of the value $B(0)$, is called the correlation time. As can be seen from the examples considered, the quantity τ_o is related to the "width" ω_o of the spectrum (i.e. to the frequency at which the spectral density $W(\omega)$ falls off appreciably) by the relation $\omega_o \tau_o \sim 1$.

1.2 Random functions with stationary increments

Actual random processes can very often be described with sufficient accuracy by using stationary random functions. An example of such a process is the fluctuating voltage appearing across a resistance in a state of thermodynamic equilibrium with the surrounding medium. However, the opposite case can also occur, where the random processes cannot be regarded as stationary. As an example of such a process in radiophysics we cite the phase fluctuations of a vacuum tube oscillator [7]. Such examples also occur very often in meteorology. For example, as already noted, as the strength of the wind gradually increases, the mean value of the velocity at any point increases, so that in this case the wind velocity is not a stationary random function. The mean values of other meteorological variables of the atmosphere, e.g., temperature, pressure and humidity, also undergo comparatively slow and smooth changes. In analyzing these variables the same difficulty continually arises, i.e., which changes of the function $f(t)$ are to be regarded as changes of the mean value and which are to be regarded as slow fluctuations? Such characteristics of a random function as the mean square fluctuation, the correlation time, the shape of the correlation function $B(\tau)$ and of the spectral density $W(\omega)$, very often depend to a considerable extent on the answer to this question.

To avoid this difficulty and to describe random functions which are more general than stationary random functions, in turbulence theory one uses instead of correlation functions (1.2) the so-called structure functions, first introduced in the papers of Kolmogorov [8,9]. The basic idea behind this method consists of the following. In the case where $f(t)$ represents a non-stationary random function, i.e., where $\overline{f(t)}$ changes in the course of time, we can consider instead of $f(t)$ the difference $F_\tau(t) = f(t + \tau) - f(t)$. For values of τ which are not too large, slow changes in the function $f(t)$ do not affect the value of this difference, and it can be a stationary random function of time, at least approximately. In the case where $F_\tau(t)$ is a stationary random function, the function $f(t)$ is called a random function with stationary first increments, or simply a random function with stationary increments [h].

If we use the algebraic identity

$$(a - b)(c - d) = \frac{1}{2}[(a - d)^2 + (b - c)^2 - (a - c)^2 - (b - d)^2],$$

then we can represent the correlation function of the increments in the following form:

$$B_F(t_1, t_2) = \overline{F_\tau(t_1)F_\tau(t_2)} = \frac{1}{2}\overline{[f(t_1 + \tau) - f(t_2)]^2} +$$

$$+ \frac{1}{2}\overline{[f(t_1) - f(t_2 + \tau)]^2} - \frac{1}{2}\overline{[f(t_1 + \tau) - f(t_2 + \tau)]^2} - \frac{1}{2}\overline{[f(t_1) - f(t_2)]^2}.$$

Thus $B_F(t_1,t_2)$ is expressed as a linear combination of the functions

$$D_f(t_i,t_j) = \overline{[f(t_i) - f(t_j)]^2}. \tag{1.13}$$

The function (1.13) of the arguments t_i and t_j, where t_i and t_j take the values $t_1 + \tau$, t_1, t_2, $t_2 + \tau$, is called the structure function of the random process. In order for $B_F(t_1,t_2)$ to depend only on $t_1 - t_2$, it is sufficient that $D_f(t_1,t_2)$ depend only on this difference, i.e., that the relation $D_f(t_1,t_2) = D_f(t_1 - t_2)$ holds.

The structure function $D_f(\tau) = \overline{[f(t + \tau) - f(t)]^2}$ is the basic characteristic of a random process with stationary increments. Roughly speaking, the value of $D_f(\tau)$ characterizes the intensity of those fluctuations of $f(t)$ with periods which are smaller than or comparable with τ. Of course, the function $D_f(\tau)$ can also be constructed for ordinary stationary functions, which are a special case of functions with stationary increments. If $f(t)$ is a stationary random function with mean value 0, then

$$D_f(\tau) = \overline{[f(t + \tau) - f(t)]^2} = \overline{[f(t + \tau)]^2} + \overline{[f(t)]^2} - \overline{2f(t + \tau)f(t)}.$$

It follows from the stationarity of $f(t)$ that

$$\overline{[f(t)]^2} = \overline{[f(t + \tau)]^2} = B_f(0).$$

Thus, for a stationary process

$$D_f(\tau) = 2[B_f(0) - B_f(\tau)]. \tag{1.14}$$

In the case where $B_f(\infty) = 0$ (and in practice this condition is almost always met), we have $D_f(\infty) = 2B_f(0)$. This relation allows us to express the correlation function $B_f(\tau)$ in terms of the structure function $D_f(\tau)$, i.e.

$$B_f(\tau) = \frac{1}{2} D_f(\infty) - \frac{1}{2} D_f(\tau). \tag{1.14'}$$

Thus, in the case of stationary random processes, the structure functions $D_f(\tau)$ can be used along with the correlation functions, and in some cases their use is even more appropriate [i].

As we have already seen, the expansion

$$B_f(\tau) = \int_{-\infty}^{\infty} e^{i\omega\tau} W(\omega)\,d\omega = \int_{-\infty}^{\infty} \cos(\omega\tau) W(\omega)\,d\omega \tag{1.6}$$

is valid for the correlation function of a stationary random process. From this we can obtain a similar expansion for the corresponding structure function. Indeed, substituting (1.6) in (1.14), we obtain

$$D_f(\tau) = 2 \int_{-\infty}^{\infty} (1 - \cos \omega\tau) W(\omega)\,d\omega. \tag{1.15}$$

It turns out that the same expansion is also valid for the structure function of the general random function with stationary increments, the only difference being that the spectral density $W(\omega)$ can now have a singularity at the origin (in this regard see below).

Just as a stationary random function can be represented as a stochastic Fourier-Stieltjes integral

$$f(t) = \int_{-\infty}^{\infty} e^{i\omega t}\, d\varphi(\omega), \tag{1.4}$$

a random function with stationary increments can be represented in the form

$$f(t) = f(0) + \int_{-\infty}^{\infty} (1 - e^{i\omega t})\,d\varphi(\omega), \tag{1.16}$$

where $f(0)$ is a random variable, and the amplitudes $d\varphi(\omega)$ obey the condition

$$\overline{d\varphi(\omega_1)d\varphi^*(\omega_2)} = \delta(\omega_1 - \omega_2) W(\omega_1)\,d\omega_1 d\omega_2. \tag{1.17}$$

Substituting the expansion (1.16) in the right hand side of (1.13) and using the relation (1.17), we obtain

$$D_f(t_1 - t_2) = \overline{[f(t_1) - f(t_2)]^2} = \overline{[f(t_1) - f(t_2)][f^*(t_1) - f^*(t_2)]} =$$

$$= \int\int_{-\infty}^{\infty} (e^{i\omega_1 t_2} - e^{i\omega_1 t_1})(e^{-i\omega_2 t_2} - e^{-i\omega_2 t_1}) \overline{d\varphi(\omega_1) d\varphi^*(\omega_2)} =$$

$$= 2 \int_{-\infty}^{\infty} [1 - \cos \omega(t_2 - t_1)] W(\omega) d\omega. \qquad (1.15')$$

Thus, the expansion (1.15) for the structure function of a stationary random process is also valid for a random process with stationary increments. Since the spectral density $W(\omega)$ which figures in (1.15) signifies the average spectral density of the power (or energy) of the fluctuations, it is natural to assume that the spectral density $W(\omega)$ figuring in (1.15') for processes with stationary increments has the same physical meaning. We note that for convergence of the integral (1.6) it is necessary that the integral

$$\int_{-\infty}^{\infty} W(\omega) d\omega$$

exist, i.e., that the power of the fluctuations be finite. On the other hand the integral (1.15) also converges when $W(\omega)$ has a singularity at zero of the form $\omega^{-\alpha}$ $(\alpha < 3)$, i.e., when the low frequency components of the fluctuation spectrum have infinite "energy" [j].

We now consider some examples.

a) We construct the structure function of the stationary random process considered in example c) on page 7. Using the formula $D_f(\tau) = 2[B_f(0) - B_f(\tau)]$, we obtain

$$D_f(\tau) = 2a^2 \left[1 - \frac{2^{1-\nu}}{\Gamma(\nu)} \left(\frac{\tau}{\tau_o}\right)^{\nu} K_{\nu}\left(\frac{\tau}{\tau_o}\right) \right].$$

For $\tau \ll \tau_o$ we can use the first two terms of the series expansion of the function $K_\nu(x)$ [k]. After some simple calculations we obtain

$$D_f(\tau) = 2a^2 \frac{\Gamma(1-\nu)}{\Gamma(1+\nu)} \left(\frac{\tau}{2\tau_o}\right)^{2\nu},$$

i.e. $D_f(\tau) \sim \tau^{2\nu}$. For $\tau \sim \tau_o$ the growth of the function $D_f(\tau)$ slows down, and it approaches the constant $2a^2$. The spectral density corresponding to $D_f(\tau)$ is the same as in the example on page 7.

b) Consider the spectral density $W(\omega) = A|\omega|^{-(p+1)}$, $(A > 0,\ 0 < p < 2)$. Substituting this function in Eq. (1.15) and carrying out the integration [ℓ], we obtain

$$D_f(\tau) = \frac{2A\pi}{\sin\frac{\pi p}{2}\,\Gamma(1+p)}\,\tau^p.$$

Thus to the structure function

$$D_f(\tau) = c^2\,\tau^p \quad (0 < p < 2)$$

corresponds the spectral function

$$W(\omega) = \frac{\Gamma(1+p)}{2\pi} \sin\frac{\pi p}{2}\, c^2 |\omega|^{-(p+1)}.$$

With $\nu = p/2$ and

$$\frac{a^2}{\tau_o^{2\nu}} = \frac{2^{2\nu-1}\,\Gamma(1+\nu)}{\Gamma(1-\nu)}\, c^2,$$

the structure function considered in the preceding example coincides with the structure function $c^2\,\tau^p$ for $\tau \ll \tau_o$. The spectra of these structure functions coincide in the region $\omega\tau_o \gg 1$. Fig. 4 shows the structure functions of examples a) and b), and Fig. 5 shows their spectra.

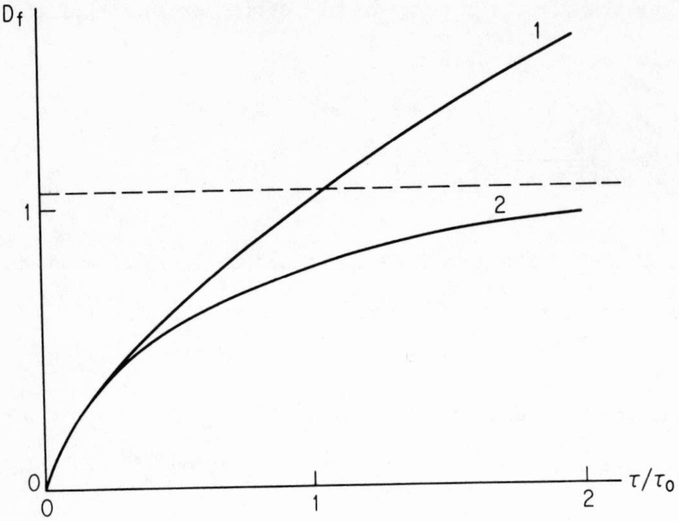

Fig. 4 The structure functions:

$$1)\quad \frac{1}{\tau_o^{2/3}}\,\tau^{2/3}$$

$$2)\quad \text{const.}\left[1 - \frac{2^{2/3}}{\Gamma(1/3)}\left(\frac{\tau}{\tau_o}\right)^{1/3} K_{1/3}\left(\frac{\tau}{\tau_o}\right)\right]$$

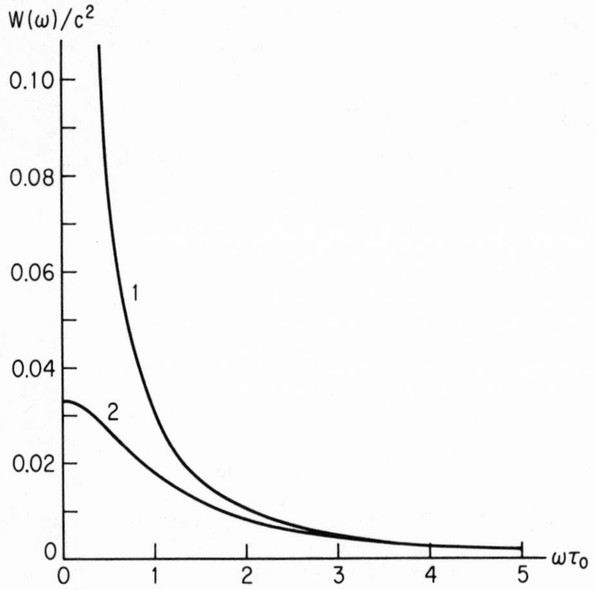

Fig. 5 The spectral densities of the structure functions of Fig. 4.

1.3 Homogeneous and isotropic random fields

We turn now to random functions of three variables (random fields). The concept of a random field is completely analogous to the concept of a random process. Examples of random fields are the wind velocity field in the turbulent atmosphere (a vector random field comprising three random velocity components), and the (scalar) fields of temperature, humidity and dielectric constant. For a random field $f(\vec{r})$ we can also define the mean value $f(\vec{r})$ and the correlation function

$$B_f(\vec{r}_1,\vec{r}_2) = \overline{[f(\vec{r}_1) - \overline{f(\vec{r}_1)}][f(\vec{r}_2) - \overline{f(\vec{r}_2)}]}. \tag{1.18}$$

In the case of random fields the concept of stationarity generalizes to the concept of homogeneity. A random field is called homogeneous if its mean value is constant and if its correlation function does not change when the pair of points $\vec{r}_1$ and $\vec{r}_2$ are both displaced by the same amount in the same direction, i.e. if

$$\overline{f(\vec{r})} = \text{const}, \quad B_f(\vec{r}_1,\vec{r}_2) = B_f(\vec{r}_1 + \vec{r}_0,\ \vec{r}_2 + \vec{r}_0).$$

Choosing $\vec{r}_0 = -\vec{r}_2$ in the last formula, we find that $B_f(\vec{r}_1,\vec{r}_2) = B_f(\vec{r}_1 - \vec{r}_2,\ 0)$ in a homogeneous field, i.e., the correlation function of a homogeneous random field depends only on $\vec{r}_1 - \vec{r}_2$, so that $B_f(\vec{r}_1,\vec{r}_2) = B_f(\vec{r}_1 - \vec{r}_2)$. A homogeneous random field is called isotropic if $B_f(\vec{r})$ depends only on $r = |\vec{r}|$, i.e. only on the distance between the observation points. Of course, a homogeneous field may also not be isotropic; for example, the field with correlation function of the form

$$B_f(\vec{r}_1 - \vec{r}_2) = B_f[\alpha(x_1 - x_2) + \beta(y_1 - y_2) + \gamma(z_1 - z_2)],$$

is homogeneous, but not isotropic.

If in a homogeneous and isotropic field we single out any straight line and consider the values of the field only along this line, then as a result we obtain a random function of one variable x, to which we can apply all the results pertaining to stationary random functions.

In particular, we can expand the correlation function as a Fourier integral.

$$B_f(x) = \int_{-\infty}^{\infty} \cos(\kappa x)\, V(\kappa)d\kappa. \tag{1.19}$$

However it is more natural to use three-dimensional expansions. A homogeneous random field can be represented in the form of a three-dimensional stochastic Fourier-Stieltjes integral:

$$f(\vec{r}) = \iiint_{-\infty}^{\infty} e^{i\vec{\kappa}\cdot\vec{r}}\, d\varphi(\kappa_1,\kappa_2,\kappa_3). \tag{1.20}$$

Here the amplitudes $d\varphi(\vec{\kappa})$ satisfy the relation [m]

$$\overline{d\varphi(\vec{\kappa}_1)d\varphi^*(\vec{\kappa}_2)} = \delta(\vec{\kappa}_1 - \vec{\kappa}_2)\Phi(\vec{\kappa}_1)d\vec{\kappa}_1 d\vec{\kappa}_2, \tag{1.21}$$

where $\Phi(\kappa) \geqq 0$. Substituting this expansion in the formula

$$B_f(\vec{r}_1 - \vec{r}_2) = \overline{f(\vec{r}_1)f(\vec{r}_2)}$$

(assuming that $\overline{f(\vec{r})} = 0$) and taking into account the relation (1.21), we obtain

$$B_f(\vec{r}_1 - \vec{r}_2) = \iiint_{-\infty}^{\infty} \exp[i\vec{\kappa}\cdot(\vec{r}_1 - \vec{r}_2)]\Phi(\vec{\kappa})d\vec{\kappa}. \tag{1.22}$$

$\Phi(\vec{\kappa}) = \Phi(-\vec{\kappa})$, since $B(\vec{r}_1 - \vec{r}_2) = B(\vec{r}_2 - \vec{r}_1)$, so that the formula can also be written in the form

$$B_f(\vec{r}) = \iiint_{-\infty}^{\infty} \cos(\vec{\kappa}\cdot\vec{r})\, \Phi(\vec{\kappa})d\vec{\kappa}. \tag{1.23}$$

The function $\Phi(\vec{\kappa})$ can be expressed in terms of $B(\vec{r})$:

$$\Phi(\vec{\kappa}) = \frac{1}{(2\pi)^3} \iiint_{-\infty}^{\infty} \cos (\vec{\kappa}\cdot\vec{r}) B_f(\vec{r}) d\vec{r}. \tag{1.24}$$

Thus, the functions $B_f(\vec{r})$ and $\Phi(\vec{\kappa})$ are Fourier transforms of each other.

If the random field $f(\vec{r})$ is isotropic, the function $B_f(\vec{r})$ depends only on $|\vec{r}|$. Then in the integral (1.24) we can introduce spherical coordinates and carry out the angular integrations. As a result we obtain the expression

$$\Phi(\vec{\kappa}) = \frac{1}{2\pi^2\kappa} \int_0^{\infty} r B_f(r) \sin (\kappa r) dr, \tag{1.25}$$

where $\kappa = |\vec{\kappa}|$. Thus, in an isotropic random field the spectral density $\Phi(\vec{\kappa})$ is a function of only one variable, the magnitude of the vector $\vec{\kappa}$. This allows us to simplify the expression (1.23) in the case of an isotropic field. Introducing spherical coordinates in the space of the vector $\vec{\kappa}$ and carrying out the angular integrations, we obtain the relation

$$B_f(r) = \frac{4\pi}{r} \int_0^{\infty} \kappa \Phi(\kappa) \sin (\kappa r) d\kappa. \tag{1.26}$$

It should be noted that the three-dimensional spectral density $\Phi(\kappa)$ of an isotropic random field is related to the one-dimensional spectral density $V(\kappa)$ by the simple relation

$$\Phi(\kappa) = - \frac{1}{2\pi\kappa} \frac{dV(\kappa)}{d\kappa} , \tag{1.27}$$

which can be obtained by substituting (1.19) in the right hand side of (1.25) [n].

We now give some examples of spatial correlation functions and their spectra:

a) $$B_f(r) = a^2 \exp \left[- \left| \frac{r}{r_0} \right| \right] . \tag{1.28}$$

Using the results of example a) on page 6 and the fact that the expansion (1.19) is completely analogous to the expansion (1.6) for a stationary random process, we can write down immediately the one-dimensional spectral density $V(\kappa)$:

$$V(\kappa) = \frac{a^2 r_o}{\pi(1 + \kappa^2 r_o^2)} . \qquad (1.29)$$

We use Eq. (1.27) to determine $\Phi(\kappa)$:

$$\Phi(\kappa) = \frac{a^2 r_o^3}{\pi^2(1 + \kappa^2 r_o^2)^2} . \qquad (1.30)$$

b) Similarly, for the correlation function

$$B(r) = a^2 \exp\left[- \left(\frac{r}{r_o}\right)^2\right] \qquad (1.31)$$

we obtain

$$V(\kappa) = \frac{a^2 r_o}{2\sqrt{\pi}} \exp\left[- \frac{\kappa^2 r_o^2}{4}\right]$$

and

$$\Phi(\kappa) = \frac{a^2 r_o^3}{8\pi\sqrt{\pi}} \exp\left[- \frac{\kappa^2 r_o^2}{4}\right]. \qquad (1.32)$$

c) Finally, for the correlation function

$$B(r) = \frac{a^2}{2^{\nu-1}\Gamma(\nu)} \left(\frac{r}{r_o}\right)^{\nu} K_{\nu}\left(\frac{r}{r_o}\right) , \quad r > 0, \qquad (1.33)$$

we have

$$V(\kappa) = \frac{a^2\Gamma(\nu + \frac{1}{2})}{\sqrt{\pi}\,\Gamma(\nu)} \frac{r_o}{(1 + \kappa^2 r_o^2)^{\nu + \frac{1}{2}}} \qquad (1.34)$$

and

$$\Phi(\kappa) = \frac{\Gamma(\nu + \frac{3}{2})}{\pi\sqrt{\pi}\,\Gamma(\nu)} \frac{a^2 r_o^3}{(1 + \kappa^2 r_o^2)^{\nu + \frac{3}{2}}} . \tag{1.35}$$

1.4 Locally homogeneous and isotropic random fields

It should be noted that it is a very rough approximation to regard actual meteorological fields as homogeneous and isotropic random fields. Atmospheric turbulence always contains large scale components which usually destroy the homogeneity and isotropy of the fields of the meteorological variables; moreover, these components cause the meteorological fields to be non-stationary. Thus, there is a close relation between the non-stationarity, inhomogeneity and anisotropy of the meteorological field of an atmospheric variable; basically they are due to the same causes. Therefore, in analyzing the spatial structure of meteorological fields (and some others) it is again appropriate to apply the method of structure functions. In fact, the difference between the values of the field $f(\vec{r})$ at two points $\vec{r}_1$ and $\vec{r}_2$ is chiefly affected only by inhomogeneities of the field f with dimensions which do not exceed the distance $|\vec{r}_1 - \vec{r}_2|$. If this distance is not too large, the largest inhomogeneities have no effect on $f(\vec{r}_1) - f(\vec{r}_2)$ and therefore the structure function

$$D_f(\vec{r}_1,\vec{r}_2) = \overline{[f(\vec{r}_1) - f(\vec{r}_2)]^2} \tag{1.36}$$

can depend only on $\vec{r}_1 - \vec{r}_2$. At the same time, the value of the correlation function $B_f(\vec{r}_1,\vec{r}_2)$ is affected by inhomogeneities of all scales, so that for the same values $\vec{r}_1$ and $\vec{r}_2$ the function $B_f(\vec{r}_1,\vec{r}_2)$ can depend on each of the arguments separately and not just on the difference $\vec{r}_1-\vec{r}_2$. Thus, we arrive at the concept of local homogeneity [8]. The random field $f(\vec{r})$ is called locally homogeneous in the region G if the distribution functions of the random variable $f(\vec{r}_1) - f(\vec{r}_2)$ are invariant with respect to shifts of the pair of points $\vec{r}_1,\vec{r}_2$, as long as these points are located in the region G. Thus, the mean value $\overline{f(\vec{r}_1) - f(\vec{r}_2)}$ and the structure function (1.36) of a locally homogemeous random field depend only on $\vec{r}_1- \vec{r}_2$:

$$D_f(\vec{r}_1 - \vec{r}_2) = \overline{[f(\vec{r}_1) - f(\vec{r}_2)]^2}. \tag{1.37}$$

A locally homogeneous random field is called locally isotropic in the region G if the distribution functions of the quantity $f(\vec{r}_1) - f(\vec{r}_2)$ are invariant with respect to rotations and mirror reflections of the vector $\vec{r}_1 - \vec{r}_2$, as long as the points $\vec{r}_1$ and $\vec{r}_2$ are located in G [8]. The structure function of a locally isotropic random field depends only on $|\vec{r}_1 - \vec{r}_2|$:

$$D_f(\vec{r}) = \overline{[f(\vec{r} + \vec{r}_1) - f(\vec{r}_1)]^2} = D_f(r). \tag{1.38}$$

A locally homogeneous random field $f(\vec{r})$ can be represented in a form similar to (1.16):

$$f(\vec{r}) = f(0) + \iiint_{-\infty}^{\infty} (1 - e^{i\vec{\kappa}\cdot\vec{r}})d\varphi(\vec{\kappa}). \tag{1.39}$$

Here f(0) is a random variable, and the random amplitudes $d\varphi(\vec{\kappa})$ satisfy the relation

$$\overline{d\varphi(\vec{\kappa}_1)d\varphi^*(\vec{\kappa}_2)} = \delta(\vec{\kappa}_1 - \vec{\kappa}_2)\Phi(\vec{\kappa}_1)d\vec{\kappa}_1 d\vec{\kappa}_2, \tag{1.40}$$

where $\Phi(\vec{\kappa}) \geqq 0$ is the spectral density of the random field f. Substituting the expansion (1.39) in Eq. (1.37) and using the relation (1.40), we obtain

$$D_f(\vec{r}) = 2 \iiint_{-\infty}^{\infty} (1 - \cos \vec{\kappa}\cdot\vec{r})\Phi(\vec{\kappa})d\vec{\kappa}. \tag{1.41}$$

In the case where the field f is locally isotropic, $D_f(\vec{r}) = D_f(r)$ and $\Phi(\vec{\kappa}) = \Phi(\kappa)$. In this case

$$D_f(r) = 8\pi \int_0^{\infty} (1 - \frac{\sin \kappa r}{\kappa r}) \Phi(\kappa)\kappa^2 d\kappa. \tag{1.42}$$

It should be noted that the integral (1.42) also converges in the case where $\Phi(\kappa)$ has a singularity at zero of the type $\kappa^{-\alpha}$ ($\alpha < 5$), which corresponds to the case where the large-scale components of the turbulence have infinite energy [j].

We can also examine a locally isotropic field along any line in space. The corresponding expansion of the field f has a form similar to the expansion of a random function with stationary increments. In this case the expansion of the structure function is similar to Eq. (1.15):

$$D_f(r) = 2 \int_{-\infty}^{\infty} (1 - \cos \kappa r)\, V(\kappa) d\kappa . \tag{1.43}$$

The functions $\Phi(\kappa)$ and $V(\kappa)$ are connected by the same relation as in the case of an isotropic random field:

$$\Phi(\kappa) = - \frac{1}{2\pi\kappa} \frac{dV}{d\kappa} . \tag{1.44}$$

In addition to the expansions (1.39) and (1.42) of a locally isotropic random field and its structure function as three-dimensional Fourier integrals, we shall also use two-dimensional expansions in the plane x = const:

$$f(x,y,z) = f(x,0,0) + \iint_{-\infty}^{\infty} \left\{1 - \exp\left[i(\kappa_2 y + \kappa_3 z)\right]\right\} d\psi(\kappa_2,\kappa_3,x) . \tag{1.45}$$

Here $f(x,0,0)$ is a random function and $\psi(\kappa_2,\kappa_3,x)$ obeys the relation

$$\overline{d\psi(\kappa_2,\kappa_3,x) d\psi^*(\kappa_2',\kappa_3',x')} =$$

$$= \delta(\kappa_2 - \kappa_2')\delta(\kappa_3 - \kappa_3')F(\kappa_2,\kappa_3,|x - x'|)d\kappa_2 d\kappa_3 d\kappa_2' d\kappa_3' . \tag{1.46}$$

Consider the difference of the values of $f(x,y,z)$ at two points of the plane x = const. Using the expansion (1.45) we obtain

$$f(x,y,z) - f(x,y',z') = \iint_{-\infty}^{\infty} \left\{ \exp[i(\kappa_2 y' + \kappa_3 z')] - \exp[i(\kappa_2 y + \kappa_3 z)] \right\} d\psi(\kappa_2,\kappa_3,x).$$

We calculate the correlation function of two such differences taken in the planes x and x':

$$\overline{[f(x,y,z) - f(x,y',z')][f(x',y,z) - f(x',y',z')]} =$$

$$= \overline{[f(x,y,z) - f(x,y',z')][f^*(x',y,z) - f^*(x',y',z')]} =$$

$$= \iiiint_{-\infty}^{\infty} \left\{ \exp[i(\kappa_2 y' + \kappa_3 z')] - \exp[i(\kappa_2 y + \kappa_3 z)] \right\} \left\{ \exp[-i(\kappa_2' y' + \kappa_3' z')] - \right.$$

$$\left. - \exp[-i(\kappa_2' y + \kappa_3' z)] \right\} \overline{d\psi(\kappa_2,\kappa_3,x) d\psi^*(\kappa_2',\kappa_3',x')}.$$

Using Eq. (1.46), we obtain

$$\overline{[f(x,y,z) - f(x,y',z')][f(x',y,z) - f(x',y',z')]} =$$

$$= 2 \iint_{-\infty}^{\infty} \left\{ 1 - \cos[\kappa_2(y - y') + \kappa_3(z - z')] \right\} \times$$

$$\times F(\kappa_2,\kappa_3,|x - x'|) d\kappa_2 d\kappa_3. \qquad (1.47)$$

Clearly, correlation between the difference $f(x,y,z) - f(x,y',z')$ and $f(x',y,z) - f(x',y',z')$ is produced only by those inhomogeneities with scales exceeding the distance $|x - x'|$ between the planes, i.e. $\ell \geq |x - x'|$. Since the wave number $\kappa \sim 2\pi/\ell$ corresponds to the scale ℓ, correlation between these differences is caused only by that part of the spectrum for which the wave numbers obey the condition $\kappa|x - x'| \lesssim 1$. Consequently, the function $F(\kappa_2,\kappa_3,|x-x'|)$, which is the spectral density of the quantity

$$\overline{[f(x,y,z) - f(x,y',z')][f(x',y,z) - f(x',y',z')]},$$

falls off rapidly for $\kappa|x - x'| > 1$. Using the algebraic identity

$$(a - b)(c - d) = \tfrac{1}{2}[(a - d)^2 + (b - c)^2 - (a - c)^2 - (b - d)^2],$$

we can express the left hand side of Eq. (1.47) in terms of the structure function of the field f, with the result that the formula takes the following form:

$$D_f(x - x', y - y', z - z') - D_f(x - x', 0,0) =$$

$$= 2 \iint_{-\infty}^{\infty} \left(1 - \cos[\kappa_2(y - y') + \kappa_3(z - z')]\right) \times$$

$$\times F(\kappa_2,\kappa_3,|x - x'|)d\kappa_2 d\kappa_3. \tag{1.48}$$

Setting $x = x'$, $y - y' = \eta$, $z - z' = \zeta$, we obtain

$$D_f(0,\eta,\zeta) = 2 \iint_{-\infty}^{\infty} [1 - \cos(\kappa_2\eta + \kappa_3\zeta)]F(\kappa_2,\kappa_3,0)d\kappa_2 d\kappa_3, \tag{1.49}$$

i.e., the function $F(\kappa_2,\kappa_3,0)$ is the two-dimensional spectral density of the quantity $D_f(0,\eta,\zeta)$. In the case of local isotropy in the plane x = const, $F(\kappa_2,\kappa_3,|x|)$ depends only on $\kappa = \sqrt{\kappa_2^2 + \kappa_3^2}$ and then [o]

$$D_f(\rho) = 4\pi \int_0^{\infty} [1 - J_0(\kappa\rho)]F(\kappa,0)\kappa d\kappa . \tag{1.50}$$

Here $\rho^2 = \eta^2 + \zeta^2$ and $F(\kappa_2,\kappa_3,0) = F(\sqrt{\kappa_2^2 + \kappa_3^2}\,,\ 0)$. In the case where the field $f(\vec{r})$ is homogeneous and isotropic in the plane x = const, its correlation function in this plane can be expressed in terms of $F(\kappa,0)$ by using the formula

$$B_f(\rho) = 2\pi \int_0^\infty J_o(\kappa\rho)F(\kappa,0)\kappa d\kappa. \tag{1.51}$$

The function $F(\kappa,x)$ of a locally isotropic random field can be expressed in terms of its three-dimensional spectral density $\Phi(\kappa)$. Substituting the expansion (1.41) in the left hand side of (1.48) and using the evenness of the function $\Phi(\kappa_1,\kappa_2,\kappa_3)$ in κ_1, we obtain the relation

$$F(\kappa_2,\kappa_3,x) = \int_{-\infty}^{\infty} \cos(\kappa_1 x)\ \Phi(\kappa_1,\kappa_2,\kappa_3)d\kappa_1. \tag{1.52}$$

Inverting this Fourier integral, we find

$$\Phi(\kappa_1,\kappa_2,\kappa_3) = \frac{1}{2\pi} \int_{-\infty}^{\infty} F(\kappa_2,\kappa_3,x)\cos(\kappa_1 x)dx. \tag{1.53}$$

We now consider some examples of structure functions.

a) The structure function of a homogeneous and isotropic random field can be expressed in terms of its correlation function by using the formula

$$D_f(r) = 2B_f(0) - 2B_f(r). \tag{1.54}$$

Setting (see example c on page 18)

$$B_f(r) = \frac{a^2}{2^{\nu-1}\,\Gamma(\nu)} \left(\frac{r}{r_o}\right)^\nu K_\nu\left(\frac{r}{r_o}\right)$$

here, we obtain

$$D_f(r) = 2a^2\left[1 - \frac{1}{2^{\nu-1}\Gamma(\nu)} \left(\frac{r}{r_o}\right)^\nu K_\nu\left(\frac{r}{r_o}\right)\right]. \qquad (1.55)$$

The spectral density corresponding to (1.55) is

$$\Phi(\kappa) = \frac{\Gamma(\nu + \frac{3}{2})}{\pi\sqrt{\pi}\,\Gamma(\nu)} \frac{a^2 r_o^3}{(1 + \kappa^2 r_o^2)^{\nu + \frac{3}{2}}}. \qquad (1.35)$$

For $r \ll r_o$

$$D_f(r) \sim 2a^2 \frac{\Gamma(1 - \nu)}{\Gamma(1 + \nu)} \left(\frac{r}{2r_o}\right)^{2\nu},$$

i.e.

$$D_f(r) \sim r^{2\nu}.$$

b) Consider the structure function

$$D_f(r) = c^2 r^p \quad (0 < p < 2). \qquad (1.56)$$

The one-dimensional spectral density corresponding to this function (see example b on page 13) is

$$V(\kappa) = \frac{\Gamma(p + 1)}{2\pi} \sin\frac{\pi p}{2}\, c^2\, \kappa^{-(p + 1)}. \qquad (1.57)$$

We use the relation (1.44) to find the three-dimensional spectral density $\Phi(\kappa)$:

$$\Phi(\kappa) = -\frac{1}{2\pi\kappa}\frac{dV}{d\kappa} = \frac{\Gamma(p + 2)}{4\pi^2} \sin\frac{\pi p}{2}\, c^2\, \kappa^{-(p + 3)}. \qquad (1.58)$$

We also calculate the two-dimensional spectral density $F(\kappa,x)$ corresponding to the structure function $c^2 r^p$. Substituting the expression (1.58) in the right hand side of Eq. (1.52) and carrying out the integration, we obtain [p]

$$F(\kappa,x) = \frac{c^2}{\pi^2} \sin\frac{\pi p}{2}\, 2^{\frac{p}{2}-1}\, \Gamma\left(1+\frac{p}{2}\right) \frac{(\kappa x)^{1+\frac{p}{2}} K_{1+\frac{p}{2}}(\kappa x)}{\kappa^{p+2}} . \tag{1.59}$$

Since for $z \gg 1$, $K_\nu(z) \sim \sqrt{\pi/2z}\, e^{-z}$, for $\kappa x \gg 1$ the function (1.59) rapidly approaches zero, which corresponds to the abovementioned property of the function $F(\kappa,x)$.

For

$$\nu = \frac{p}{2}\ , \quad \frac{a^2}{r_o^{2\nu}} = \frac{2^{2\nu-1}\,\Gamma(1+\nu)}{\Gamma(1-\nu)}\, c^2\ ,$$

the structure function of the preceding example coincides with the structure function $c^2 r^p$ for $r \ll r_o$. The spectra of these functions agree for $\kappa r_o \gg 1$ (see Fig. 3).

Chapter 2

THE MICROSTRUCTURE OF TURBULENT FLOW

Introductory Remarks

In what follows we shall repeatedly need basic information about the statistical properties of developed turbulent flow. The statistical theory of turbulence, which was initiated in the papers of Friedmann and Keller, has undergone great development in the last two decades. A very important advance was achieved in the year 1941, when Kolmogorov and Obukhov established the laws which characterize the basic properties of the microstructure of turbulent flow at very large Reynolds numbers; some years later certain foreign scientists (Onsager, von Weizsäcker, Heisenberg) arrived at the same results. In this chapter we present only those results of the Kolmogorov theory which are most important for our purposes, and refer to the original sources [8,9,11-16] for more detailed information.

2.1 Onset and development of turbulence

Consider an initially laminar flow of a viscous fluid. This flow can be characterized by the values of the kinematic viscosity ν, the characteristic velocity scale v and the characteristic length L. The quantity L characterizes the dimensions of the flow as a whole, and arises from the boundary conditions of the fluid dynamics problem. The laminar flow of the fluid is stable only in the case where the Reynolds number $Re = vL/\nu$ does not exceed a certain critical value Re_{cr}. As the number Re is increased (e.g. by increasing the velocity of the flow) the motion becomes unstable. This stability criterion can be explained by the following simple considerations.

Suppose that for some reason or other a velocity fluctuation v'_ℓ occurs in a region of size ℓ of the basic laminar flow. The characteristic period $\tau = \ell/v'_\ell$ which corresponds to this fluctuation specifies the order of magnitude of the time required for the occurrence of the fluctuation. The energy (per unit mass) of the given fluctuation is v'^2_ℓ. Thus, when the velocity fluctuation under consideration occurs, the amount of energy per unit time which goes over from the initial flow to the fluctuational motion is equal in order of magnitude to

$v_\ell'^2/\tau \sim v_\ell'^3/\ell$. On the other hand, the local velocity gradients of our fluctuation are given by the ratio v_ℓ'/ℓ, and therefore the energy dissipated as heat per unit mass of the fluid per unit time is of the order of magnitude $\epsilon = \nu v_\ell'^2/\ell^2$. If the velocity fluctuation which arises is to exist, it is clearly necessary that the inequality $v_\ell'^3/\ell > \nu v_\ell'^2/\ell^2$ hold, i.e.

$$\frac{v_\ell'^3/\ell}{\nu v_\ell'^2/\ell^2} = \frac{\ell v'_\ell}{\nu} = Re_\ell > 1.$$

Since all these calculations are accurate only to within undetermined numerical factors, it would be more correct to write the relation we have just obtained in the form $Re_\ell > Re_{cr}$. Here Re_ℓ denotes the "inner" Reynolds number corresponding to fluctuations of size ℓ, and Re_{cr} is some fixed number which cannot be determined precisely. These considerations show that, generally speaking, large perturbations, corresponding to large values of the number Re_ℓ, are most easily excited. But if the condition $vL/\nu > Re_{cr}$ is not met for the flow as a whole, then the laminar motion is stable.

Let us assume that as the number Re is gradually increased the laminar motion loses stability and there occur velocity fluctuations v_ℓ' with geometric dimensions ℓ. If the initial number $Re = vL/\nu$ was only a little larger than Re_{cr}, then the fluctuations which arise have small velocities and $Re_\ell = v_\ell'\ell/\nu < Re_{cr}$, i.e., the velocity fluctuations which occur are stable. As $Re = vL/\nu$ is increased further, the velocities of the fluctuations which occur increase and their inner Reynolds number Re_ℓ may exceed the critical value. This means that the "first order" velocity fluctuations which arise lose stability themselves and can transfer energy to new "second order" fluctuations. As the number Re is increased further the "second order" fluctuations become unstable, and so on.

Let the geometrical dimensions of the smallest fluctuations which occur be ℓ_o, and let their velocities be v_o. For all the velocity fluctuations with sizes $\ell > \ell_o$ the inner number Re_ℓ is large (exceeds Re_{cr}). It follows from this that their direct energy dissipation is small compared to the energy which they receive from larger perturbations; thus, these fluctuations transfer almost all the energy they receive to smaller perturbations. Consequently, the quantity $v_\ell'^3/\ell$, which represents the energy per unit mass received per unit time by eddies of the n'th order from eddies of the (n-1)'th order and transferred by them to eddies of the (n+1)'th order, is constant for perturbations of almost all sizes (with the exception of the very smallest). In the smallest velocity perturbations with sizes ℓ_0, this energy is converted into heat. The rate of dissipation of energy into heat is determined by the local velocity gradients in these smallest perturbations, i.e. is of order $\epsilon \sim \nu v_0^2/\ell_0^2$. Thus, for velocity fluctuations of all scales, except the very smallest, we have $v_\ell'^3/\ell \sim \epsilon$ and

$$v_\ell' \sim (\epsilon\ell)^{1/3}, \tag{2.1}$$

i.e., the size of the fluctuational energy belonging to perturbations with sizes of the order ℓ is proportional to $\ell^{1/3}$. Moreover, for all scales the size of these fluctuations depends only on one parameter, the energy dissipation rate ϵ.

We now calculate the dimension ℓ_0 of the smallest inhomogeneities. For them the relations $v_0 \sim (\epsilon\ell_0)^{1/3}$ and $\nu v_0^2/\ell_0^2 \sim \epsilon$ hold. Solving this system of equations, we find that

$$\ell_0 \sim \sqrt[4]{\frac{\nu^3}{\epsilon}}, \quad v_0 \sim \sqrt[4]{\nu\epsilon}. \tag{2.2}$$

The quantity ℓ_0 can also be expressed in terms of the dimensions of the largest eddies L, which are comparable with the dimension of the flow as a whole. Since $v_L^3/L \sim \epsilon$, then substituting this expression for ϵ in Eq. (2.2) we obtain

$$\ell_0 \sim \frac{L}{(Re)^{3/4}}, \quad v_0 \sim \frac{v_L}{(Re)^{1/4}}. \tag{2.3}$$

Thus, the larger the Reynolds number of the flow as a whole, the smaller the size of the velocity inhomogeneities which can arise.

The considerations given above are essentially only of a qualitative nature, but they can be used as the basis for constructing a more rigorous theory.

2.2 Structure functions of the velocity field in developed turbulent flow

The largest eddies which arise as a result of the instability of the basic flow are of course not isotropic, since they are influenced by the special geometric properties of the flow. However these special properties no longer influence the eddies of sufficiently high order, and therefore there are good grounds for considering the latter to be isotropic. Since eddies with dimensions much larger than $|\vec{r}_1 - \vec{r}_2|$ do not influence the two point velocity difference $\vec{v}(\vec{r}_1) - \vec{v}(\vec{r}_2)$, then for values of $|\vec{r}_1 - \vec{r}_2|$ which are not very large, this difference will depend only on isotropic eddies. Thus, we arrive at the scheme of a locally isotropic random field. Since the field $\vec{v}(\vec{r})$ is a vector field, it is characterized by a set of nine structure functions (instead of by one structure function) composed of the different components of the vector $\vec{v}$:

$$D_{ik}(\vec{r}) = \overline{(v_i - v_i')(v_k - v_k')}. \qquad (2.4)$$

Here i,k = 1,2,3, the v_i are the components with respect to the x,y,z axes of the velocity vector at the point $\vec{r}_1$, and the v_i' are the components of the velocity at the point $\vec{r}_1' = \vec{r}_1 + \vec{r}$.

It follows from the local isotropy of the velocity field that $D_{ik}(\vec{r})$ has the form (see e.g. [14,15,16])

$$D_{ik}(\vec{r}) = [D_{rr}(r) - D_{tt}(r)]n_i n_k + D_{tt}\delta_{ik}, \qquad (2.5)$$

where $\delta_{ik} = 1$ for $i = k$, $\delta_{ik} = 0$ for $i \neq k$, and the n_i are the components of the unit vector directed along $\vec{r}$. $D_{rr} = \overline{(v_r - v_r')^2}$, where v_r is the projection of the velocity at the point $\vec{r}_1$ along the direction of $\vec{r}$, and v_r' is the same quantity at the point $\vec{r}_1' = \vec{r}_1 + \vec{r}$; $D_{tt} = \overline{(v_t - v_t')^2}$, where v_t is the projection of the velocity at the point $\vec{r}_1$ along some direction perpendicular to the vector $\vec{r}$, and v_t' is the same quantity at the point $\vec{r}_1'$. D_{rr} is called the longitudinal structure function and D_{tt} the transverse structure function of the velocity field. In the case where the velocities v are small compared to the velocity of sound, the motion of the fluid can be regarded as incompressible. In this case div $\vec{v} = 0$. It follows from this relation that the tensor $D_{ik}(\vec{r})$ satisfies the condition

$$\frac{\partial D_{ik}}{\partial x_i} = 0,$$

where we sum from 1 to 3 with respect to repeated indices. Substituting from Eq. (2.5), we find that

$$D_{tt} = \frac{1}{2r}\frac{d}{dr}(r^2 D_{rr}). \tag{2.6}$$

Thus, the tensor D_{ik} is determined by the single function $D_{rr}(r)$ (or $D_{tt}(r)$). For values of r which are not very large, the form of the function $D_{rr}(r)$ can be established by using the qualitative considerations developed above.

Let r be large compared to the inner scale ℓ_o of the turbulence (i.e. compared to the size of the smallest eddies) and small compared with the outer scale L of the turbulence (i.e. compared to the size of the largest, anisotropic eddies). Then the velocity difference at the points $\vec{r}_1$ and $\vec{r}_1' = \vec{r}_1 + \vec{r}$ is mainly due to eddies with dimensions comparable to r. As explained above, the only parameter which characterizes such eddies is the energy dissipation rate ϵ. Thus, we can assert that $D_{rr}(r)$ is a function only of r and ϵ, i.e. $D_{rr}(r) = F(r,\epsilon)$. But the only combination of the quantities r and ϵ with the dimensions of velocity squared is the quantity $(\epsilon r)^{2/3}$, and it is impossible to construct dimensionless combinations of these quantities. Thus, we arrive at the conclusion that D_{rr} is proportional to $(\epsilon r)^{2/3}$, i.e.

$$D_{rr}(r) = C(\epsilon r)^{2/3} \qquad (\ell_o \ll r \ll L), \tag{2.7}$$

where C is a dimensionless constant of order unity [a].

We can arrive at the same conclusion by starting with Eq. (2.1). In fact,

$$D_{rr}(r) = \overline{[v_r(\vec{r}_1 + \vec{r}) - v_r(\vec{r}_1)]^2}$$

is mainly due to eddies with sizes r, i.e. $D_{rr}(r) \sim v_r^2$. But by (2.1) $v_r \sim (\epsilon r)^{1/3}$, whence we again arrive at (2.7). Eq. (2.7) was first obtained by Kolmogorov and Obukhov [8,11] and bears the name of the "two-thirds law". Using the relation (2.6) we can also obtain the quantity $D_{tt}(r)$:

$$D_{tt}(r) = \frac{4}{3}C(\epsilon r)^{2/3} \qquad (\ell_o \ll r \ll L). \tag{2.8}$$

We now consider the value of the structure functions for $r \ll \ell_o$. In this case the changes of velocity occur smoothly, since now the relative motions are laminar. The velocity difference $v_r(\vec{r}_1) - v(\vec{r}_1 + \vec{r})$ can therefore be expanded as a series of powers of the quantity r. Retaining only the first non-vanishing term of the expansion, we obtain

$$v_r(\vec{r}_1) - v_r(\vec{r}_1 + \vec{r}) = \vec{\alpha}\cdot\vec{r},$$

where $\vec{\alpha}$ is a constant vector. From this we find that

$$D_{rr}(r) = ar^2$$

for $r \ll \ell_o$, where a is some constant. The quantity a can be related to the quantities ν and ϵ by a more careful argument (see e.g. [8,14]). It turns out that

$$D_{rr}(r) = \frac{1}{15}\frac{\epsilon}{\nu} r^2 \quad (r \ll \ell_o). \tag{2.9}$$

It follows from (2.6) that in this case

$$D_{tt}(r) = \frac{2}{15}\frac{\epsilon}{\nu} r^2 \quad (r \ll \ell_o). \tag{2.10}$$

Thus

$$D_{rr}(r) = \begin{cases} C\epsilon^{2/3} r^{2/3} & (\text{for } r \gg \ell_o), \\ \frac{1}{15}\frac{\epsilon}{\nu} r^2 & (\text{for } r \ll \ell_o), \end{cases}$$

$$D_{tt}(r) = \begin{cases} \frac{4}{3} C\epsilon^{2/3} r^{2/3} & (\text{for } r \gg \ell_o), \\ \frac{2}{15}\frac{\epsilon}{\nu} r^2 & (\text{for } r \ll \ell_o). \end{cases} \tag{2.11}$$

In Eqs. (2.11) it is assumed that $r \ll L$, where L is the outer scale of the turbulence. Further hypotheses are needed to determine the form of the functions D_{rr} and D_{tt} for intermediate values of the argument r (see [12] and [13]).

When r is increased, the condition $r \ll L$ is violated. Then the large eddies, which cannot be regarded as isotropic and homogeneous, begin to influence the value of $v_r(\vec{r}_1) - v_r(\vec{r}_1+\vec{r})$. In this case, the structure functions D_{rr} and D_{tt} depend on the coordinates of both observation points, and no universal law can be given which describes the structure functions for large values of r. We can only state that the growth of the structure functions $D_{rr}(r)$ and $D_{tt}(r)$ slows down for $r \gg L$ [b]. Fig. 6 shows the general shape of the function $D_{rr}(r)$. For small values of r, the curve can be replaced by a parabola with great accuracy, then the part of the curve corresponding to the "two-thirds law" begins, and finally, in the region of the outer scale of the turbulence, the curve starts to "saturate". The dashed parts of the curve show the asymptotic behavior of the function $D_{rr}(r)$ for $r \ll \ell_o$ and $r \gg \ell_o$. To make more precise the definition of ℓ_o, the inner scale of the turbulence, we shall call the inner scale of the turbulence that value of r for which the functions $\epsilon r^2/15\nu$ and $C\epsilon^{2/3}r^{2/3}$ intersect, i.e.

$$\ell_o = \sqrt[4]{\frac{(15\ C\nu)^3}{\epsilon}} . \tag{2.12}$$

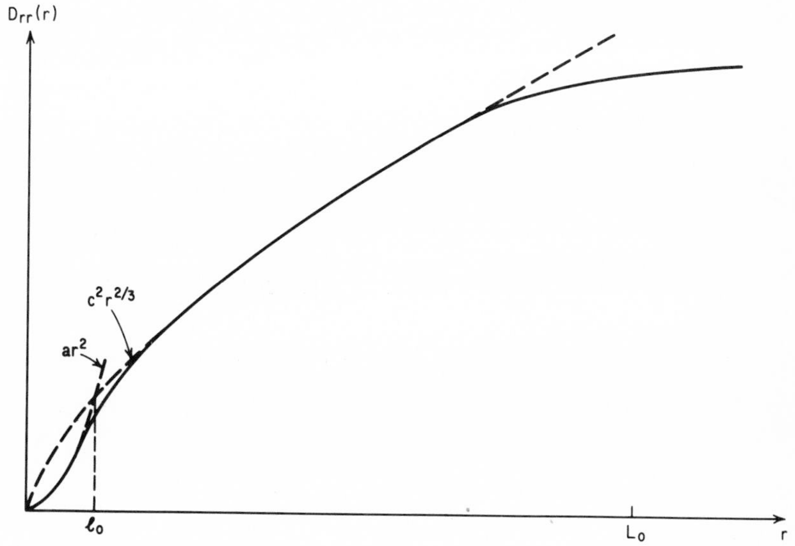

Fig. 6 General shape of the structure function $D_{rr}(r)$.
(L_o is the outer scale and ℓ_o the inner scale of the turbulence.)

In many applications of turbulence theory an important role is played by the isotropic eddies described by the structure functions (2.11). In these cases, it is often expedient to regard the values of r in Eqs. (2.11) as not being bounded above by the value L. This is almost always the case in the problems considered in this book. However, if we cannot neglect the "saturation" of the structure function, it is necessary to use interpolation formulas which approximately describe the behavior of the structure function for large values of r. For small values of r these formulas must reduce to the same values of D_{rr} as given in the expression (2.11). One of the functions satisfying the stipulated requirements is the function

$$D_{rr}(r) = \frac{2}{3}\overline{v'^2}\left[1 - \frac{2^{2/3}}{\Gamma(1/3)}\left(\frac{r}{L_o}\right)^{1/3} K_{1/3}\left(\frac{r}{L_o}\right)\right] \qquad (2.13)$$

proposed by von Kármán. Here $\overline{v'^2}$ is the mean square velocity fluctuation and L_o is the outer scale of the turbulence. As shown in example a) on page 12, for $r \ll L_o$ the function (2.13) is approximately equal to

$$D_{rr}(r) \sim \frac{\sqrt{\pi}}{3\Gamma(7/6)} \frac{\overline{v'^2}}{L_o^{2/3}} r^{2/3}, \qquad (2.14)$$

i.e. coincides for $r \ll L_o$ with the "two-thirds law". We can also write down other functions satisfying the same requirements.

2.3 Spectrum of the velocity field in turbulent flow

We now study the spectrum of turbulence. As shown in Chapter 1, the structure function $D_f(\vec{r})$ of a locally isotropic scalar field can be represented in the form

$$D_f(\vec{r}) = 2\iiint_{-\infty}^{\infty} [1 - \cos(\vec{\kappa}\cdot\vec{r})]\Phi(\vec{\kappa})d\vec{\kappa}.$$

Similarly, the structure tensor $D_{ik}(\vec{r})$ can be represented in the form

$$D_{ik}(\vec{r}) = 2 \iiint_{-\infty}^{\infty} [1 - \cos(\vec{\kappa}\cdot\vec{r})] \, \Phi_{ik}(\vec{\kappa}) d\vec{\kappa}, \tag{2.15}$$

where $\Phi_{ik}(\vec{\kappa})$ is the spectral tensor of the velocity field. The form of this tensor can be determined from the incompressibility equation and the local isotropy condition, i.e., the tensor $\Phi_{ik}(\vec{\kappa})$ can be expressed in terms of the vector $\vec{\kappa}$ and the unit tensor δ_{ik} [16] as

$$\Phi_{ik}(\vec{\kappa}) = G(\kappa)\kappa_i\kappa_k + E(\kappa)\delta_{ik}, \tag{2.16}$$

where $G(\kappa)$ and $E(\kappa)$ are scalar functions of a single argument, the magnitude of the vector $\vec{\kappa}$. It follows from the incompressibility equation that

$$\frac{\partial D_{ik}}{\partial x_i} = 0$$

(see page 30). Taking the divergence of Eq. (2.15), we obtain

$$\iiint_{-\infty}^{\infty} \sin(\vec{\kappa}\cdot\vec{r})\kappa_i \, \Phi_{ik}(\vec{\kappa}) d\vec{\kappa} = 0.$$

Thus the condition $\kappa_i \, \Phi_{ik}(\vec{\kappa}) = 0$ must be met. Substituting Eq. (2.16) into this condition, we get $G\kappa^2\kappa_k + E\kappa_k = 0$, whence $G = - E/\kappa^2$. Consequently we have

$$\Phi_{ik}(\vec{\kappa}) = (\delta_{ik} - \frac{\kappa_i\kappa_k}{\kappa^2})E(\kappa). \tag{2.17}$$

Thus, Eq. (2.15) takes the form

$$D_{ik}(\vec{r}) = 2 \iiint_{-\infty}^{\infty} [1 - \cos\,(\vec{\kappa}\cdot\vec{r})](\delta_{ik} - \frac{\kappa_i\kappa_k}{\kappa^2})E(\kappa)d\vec{\kappa}. \tag{2.18}$$

To explain the physical meaning of the function $E(\kappa)$ let us assume temporarily that the velocity field is isotropic and that the correlation tensor $B_{ik}(\vec{r})$ exists as well as the structure tensor $D_{ik}(\vec{r})$. Then we have

$$B_{ik}(\vec{r}) = \iiint_{-\infty}^{\infty} \cos(\vec{\kappa}\cdot\vec{r})(\delta_{ik} - \frac{\kappa_i\kappa_k}{\kappa^2})E(\kappa)d\vec{\kappa}.$$

We contract this expression with respect to the indices i and k. Taking into account that $\delta_{ii} = 3$ and $\kappa_i\kappa_i = \kappa^2$, we obtain

$$B_{ii}(\vec{r}) = \iiint_{-\infty}^{\infty} \cos(\vec{\kappa}\cdot\vec{r})2E(\kappa)d\vec{\kappa}.$$

Setting $r = 0$ in this equation, we get

$$\frac{1}{2}\overline{v'^2} = \iiint_{-\infty}^{\infty} E(\kappa)d\vec{\kappa}.$$

Thus, the quantity $E(\kappa)$ is the spectral density in three-dimensional wave vector space of the distribution of the energy of the velocity fluctuations.

We now find the form of the function $E(\kappa)$ corresponding to the "two-thirds law". To do this we contract the expression (2.18) with respect to the indices i and k

$$D_{ii}(r) = 4 \iiint_{-\infty}^{\infty} [1 - \cos(\vec{\kappa}\cdot\vec{r})]E(\kappa)d\vec{\kappa}. \qquad (2.19)$$

It follows from (2.5) that

$$D_{ii}(r) = D_{rr}(r) + 2D_{tt}(r).$$

Setting

$$D_{rr}(r) = C\epsilon^{2/3}r^{2/3} \quad , \quad D_{tt} = \frac{4}{3} C\epsilon^{2/3}r^{2/3},$$

we obtain

$$\frac{11}{3} C\epsilon^{2/3}r^{2/3} = 4 \iiint_{-\infty}^{\infty} [1 - \cos(\vec{\kappa}\cdot\vec{r})] E(\kappa) d\vec{\kappa}.$$

Comparing this expression with Eqs. (1.56) and (1.58) in example b) on page 25, we find that

$$E(\kappa) = A\epsilon^{2/3}\kappa^{-11/3}, \tag{2.20}$$

where

$$A = \frac{11\Gamma(\frac{8}{3}) \sin \frac{\pi}{3}}{24\pi^2} C = 0.061C.$$

Many papers on turbulence theory use the one-dimensional spectral expansion of the quantity D_{rr} with respect to the magnitude of the vector $\vec{\kappa}$, i.e.

$$D_{rr}(r) = 2 \int_{-\infty}^{\infty} [1 - \cos(\kappa r)] E_1(\kappa) d\kappa, \tag{2.21}$$

instead of the three-dimensional spectral expansion of the structure tensor (2.18). Using Eqs. (1.56) and (1.57) of example b) on page 25, we obtain

$$E_1(\kappa) = A_1\epsilon^{2/3}\kappa^{-5/3}, \tag{2.22}$$

where

$$A_1 = \frac{\Gamma(\frac{5}{3}) \sin \frac{\pi}{3}}{2\pi} C.$$

The spectral energy densities (2.20) and (2.22) correspond to the struction function $D_{rr} = C\epsilon^{2/3}r^{2/3}$ and do not reflect the fact that the structure functions $D_{rr}(r)$ and

$D_{tt}(r)$ have a parabolic character for $r \ll \ell_0$, because of the smoothing action of the viscous forces. As we have already seen above, the action of these forces is apparent from the fact that eddies with sizes of the order of ℓ_0 are stable. Thus, in a turbulent flow there are no inhomogeneities with sizes much smaller than ℓ_0. This means that the spectral density $E(\kappa)$ rapidly dies off to zero when $\kappa \gtrsim 2\pi/\ell_0$. The character of this cutoff is related to the form of the structure function $D_{rr}(r)$ in the transition region from $r \ll \ell_0$ to $r \gg \ell_0$, and at present has not yet been ascertained exactly. The spectral density (2.20) goes to infinity at $\kappa = 0$. This is related to the fact that the structure function $D_{rr} = C\epsilon^{2/3}r^{2/3}$ goes to infinity at $r = \infty$. In all actual cases, of course, $D_{rr}(\infty) < \infty$ and the growth of the spectral density $E(\kappa)$ for $\kappa < \kappa_{min}$ slows down (the quantity $\kappa_{min} \sim 2\pi/L_0$ corresponds to the outer scale of the turbulence). The form of the function $E(\kappa)$ for $\kappa < \kappa_{min}$ obviously has to depend on the concrete conditions which determine the formation of the largest eddies, and therefore it cannot be universal [c].

As an example of a spectral density $E(\kappa)$ which is finite for $\kappa = 0$, we can give the spectrum of the von Kármán function (2.13). Instead of the rather formidable expression for $E(\kappa)$ we give here the relatively simple formula for $E_1(\kappa)$:

$$E_1(\kappa) = \frac{\Gamma(5/6)}{3\sqrt{\pi}\,\Gamma(1/3)} \frac{L_0 \overline{v'^2}}{(1 + \kappa^2 L_0^2)^{5/6}} . \tag{2.23}$$

For $\kappa = 0$, E_1 is finite and for $\kappa L_0 \gg 1$, $E(\kappa) \sim \kappa^{-5/3}$, i.e. coincides with the spectral density $E_1(\kappa)$ corresponding to the "two-thirds law".

Numerous experimental investigations of the form of structure functions in the atmosphere (mainly in the layer of the atmosphere near the earth), where the Reynolds numbers are very large [d], give good confirmation of the "two-thirds law" for distances of the order of centimeters and meters [17]. These experiments also allow the constant C figuring in (2.11) to be rather accurately determined. Some as yet rather sparse measurements of the structure function in the lower troposphere also agree with this law for distances of the order of tens of meters [18]. One can arrive at a similar conclusion by analyzing the spectrum of airplane buffeting [19].

We defer a more detailed presentation of the results of experimental investigation of the structure of the wind in the atmosphere until Part IV. We turn now to the microstructure of the concentration of a passive additive in a turbulent flow.

Chapter 3

MICROSTRUCTURE OF THE CONCENTRATION OF A CONSERVATIVE PASSIVE ADDITIVE IN A TURBULENT FLOW

3.1 Turbulent mixing of conservative passive additives

As already noted above, the microstructure of the refractive index of the atmosphere is determined by the structure of the temperature, humidity and wind velocity fields. The temperature, humidity and some other characteristics of the atmosphere can very often be regarded approximately (to a high degree of accuracy) as conservative passive additives.

If a volume of air is characterized by a concentration ϑ of additive, then by saying that the additive is conservative we mean that the quantity ϑ does not change when the volume element is shifted about in space. By the additive being passive is meant that the quantity ϑ does not affect the dynamical regime of the turbulence [a]. The problem of the microstructure of the concentration of a conservative passive additive was first considered by Obukhov and Yaglom [21,22] for the case of the temperature field.

We shall start from the equation of molecular diffusion

$$\frac{d\vartheta}{dt} + \operatorname{div}(- D \operatorname{grad} \vartheta) = 0, \tag{3.1}$$

which must be obeyed by the concentration ϑ of a passive conservative additive. Here D is the molecular diffusion coefficient of the additive and

$$\frac{d\vartheta}{dt} = \frac{\partial\vartheta}{\partial t} + \vec{v}\cdot\operatorname{grad} \vartheta$$

is the total time derivative taken along the moving parcel of air. We shall assume that the air can be regarded as incompressible, i.e. that $\operatorname{div} \vec{v} = 0$. In this case

$$\vec{v}\cdot\operatorname{grad} \vartheta = \operatorname{div}(\vec{v}\vartheta),$$

and Eq. (3.1) takes the form

$$\frac{\partial\vartheta}{\partial t} + \mathrm{div}(\vec{v}\vartheta - D\ \mathrm{grad}\ \vartheta) = 0,$$

or

$$\frac{\partial\vartheta}{\partial t} + \frac{\partial}{\partial x_i}(v_i\vartheta - D\frac{\partial\vartheta}{\partial x_i}) = 0. \tag{3.2}$$

As usual, we separate the value of the quantity ϑ into the mean value $\overline{\vartheta}$ and the departure ϑ' from the mean value, i.e. $\vartheta = \overline{\vartheta} + \vartheta'$. Similarly, we set $v_i = \overline{v}_i + v_i'$. Averaging Eq. (3.2), we obtain

$$\frac{\partial\overline{\vartheta}}{\partial t} + \frac{\partial}{\partial x_i}(\overline{v}_i\ \overline{\vartheta} + \overline{v_i'\vartheta'} - D\frac{\partial\overline{\vartheta}}{\partial x_i}) = 0. \tag{3.3}$$

The expression in parentheses represents the mean density of flow of the quantity ϑ. The quantity $\vec{q}_m = -D\ \mathrm{grad}\ \overline{\vartheta}$ represents the mean flow of ϑ caused by molecular diffusion. The quantity $\vec{q}_a = \overline{\vec{v}}\ \overline{\vartheta}$ is connected with the transport of ϑ by the mean velocity of the flow; it is usually constant and drops out of the equation. Finally, the quantity $\vec{q}_T = \overline{\vec{v}'\vartheta'}$ represents the density of turbulent flow of ϑ. It is natural to assume that q_T is proportional to the gradient of the mean concentration [b], i.e.

$$\vec{q}_T = -K\ \mathrm{grad}\ \overline{\vartheta}. \tag{3.4}$$

The quantity K is called the coefficient of turbulent diffusion and usually exceeds the coefficient of molecular diffusion by several orders of magnitude. Of course, the value of K depends on the intensity of the turbulence.

It should be remarked that there is an essential difference between the mechanisms of molecular and turbulent diffusion, which the following example clarifies. Let the mean value $\overline{\vartheta}$ depend only on one coordinate z, say. Assume for definiteness that $\overline{\vartheta}$ increases as z increases. Consider the values of ϑ at two different levels z_1 and z_2. Because of the turbulent mixing, parcels of air from the level z_2 will arrive at the level z_1, and conversely parcels of air from the level z_1 will arrive at the level z_2. Thus, at each of these levels parcels of air characterized by the value $\overline{\vartheta}(z_1)$ appear next to parcels of air characterized by the value $\overline{\vartheta}(z_2)$. As a result, the mean concentrations taken over each level change in such a way that the difference between them decreases, while the "variegation" of the values of ϑ at each level is greatly increased. Thus, as a result of turbulent mixing the inhomogeneity of the spatial distribution of ϑ is increased and large "local" gradients of ϑ are created. Only after large local gradients of ϑ have appeared does the process of molecular diffusion play a significant role by smoothing out the spatial distribution of ϑ.

The inhomogeneity of the spatial distribution of ϑ can be characterized quantitatively by the following measure of inhomogeneity in the volume V:

$$G = \frac{1}{2} \int_V \overline{\vartheta'^2}\, dV , \quad \vartheta' = \vartheta - \overline{\vartheta}. \tag{3.5}$$

Clearly $G = 0$ only when $\vartheta' = 0$ in the whole volume V. Subtracting Eq. (3.2) from Eq. (3.3), we obtain an equation which determines $\partial\vartheta'/\partial t$:

$$\frac{\partial\vartheta'}{\partial t} + \frac{\partial}{\partial x_i}\left(v_i\vartheta' + v_i'\overline{\vartheta} - \overline{v_i'\vartheta'} - D\frac{\partial\vartheta'}{\partial x_i}\right) = 0. \tag{3.6}$$

Multiplying this equation by ϑ' and using the obvious relations [c]

$$\vartheta'\frac{\partial\vartheta'}{\partial t} = \frac{\partial}{\partial t}\left(\frac{1}{2}\vartheta'^2\right),$$

$$\vartheta'\frac{\partial}{\partial x_i}(v_i\vartheta') = \vartheta' v_i\frac{\partial\vartheta'}{\partial x_i} = v_i\frac{\partial}{\partial x_i}\left(\frac{1}{2}\vartheta'^2\right) = \frac{\partial}{\partial x_i}\left(\frac{1}{2}v_i\vartheta'^2\right),$$

$$\vartheta'\frac{\partial}{\partial x_i}(v_i'\overline{\vartheta}) = v_i'\vartheta'\frac{\partial\overline{\vartheta}}{\partial x_i}, \quad \vartheta'\frac{\partial}{\partial x_i}\left(D\frac{\partial\vartheta'}{\partial x_i}\right) = \frac{\partial}{\partial x_i}\left(\vartheta' D\frac{\partial\vartheta'}{\partial x_i}\right) - D\left(\frac{\partial\vartheta'}{\partial x_i}\right)^2,$$

we obtain

$$\frac{\partial}{\partial t}\frac{\vartheta'^2}{2} + \operatorname{div}\left(\frac{\vec{v}\vartheta'^2}{2} - D\,\vartheta'\operatorname{grad}\vartheta'\right) + \vartheta'\vec{v}'\cdot\operatorname{grad}\overline{\vartheta} + D(\operatorname{grad}\vartheta')^2 - \vartheta'\operatorname{div}(\overline{\vec{v}'\vartheta'}) = 0.$$

Averaging this equation and using the fact that

$$\overline{\vartheta' \frac{\partial}{\partial x_i} (\overline{v_i' \vartheta'})} = 0,$$

we have

$$\frac{\partial}{\partial t} \frac{\overline{\vartheta'^2}}{2} + \mathrm{div}\left(\frac{1}{2} \overline{\vec{v}\vartheta'^2} - D \overline{\vartheta' \,\mathrm{grad}\, \vartheta'} \right) + \vartheta' \vec{v} \cdot \mathrm{grad}\, \overline{\vartheta} +$$

$$+ D \overline{(\mathrm{grad}\, \vartheta')^2} = 0. \qquad (3.7)$$

We now integrate (3.7) over the volume V. The integral of the divergence can be transformed into a surface integral, which is small compared to the volume integrals. Neglecting the surface integral, we find

$$\frac{\partial G}{\partial t} + \int_V \left[\overline{v_i' \vartheta'} \frac{\partial \overline{\vartheta}}{\partial x_i} + D\overline{\left(\frac{\partial \vartheta'}{\partial x_i}\right)^2} \right] dV = 0. \qquad (3.8)$$

Substituting into (3.8) the value of the quantity $\overline{\vec{v}'\vartheta} = \vec{q}_T$ from Eq. (3.4), we obtain

$$\frac{\partial G}{\partial t} = \int_V \left[K(\mathrm{grad}\, \overline{\vartheta})^2 - D\overline{(\mathrm{grad}\, \vartheta')^2} \right] dV = 0. \qquad (3.9)$$

Thus, the amount G of inhomogeneity increases due to the presence of turbulent mixing ("turbulent flow") of the substance in question and decreases due to the presence of the process of molecular diffusion. In the stationary case, dG/dt = 0 and both processes must balance each other:

$$\int_V K(\mathrm{grad}\, \overline{\vartheta})^2 \, dV = \int_V D\overline{(\mathrm{grad}\, \vartheta')^2} \, dV. \qquad (3.10)$$

If the inhomogeneity measure is stationary not only for the volume as a whole but for its separate parts as well, then Eq. (3.10) can be written in the form

$$K(\text{grad}\ \overline{\vartheta})^2 = D\overline{(\text{grad}\ \vartheta')^2}. \tag{3.11}$$

The quantity

$$\overline{N} = D\overline{(\text{grad}\ \vartheta')^2}$$

represents the amount of inhomogeneity which disappears per unit time due to molecular diffusion; this quantity is analogous to the energy dissipation rate ϵ. The quantity $K(\text{grad}\ \overline{\vartheta})^2$ represents the amount of inhomogeneity which appears per unit time due to the turbulence, and is similar to v^3/ℓ, the rate of production of the energy of the fluctuations. We can carry out an even more detailed analogy between the velocity fluctuations in a turbulent flow and the concentration fluctuations of a conservative passive additive ϑ.

3.2 Structure functions and spectral functions of the field of a conservative passive additive in a turbulent flow

Concentration inhomogeneities ϑ'_ℓ with geometrical dimensions ℓ appear as a result of the action of velocity field perturbations with dimensions ℓ and characteristic velocities v_ℓ. The amount of inhomogeneity appearing per unit time is clearly equal to $v_\ell \vartheta'^2_\ell/\ell$ (ℓ/v_ℓ is the time of formation of the velocity fluctuation v_ℓ and ϑ'^2_ℓ is the measure of inhomogeneity). According to the second term on the right of Eq. (3.9), the rate of levelling out of the inhomogeneity ϑ'_ℓ is of the order $D\vartheta'^2_\ell/\ell^2$. In the case where $v_\ell \vartheta'^2_\ell/\ell \gg D\vartheta'^2_\ell/\ell^2$ or $\ell v_\ell/D \gg 1$, the inhomogeneity ϑ'_ℓ which appears is not dissipated by the action of molecular diffusion, but rather has a stable existence and can subsequently subdivide into smaller eddies. This process of subdivision proceeds until inhomogeneities appear for which $v_{\ell_1} \vartheta'^2_{\ell_1}/\ell_1 \sim D\vartheta'^2_{\ell_1}/\ell_1^2$ or $\ell_1 v_{\ell_1} \sim D$. These inhomogeneities are dissipated by the process of molecular diffusion. It follows from Eq. (3.10) that G, the amount of inhomogeneity appearing per unit time due to the largest eddies, is equal to $\overline{N}$, the rate at which the inhomogeneity is levelled out in the smallest eddies. Thus, the amount of inhomogeneity transferred per unit time from the largest to the smallest eddies is constant and is equal to the rate $\overline{N}$ at which the inhomogeneity is dissipated. Consequently, for inhomogeneities with $\ell v_\ell \gg D$ (i.e. for all inhomogeneities except the very smallest) the relation $v_\ell \vartheta_\ell'^2/\ell \sim \overline{N}$ holds, whence, since $v_\ell \sim (\epsilon\ell)^{1/3}$, we obtain

$$\vartheta_\ell'^2 \sim \frac{\overline{N}\,\ell^{2/3}}{\epsilon^{1/3}} \, . \tag{3.12}$$

The size of the smallest inhomogeneities in the distribution of ϑ is defined by the relation $\ell_1 v_{\ell_1} \sim D$, whence, since $v_{\ell_1} \sim (\epsilon\ell_1)^{1/3}$, we obtain

$$\ell_1 \sim \left(\frac{D^3}{\epsilon}\right)^{1/4} \tag{3.13}$$

The quantity $\ell v_\ell/D$, which determines the "stability" of inhomogeneities ϑ_ℓ' with dimensions ℓ, is analogous to the Reynolds number which determines the stability of velocity perturbations. Since the values of D are near ν, the numbers $\ell v_\ell/\nu$ and $\ell v_\ell/D$ are always of the same order. (For air $\nu = 0.15$ cm^2/sec, the coefficient of temperature conductivity $D_t = 0.19$ cm^2/sec, the diffusion coefficient for atmospheric water vapor is $D_e = 0.20$ cm^2/sec, the diffusion coefficient for atmospheric CO_2 is $D_{CO_2} = 0.14$ cm^2/sec, etc.) Thus, the range of sizes within which the relations $v_\ell \sim (\epsilon\ell)^{1/3}$ and $\vartheta_\ell'^2 \sim \overline{N}\ell^{2/3}\epsilon^{-1/3}$ hold, are always the same. The size of the smallest eddies and the size ℓ of the smallest inhomogeneities in the distribution of ϑ have the same order of magnitude, i.e. $(\nu^3\,\epsilon^{-1})^{3/4} \sim (D^3\,\epsilon^{-1})^{3/4}$. Because of this, we shall henceforth make no distinction between these quantities.

A more rigorous theory can be constructed on the basis of the above qualitative considerations. The largest inhomogeneities in the distribution of ϑ originate from the largest eddies and are not isotropic. However the smallest inhomogeneities in the distribution of ϑ can be considered isotropic. Since the difference of the values of ϑ at two points $\vec{r}_1$ and $\vec{r}_2$ is determined mainly by inhomogeneities of sizes $|\vec{r}_1 - \vec{r}_2|$, then in the case where $|\vec{r}_1 - \vec{r}_2| \ll L_0$ the quantity $\vartheta(\vec{r}_1) - \vartheta(\vec{r}_2)$ can be considered statistically isotropic. Thus, $\vartheta(\vec{r})$ is a locally isotropic random field. For the range of values $\ell_0 \ll |\vec{r}_1 - \vec{r}_2| \ll L_0$, the structure function

$$D_\vartheta(|\vec{r}_1 - \vec{r}_2|) = \overline{[\vartheta(\vec{r}_1) - \vartheta(\vec{r}_2)]^2} \tag{3.14}$$

depends on $r = |\vec{r}_1 - \vec{r}_2|$, $\overline{N}$ and the quantity ϵ characterizing the turbulence, i.e.

$D_\vartheta(r) = F(\overline{N}, \epsilon, r)$. Dimensional considerations lead to the formula [21]

$$D_\vartheta(r) = a^2 \frac{\overline{N}}{\epsilon^{1/3}} r^{2/3} \quad (\ell_o \ll r \ll L_o), \tag{3.15}$$

where a is a numerical constant. The expression (3.15), which corresponds to Eq. (3.12) and is derived on the basis of qualitative considerations, was first obtained in the paper of Obukhov [21] and is called the "two-thirds law" for the concentration of a conservative passive additive. For $r \ll \ell_o$, the difference $\vartheta(\vec{r}_1 + \vec{r}) - \vartheta(\vec{r}_1)$ is a smooth function of r and can be expanded in a series beginning with the first power of r. Consequently, $D_\vartheta(r) \sim r^2$ for $r \ll \ell_o$. More detailed considerations lead to the formula [21]

$$D_\vartheta(r) = \frac{1}{3}\frac{\overline{N}}{D} r^2 \quad (r \ll \ell_o). \tag{3.16}$$

We now make more precise the definition of ℓ_o for inhomogeneities in the distribution of ϑ. We shall assume that the quantity ℓ_o is defined as the point of intersection of the asymptotic expansions (3.15) and (3.16), i.e.

$$a^2 \frac{\overline{N}}{\epsilon^{1/3}} \ell_o^{2/3} = \frac{1}{3}\frac{\overline{N}}{D} \ell_o^2.$$

Solving this equation, we obtain

$$\ell_o = \sqrt[4]{\frac{27a^6D^3}{\epsilon}} . \tag{3.17}$$

Thus, the structure function $D_\vartheta(r)$ can be represented in the form

$$D_\vartheta(r) = \begin{cases} C_\vartheta^2 \, r^{2/3} & \text{for } r \gg \ell_o, \\ C_\vartheta^2 \, \ell_o^{2/3} \left(\frac{r}{\ell_o}\right)^2 & \text{for } r \ll \ell_o, \end{cases} \tag{3.18}$$

where

$$C_{\vartheta}^2 = a^2 \frac{\overline{N}}{\epsilon^{1/3}}, \tag{3.19}$$

and ℓ_0 is defined by Eq. (3.17).

According to the general formula (1.39), a locally isotropic random field can be represented in the form of a stochastic integral

$$\vartheta(\vec{r}) = \vartheta(0) + \iiint_{-\infty}^{\infty} (1 - e^{i\vec{\kappa}\cdot\vec{r}})d\varphi(\vec{\kappa}), \tag{3.20}$$

where the random amplitudes $d\varphi(\vec{\kappa})$ satisfy the relation

$$\overline{d\varphi(\vec{\kappa}_1)d\varphi^*(\vec{\kappa}_2)} = \delta(\vec{\kappa}_1 - \vec{\kappa}_2)\, \Phi_{\vartheta}(\vec{\kappa}_1)\, d\vec{\kappa}_1 \; d\vec{\kappa}_2 . \tag{3.21}$$

The function $\Phi_{\vartheta}(\vec{\kappa})$ is the spectral density of the structure function $D_{\vartheta}(\vec{r})$, i.e.

$$D_{\vartheta}(\vec{r}) = 2 \iiint_{-\infty}^{\infty} (1 - \cos \vec{\kappa}\cdot\vec{r})\Phi_{\vartheta}(\vec{\kappa})\, d\vec{\kappa} . \tag{3.22}$$

The expression (3.22) can also be written in the form

$$D_{\vartheta}(r) = 8\pi \int_0^{\infty} (1 - \frac{\sin \kappa r}{\kappa r})\Phi_{\vartheta}(\kappa)\kappa^2 d\kappa . \tag{3.23}$$

The function $\Phi_{\vartheta}(\kappa)$ is the spectral density in the three-dimensional space of wave numbers κ_1, κ_2, κ_3 of the distribution of the amount of inhomogeneity in a unit volume. The form of this function corresponding to the "two-thirds law" for the concentration ϑ, was given in example b) on page 25, i.e.

$$\Phi_\vartheta(\kappa) = \frac{\Gamma(\frac{8}{3}) \sin\frac{\pi}{3}}{4\pi^2} C_\vartheta^2 \kappa^{-11/3}$$

and

$$\Phi_\vartheta(\kappa) = 0.033\, C_\vartheta^2 \kappa^{-11/3}. \tag{3.24}$$

However, we note that for $r \ll \ell_o$ the structure function $D_\vartheta(r)$ behaves quadratically, corresponding to a rapid decrease of $\Phi_\vartheta(\kappa)$ for $\kappa \gtrsim 1/\ell_o$ (see page 38). At present, the exact cut-off law of $\Phi_\vartheta(\kappa)$ for $\kappa \sim 1/\ell_o$ has not yet been ascertained exactly. In some calculations we shall use a function $\Phi_\vartheta(\kappa)$ which vanishes for $\kappa > \kappa_m$. Of course, such a definition of $\Phi_\vartheta(\kappa)$ is not rigorously founded, but is recommended by its simplicity; it simply means that a certain interpolation formula has been chosen for $D_\vartheta(r)$. Thus we shall assume that

$$\Phi_\vartheta(\kappa) = \begin{cases} 0.033\, C_\vartheta^2 \kappa^{-11/3} & \text{for } \kappa < \kappa_m, \\ 0 & \text{for } \kappa > \kappa_m. \end{cases} \tag{3.25}$$

The quantity κ_m can be related to the quantity ℓ_o defined in Eq. (3.17). Substituting the function (3.25) in the expression (3.23), we obtain

$$D_\vartheta(r) = 8\pi(0.033)C_\vartheta^2 \int_0^{\kappa_m} \left(1 - \frac{\sin\kappa r}{\kappa r}\right) \kappa^{-11/3} \kappa^2 d\kappa. \tag{3.26}$$

For $\kappa_m r \gg 1$ the integral (3.26) is practically the same as the function (3.15). For $\kappa_m r \ll 1$

$$\left(1 - \frac{\sin\kappa r}{\kappa r}\right) \sim \frac{\kappa^2 r^2}{6}$$

and

$$D_\vartheta(r) = 8\pi(0.033)C_\vartheta^2 \int_0^{\kappa_m} \frac{r^2}{6} \kappa^{1/3} d\kappa = 8\pi(0.033)C_\vartheta^2 \frac{1}{6}\cdot\frac{3}{4} \kappa_m^{4/3} r^2.$$

Comparing this expression with the formula $D_\vartheta(r) = C_\vartheta^2 \ell_o^{2/3}(\frac{r}{\ell_o})^2$, we obtain the relation between κ_m and ℓ_o:

$$\kappa_m \ell_o = (0.033\pi)^{-3/4} = 5.48. \tag{3.27}$$

The expression $C_\vartheta^2 = a^2 \overline{N} \epsilon^{-1/3}$ can be transformed into a form which permits this quantity to be calculated in terms of data on the mean value profiles of the wind velocity and concentration ϑ. To do this we have to use the relation

$$K(\text{grad } \overline{\vartheta})^2 = D\overline{(\text{grad } \vartheta')^2} = \overline{N},$$

which expresses the quantity $\overline{N}$ in terms of characteristics of the mean profile of ϑ. A similar relation holds for the quantity

$$\epsilon = \frac{1}{2} \nu \overline{\left(\frac{\partial v_i}{\partial x_k} - \frac{\partial v_k}{\partial x_i}\right)^2}$$

as well [d], i.e.

$$\epsilon = K\left(\frac{\partial \overline{u}_i}{\partial x_j}\right)^2 . \tag{3.28}$$

Here $\overline{u}_i$ is the average value of the wind velocity. Substituting the expressions (3.28) and (3.11) into the formula for C_ϑ^2, we obtain

$$C_\vartheta^2 = a^2 \left[\frac{K^2}{\left(\frac{\partial \overline{u}_i}{\partial x_j}\right)^2}\right]^{1/3} (\text{grad } \overline{\vartheta})^2. \tag{3.29'}$$

All the quantities figuring in the right hand side of (3.29') can be obtained from observations of the average atmospheric profiles of the wind, the temperature and the quantity ϑ. Methods of determining K from observations of wind and temperature profiles in the atmosphere are described in [23-26]. It should be noted that a large amount of observational material is required to check the formulas recommended for calculation of K in the papers cited, but they do give the correct order of magnitude.

Eq. (3.29') can be used to calculate the range of sizes within which the "two-thirds law" is valid. The mean square difference which the fluctuations produce in the difference of the values of ϑ at two points grows like $\ell^{2/3}$ (ℓ is the distance between the observation points). At the same time there exists between these two observation points a systematic difference in the values of ϑ, equal to $|\text{grad}\,\bar{\vartheta}|\ell$, with square $|\text{grad}_\ell\,\bar{\vartheta}|^2\ell^2$. It is clear that for sufficiently small values of ℓ, the fluctuational difference in the values of ϑ is much larger than the systematic difference (since $x^{2/3}$ is always $\gg x^2$ for $x \ll 1$). Thus, over small distances the presence of a systematic difference in ϑ does not affect the size of the fluctuations and does not affect their homogeneity and isotropy. However, as the distance ℓ is increased, the systematic difference in the values of ϑ becomes larger than the fluctuational difference and for such scales the field of fluctuations of ϑ cannot be considered locally isotropic. Let us designate by L the dimension for which the relation

$$C_\vartheta^2 L^{2/3} = (\text{grad}\,\bar{\vartheta})^2 L^2$$

holds. Substituting Eq. (3.29') in this relation, we obtain

$$L = a^{3/2}\sqrt{\frac{K}{\sqrt{\left(\frac{\partial\bar{u}_i}{\partial x_j}\right)^2}}}\,. \tag{3.30}$$

We shall call the quantity $L_o = La^{-3/2}$, which differs from L only by a numerical factor, the outer scale of the turbulence. In the free troposphere L_o ranges from tens to hundreds of meters in order of magnitude [95]. In practice $\bar{u} = \bar{u}(z)$, i.e.

$$\left(\frac{\partial\bar{u}_i}{\partial x_j}\right)^2 = \left(\frac{\partial\bar{u}}{\partial z}\right)^2 = \beta^2\,,$$

and then

$$L_o = \sqrt{\frac{K}{\beta}}\,. \tag{3.31}$$

Using the quantity L_o, we can write Eq. (3.29') in the following convenient form

$$C_\vartheta^2 = L_o^{4/3} (\text{grad } \bar{\vartheta})^2. \qquad (3.29'')$$

Experimental investigations of concentration fluctuations of a conservative passive additive ϑ have been carried out mainly in the layer of the atmosphere near the earth (temperature fluctuations) and in the lower troposphere (fluctuations of the air's refractive index for centimeter radio waves). Measurements of the temperature fluctuations in the layer of the atmosphere near the earth have confirmed the "two-thirds law" as well as the dependence (3.29) of the quantity C_ϑ on the mean conditions, and have permitted determination of the numerical constant a figuring in (3.29') [e]. Measurements of the spectrum of the air's refractive index fluctuations in the free troposphere also agree very well with the "two-thirds law", according to which the one-dimensional spectral density of the fluctuations is proportional to $\kappa^{-5/3}$ [95,96].

3.3 Locally isotropic turbulence with smoothly varying mean characteristics

So far we have considered the case of locally homogeneous and isotropic turbulence, where the structure function

$$D_f(\vec{r}_1,\vec{r}_2) = \overline{[f(\vec{r}_1) - f(\vec{r}_2)]^2}$$

satisfies the condition

$$D_f(\vec{r}_1,\vec{r}_2) = D_f(|\vec{r}_1 - \vec{r}_2|)$$

inside some region G with dimensions of the order of magnitude of the outer scale of turbulence L_o. In the case where $\ell_o \ll |\vec{r}_1 - \vec{r}_2| \ll L_o$, $D_f(r) = C_f^2 r^{2/3}$. If we consider another region G' which also has dimensions of the order L_o and which is separated from G by a distance of order L_o, then the field f will also be locally homogeneous and isotropic in G'. The structure function $D_f(\vec{r}_1,\vec{r}_2)$ in the region G' will also be expressed by a "two-thirds law", but in general with another value of the constant C_f^2. Thus, we can assume that the quantity C_f^2 is a smooth function of the coordinates, which changes appreciably only in distances of order L_o. It is natural that C_f^2 should depend on the position of the center of mass $\vec{R} = \frac{1}{2}(\vec{r}_1 + \vec{r}_2)$ of the two observation points. Thus, we arrive at the formula

$$D_f(\vec{r}_1,\vec{r}_2) = C_f^2\left(\frac{\vec{r}_1 + \vec{r}_2}{2}\right)|\vec{r}_1 - \vec{r}_2|^{2/3}.$$

In the general case

$$D_f(\vec{r}_1,\vec{r}_2) = C_f^2\left(\frac{\vec{r}_1 + \vec{r}_2}{2}\right) D_f^{(o)}(|\vec{r}_1 - \vec{r}_2|). \tag{3.32}$$

The function $D_f^{(o)}(r)$, which describes the local properties of the field f, is the same in all the regions G,G',... in which the turbulence differs only by its "intensity", characterized by the size of C_f^2. Just as we previously defined the spectral expansion

$$D_f(\vec{r}_1 - \vec{r}_2) = 2\iiint_{-\infty}^{\infty}\left\{1 - \cos\left[\vec{\kappa}\cdot(\vec{r}_1 - \vec{r}_2)\right]\right\}\Phi_f(\vec{\kappa})d\vec{\kappa} \tag{3.33}$$

for points $\vec{r}_1,\vec{r}_2$ belonging to the region G, we can also define a similar expansion in each of the regions G,G',... by considering C_f^2 to be constant in each such region. Thus, we obtain the spectral expansion

$$D_f(\vec{r}_1,\vec{r}_2) = 2\iiint_{-\infty}^{\infty}\left\{1 - \cos\left[\vec{\kappa}\cdot(\vec{r}_1 - \vec{r}_2)\right]\right\}\Phi_f\left(\vec{\kappa}, \frac{\vec{r}_1 + \vec{r}_2}{2}\right)d\vec{\kappa}, \tag{3.34}$$

where [f]

$$\Phi_f\left(\vec{\kappa}, \frac{\vec{r}_1 + \vec{r}_2}{2}\right) = C_f^2\left(\frac{\vec{r}_1 + \vec{r}_2}{2}\right)\Phi_f^{(o)}(\vec{\kappa}). \tag{3.35}$$

The functions $\Phi_f^{(o)}(\kappa)$ and $D_f^{(o)}(\vec{r})$ are connected by the relation

$$D_f^{(o)}(\vec{r}) = 2 \iiint_{-\infty}^{\infty} \left[1 - \cos \vec{\kappa}\cdot\vec{r}\right]\Phi_f^{(o)}(\vec{\kappa})d\vec{\kappa}. \tag{3.36}$$

Thus, the relative spectral distribution of the fluctuations of the quantity f is identical in all the regions G,G',... and is described by the function $\Phi_f^{(o)}(\vec{\kappa})$; only the overall intensity of the fluctuations, expressed by the quantity [g]

$$C_f^2\left(\frac{\vec{r}_1 + \vec{r}_2}{2}\right)$$

varies from region to region. As in Chapter 1 we can introduce the two-dimensional spectral density

$$F_f\left(\kappa_2, \kappa_3, |\kappa - \kappa'|, \frac{\vec{r} + \vec{r}'}{2}\right),$$

connected with the functions $D_f(\vec{r},\vec{r}')$ and $\Phi_f(\vec{\kappa}, \frac{\vec{r} + \vec{r}'}{2})$ by relations similar to (1.48), (1.52) and (1.53), i.e.

$$F_f\left(\kappa_2,\kappa_3,|\kappa-\kappa'|, \frac{\vec{r} + \vec{r}'}{2}\right) = \int_{-\infty}^{\infty} \cos \kappa_1(x - x')\Phi_f\left(\kappa_1,\kappa_2,\kappa_3, \frac{\vec{r} + \vec{r}'}{2}\right) d\kappa_1. \tag{3.37}$$

(In Eqs. (3.34) - (3.37) we neglect the difference between $C_f^2\left(\frac{\vec{r}_1 + \vec{r}_2}{2}\right)$ at two nearby points which are separated from each other by the distance $|\vec{r}_1 - \vec{r}_2| \ll L_o$, since this function changes appreciably only when its argument changes by a quantity of order L_o.)

We now consider briefly the spectral expansion of the random field $f(\vec{r})$ itself. For simplicity we consider an example where there exists a correlation function of the fluctuations of f, of the form

$$B_f(\vec{r}_1,\vec{r}_2) = \sigma_f^2\left(\frac{\vec{r}_1 + \vec{r}_2}{2}\right) b_f(|\vec{r}_1 - \vec{r}_2|).$$

(Similar questions were considered by Silverman [92].) Let $f(\vec{r})$ be represented by a stochastic Fourier-Stieltjes integral [h]

$$f(\vec{r}) = \iiint_{-\infty}^{\infty} e^{i\vec{\kappa}\cdot\vec{r}}\, d\varphi(\vec{\kappa}) \tag{3.38}$$

where it is assumed that $\overline{f} = 0$. Consider the expression

$$B_f(\vec{r},\vec{r}\,') = \overline{f(\vec{r})f^*(\vec{r}\,')} = \iiiint\!\!\iint_{-\infty}^{\infty} e^{i(\vec{\kappa}\cdot\vec{r} - \vec{\kappa}\,'\cdot\vec{r}\,')}\overline{d\varphi(\vec{\kappa})d\varphi^*(\vec{\kappa}\,')} \tag{3.39}$$

and introduce the coordinates $\vec{\rho} = \vec{r} - \vec{r}\,'$ and $\vec{R} = \frac{1}{2}(\vec{r} + \vec{r}\,')$. Then we have

$$\vec{\kappa}\cdot\vec{r} - \vec{\kappa}\,'\cdot\vec{r}\,' = (\vec{\kappa} - \vec{\kappa}\,')\cdot\vec{R} + \frac{1}{2}(\vec{\kappa} + \vec{\kappa}\,')\cdot\vec{\rho}$$

and

$$\overline{f(\vec{r})f^*(\vec{r}\,')} = \iiiint\!\!\iint_{-\infty}^{\infty} e^{i(\vec{\kappa} - \vec{\kappa}\,')\cdot\vec{R}}\, e^{i\left(\frac{\vec{\kappa} + \vec{\kappa}\,'}{2}\right)\cdot\vec{\rho}}\, \overline{d\varphi(\vec{\kappa})d\varphi^*(\vec{\kappa}\,')}. \tag{3.40}$$

By assumption

$$\overline{f(\vec{r})f^*(\vec{r}\,')} = \sigma_f^2(\vec{R})b_f(\vec{\rho}),$$

whence it follows that $\overline{d\varphi(\vec{\kappa})d\varphi^*(\vec{\kappa}\,')}$ must have the form

$$\overline{d\varphi(\vec{\kappa})d\varphi^*(\vec{\kappa}\,')} = M(\vec{\kappa} - \vec{\kappa}\,')\Phi_f^{(0)}\left(\frac{\vec{\kappa} + \vec{\kappa}\,'}{2}\right) d\vec{\kappa}\;\; d\vec{\kappa}\,', \tag{3.41}$$

where obviously $M(0) \geq 0$ and $\Phi_f^{(0)}(\vec{\kappa}) \geq 0$. Substituting this expression in (3.40) and carrying out the change of variables, we obtain

$$\sigma_f^2(\vec{R}) = \iiint_{-\infty}^{\infty} M(\vec{\kappa}) e^{i\vec{\kappa}\cdot\vec{R}}\, d\vec{\kappa}, \tag{3.42}$$

$$b_f(\vec{\rho}) = \iiint_{-\infty}^{\infty} \Phi_f^{(o)}(\kappa) e^{i\vec{\kappa}\cdot\vec{\rho}}\, d\vec{\kappa}. \tag{3.43}$$

In the case where σ_f^2 = const, $M(\vec{\kappa} - \vec{\kappa}') = \sigma_f^2\, \delta(\vec{\kappa} - \vec{\kappa}')$ and Eq. (3.41) reduces to (3.21). As follows from (3.41), in the case of variable σ_f^2, correlation appears between the neighboring spectral components $d\varphi(\vec{\kappa})$ and $d\varphi^*(\vec{\kappa}')$, i.e. if $|\vec{\kappa} - \vec{\kappa}'| \lesssim L_o^{-1}$, then [i]

$$\overline{d\varphi(\vec{\kappa})\, d\varphi^*(\vec{\kappa}')} \neq 0.$$

(It follows from (3.42) that the function $M(\vec{\kappa})$ differs appreciably from zero in an interval of order $1/L_o$, since $\sigma_f^2(R)$ changes appreciably in an interval of order L_o.)

3.4 Microstructure of the refractive index in a turbulent flow

The refractive index n for radio waves in the centimeter range is a function of the absolute temperature T, the pressure p (in millibars) and the water vapor pressure e (in millibars), i.e.

$$n - 1 = 10^{-6} \times \frac{79}{T} \left(p + \frac{4800e}{T}\right). \tag{3.44}$$

It is not hard to see that the quantities T and e figuring in this formula are not, strictly speaking, conservative additives. In fact, it is well known that when small parcels of air are displaced vertically their pressure undergoes a continuous equalization with the pressure of the surrounding air at the given height. The changes in pressure produce changes in temperature satisfying the equation of the adiabat

$$\frac{dT}{T} = \frac{\gamma - 1}{\gamma}\frac{dp}{p},$$

where $\gamma = c_p/c_v$ is Poisson's constant. The quantity dp is related to the change in height by the barometric formula $dp = -\rho g dz$, where ρ is the density of the air and g is the acceleration due to gravity. Thus we have

$$\frac{dT}{T} = -\frac{\gamma - 1}{\gamma}\frac{\rho g}{p}dz = -\frac{\gamma - 1}{\gamma}\frac{g}{RT}dz,$$

and

$$\frac{dT}{dz} = -\frac{\gamma - 1}{\gamma}\frac{g}{R} = -\frac{g}{c_p} = -\gamma_a. \tag{3.45}$$

The quantity $\gamma_a = 0.98^\circ/100$ m is called the adiabatic temperature gradient (a rising parcel of air cools off 0.98° for every 100 m of elevation). Integrating Eq. (3.45), we obtain $T + \gamma_a z = \text{const}$. Consequently, when parcels of air are displaced vertically, the quantity

$$H = T + \gamma_a z, \tag{3.46}$$

called in meteorology the potential temperature, preserves its value and may be regarded as a conservative additive.

The water vapor pressure e which figures in Eq. (3.44) is also not a conservative quantity, since it depends on the pressure. It can be expressed in terms of the so-called specific humidity q, which represents the concentration of water vapor in the air (i.e. the ratio of the mass of water vapor to the mass of moist air in a unit volume), by using the approximate formula

$$e = 1.62\ pq. \tag{3.47}$$

The quantity q is a conservative additive. (It is assumed that while the moist air is being displaced there is no condensation of water vapor.) Replacing the quantities T and e in Eq. (3.44) by $H - \gamma_a z$ and $1.62\ pq$, we obtain the formula

$$(n - 1) \times 10^6 = N = \frac{79p}{H - \gamma_a z}\left(1 + \frac{7800q}{H - \gamma_a z}\right), \tag{3.48}$$

which expresses the refractive index in terms of the conservative passive additives H and q. The quantity N depends on z through p(z), H(z), q(z) as well as on z directly, i.e.

$$N = N(z\ ,\ p(z),\ H(z),\ q(z)).$$

Suppose a parcel of air from the level z_1, characterized by the value $N_1 = N(z_1,\ p(z_1),\ H(z_1),\ q(z_1))$, appears at the level z_2 as a result of the action of turbulent mixing. Since the quantities H(z) and q(z) do not change when the parcel is displaced, while the quantities z and p(z) take on the new values z_2 and $p(z_2)$ at the level z_2, the same parcel will be characterized at the level z_2 by the value $N_1' = N(z_2,\ p(z_2),\ H(z_1),\ q(z_1))$. The value of N_1' differs from the "local" value of N at the level z_2 by the quantity

$$\delta N = N(z_2,\ p(z_2),\ H(z_1),\ q(z_1)) -$$

$$- N(z_2,\ p(z_2),\ h(z_2),\ q(z_2)) \sim \left(\frac{\partial N}{\partial H}\frac{dH}{dz} + \frac{\partial N}{\partial q}\frac{dq}{dz}\right)\delta z.$$

Thus, the fluctuations of N which appear are not proportional to the "full" gradient n, but rather to the quantity

$$M = \left(\frac{\partial N}{\partial H}\frac{dH}{dz} + \frac{\partial N}{\partial q}\frac{dq}{dz}\right) \times 10^{-6} =$$

$$= -\frac{79 \times 10^{-6} p}{T^2}\left(1 + \frac{15,500q}{T}\right)\left(\frac{dH}{dz} - \frac{7800}{1 + \frac{15,500q}{T}}\frac{dq}{dz}\right) =$$

$$= -\frac{79 \times 10^{-6} p}{T^2}\left(1 + \frac{15,500q}{T}\right)\left(\frac{dT}{dz} + \gamma_a - \frac{7800}{1 + \frac{15,500q}{T}}\frac{dq}{dz}\right). \tag{3.49}$$

The expression (3.49) has to be used to find the size of the fluctuations of the refractive index n.

The structure function of the refractive index of the atmosphere can be represented by Eqs. (3.18), i.e.

$$D_n(r) = \begin{cases} C_n^2 \, r^{2/3} & \text{for } \ell_o \ll r \ll L, \\ C_n^2 \, \ell_o^{2/3} \left(\frac{r}{\ell_o}\right)^2 & \text{for } r \ll \ell_o, \end{cases} \tag{3.50}$$

where the quantity C_n is defined by the expressions (3.29) and (3.49), i.e.

$$C_n^2 = a^2 \left[\frac{K^2}{\left(\frac{\partial \vec{u}}{\partial z}\right)^2} \right]^{1/3} M^2 = a^2 L_o^{4/3} M^2. \tag{3.51}$$

For the spectrum of the refractive index fluctuations we write the formula

$$\Phi_n(\kappa) = 0.033 C_n^2 \, \kappa^{-11/3} \quad (\kappa_o < \kappa < \kappa_m) , \tag{3.52}$$

where $\kappa_o \sim 1/L_o$ and L_o is the outer scale of the turbulence. The formulas given can be used to calculate the size of the refractive index fluctuations.

Part II

SCATTERING OF ELECTROMAGNETIC AND ACOUSTIC WAVES IN THE TURBULENT ATMOSPHERE

Chapter 4

SCATTERING OF ELECTROMAGNETIC WAVES IN THE TURBULENT ATMOSPHERE

Introductory remarks

The problem of scattering of electromagnetic waves in the turbulent atmosphere has attracted considerable attention, since this phenomenon is related to long-range atmospheric propagation of short waves beyond the limits of the "radio horizon". We cannot linger here on all the numerous problems associated with the use of radio scattering for the purpose of long range communication. Instead, we consider only theoretical aspects and try to indicate the physical content of the problem.

The problem which we consider in this chapter can be formulated as follows. A plane monochromatic electromagnetic wave is incident on a volume V of a turbulent medium; because of turbulent mixing within the volume V, there appear irregular refractive index fluctuations, which scatter the incident electromagnetic wave. It is required to find the mean density of the energy scattered in a given direction. To solve the problem, we shall assume that the refractive index field within the volume V is a random function of the coordinates and does not depend on time. The time changes in n which actually occur will simply be regarded as changes in the different realizations of the random field $n(\vec{r})$. Thus, we do not consider the problem of frequency fluctuations and change of the frequency spectrum of the scattered field [a].

4.1 Solution of Maxwell's equations

We shall assume that the conductivity of the medium is zero and that the magnetic permeability is unity. Furthermore, we shall assume that the electromagnetic field under consideration has a time dependence given by the factor $e^{-i\omega t}$. In this case Maxwell's equations take the following form:

$$\text{curl}\ \vec{E} = ik\vec{H},$$
$$\text{curl}\ \vec{H} = -ik\epsilon\vec{E}, \tag{4.1}$$
$$\text{div}\ \epsilon\vec{E} = 0.$$

Here $k = \omega/c$ is the wave number of the electromagnetic wave, ϵ is the dielectric constant (as already stated above, we regard ϵ as time independent), and $\vec{E}$ and $\vec{H}$ are the amplitudes of the electric and magnetic fields, so that the fields themselves are equal to $\vec{E}e^{-i\omega t}$ and $\vec{H}e^{-i\omega t}$, respectively. Taking the curl of the first of the equations (4.1) and using the second equation, we have [b]

$$-\Delta\vec{E} + \text{grad div}\ \vec{E} = k^2\epsilon\vec{E}. \tag{4.2}$$

Since

$$\text{div}\ \epsilon\vec{E} = \epsilon\ \text{div}\ \vec{E} + \vec{E}\cdot\text{grad}\ \epsilon = 0,$$

we have

$$\text{div}\ \vec{E} = -\vec{E}\cdot\text{grad}\log\epsilon.$$

Using this equality and setting $\epsilon = n^2$, we obtain

$$\Delta\vec{E} + k^2n^2\vec{E} + 2\ \text{grad}(\vec{E}\cdot\text{grad}\log n) = 0. \tag{4.3}$$

We assume that the fluctuations of the refractive index n are small, i.e. that $|n - \bar{n}| \ll 1$. Let n_1 denote the deviation of n from its mean value, so that $n = \bar{n} + n_1$. Since $\bar{n}$ is near unity, we shall henceforth assume that $\bar{n} = 1$ (if necessary we can change k to $k\bar{n}$ in all the results).

Substituting $n = 1 + n_1$ in Eq. (4.3), we obtain

$$\Delta\vec{E} + k^2\vec{E} = -2\ \text{grad}(\vec{E}\cdot\text{grad}\log(1 + n_1)) - 2k^2n_1\vec{E} - k^2n_1^2\vec{E}. \tag{4.4}$$

To solve Eq. (4.4), we can apply the method of small perturbations, whereby a solution is sought in the form of a series

$$\vec{E} = \vec{E}_o + \vec{E}_1 + \vec{E}_2 + \dots ,$$

where the k'th term of the series has the order of smallness n_1^k. Substituting this series in (4.4) and equating to zero each group of terms of the same order of smallness, we obtain

$$\Delta \vec{E}_o + k^2 \vec{E}_o = 0, \quad (4.5)$$

$$\Delta \vec{E}_1 + k^2 \vec{E}_1 = - 2k^2 n_1 \vec{E}_o - 2 \operatorname{grad}(\vec{E}_o \operatorname{grad} n_1). \quad (4.6)$$

In deriving Eq. (4.6), the quantity $\log(1 + n_1)$ has to be expanded in a series of powers of n_1, i.e. $\log(1 + n_1) \sim n_1 - (n_1^2/2) + \dots$. The quantity $\vec{E}_o$ represents the amplitude of the electric vector of the incident wave. Assuming that the incident wave is plane [c], we set $\vec{E}_o = \vec{A}_o \exp(i\vec{k}\cdot\vec{r})$. The quantity $\vec{E}_1$ represents the amplitude of the electric vector of the scattered wave. (The terms of the series $\vec{E} = \vec{E}_o + \vec{E}_1 + \vec{E}_2 + \dots$ which come after $\vec{E}_1$ are neglected because of their smallness [d].)

As is well known, the solution of the equation

$$\Delta u + k^2 u = f(\vec{r}) \quad (a)$$

corresponding to outgoing waves is of the form

$$u(\vec{r}) = - \frac{1}{4\pi} \int_V f(\vec{r}\,') \frac{e^{ik|\vec{r} - \vec{r}\,'|}}{|\vec{r} - \vec{r}\,'|} dV', \quad (b)$$

where $\vec{r}\,'$ is a variable vector ranging over the scattering volume V. We choose the origin of coordinates inside the scattering volume. If the observation point $\vec{r}$ is at a great distance from the scattering volume V as compared to the dimensions of V, then for all $\vec{r}\,'$ the quantity

$|\vec{r} - \vec{r}'|$ is almost constant and close to $r = |\vec{r}|$. In this case, the quantity $|\vec{r} - \vec{r}'|$ can be expanded in a series of powers of r'/r, i.e.

$$|\vec{r} - \vec{r}'| = r - \vec{m}\cdot\vec{r}' + \frac{1}{2r}\left[r'^2 - (\vec{m}\cdot\vec{r}')^2\right] + \dots ,$$

where $\vec{m} = \vec{r}/r$ is a unit vector directed from the origin of coordinates (chosen within the scattering volume) to the observation point. If the inequality

$$\frac{k}{2r}\left[r'^2 - (\vec{m}\cdot\vec{r}')^2\right] \ll 1,$$

holds for all values of r', i.e. if the dimensions L of the scattering volume satisfy the condition $\lambda r \gg L^2$, then

$$\exp\left(ik|\vec{r} - \vec{r}'|\right) \sim \exp\left[ik(r - \vec{m}\cdot\vec{r}')\right] .$$

Moreover, in the denominator of Eq. (b) we can replace $|\vec{r} - \vec{r}'|$ by r. Thus, the formula

$$u(\vec{r}) \sim \frac{1}{4\pi}\frac{e^{ikr}}{r}\int_V f(\vec{r}')\, e^{-ik\vec{m}\cdot\vec{r}'} dV' \tag{c}$$

is valid in the Fraunhofer zone. We use Eq. (c) to solve Eq. (4.6), obtaining

$$\vec{E}_1(\vec{r}) = \frac{k^2}{2\pi}\frac{e^{ikr}}{r}\int_V n_1(\vec{r}')\,\vec{A}_o\, e^{i\vec{k}\cdot\vec{r}' - ik\vec{m}\cdot\vec{r}'}\, dV' +$$

$$+ \frac{1}{2\pi}\frac{e^{ikr}}{r}\int_V \operatorname{grad}(e^{i\vec{k}\cdot\vec{r}'}\vec{A}_o\cdot\operatorname{grad} n_1(\vec{r}'))e^{-ik\vec{m}\cdot\vec{r}'} dV' . \tag{4.7}$$

The second of the integrals figuring in (4.7) can be transformed by using Gauss' theorem:

$$\int_V u \,\mathrm{grad}\, \varphi \, dV' = \int_S \varphi\, u\, d\vec{\sigma} - \int_V \varphi \,\mathrm{grad}\, u \, dV'.$$

The surface integral vanishes, since the surface of integration can be moved beyond the limits of the volume V. Since

$$\mathrm{grad}\, e^{-ik\vec{m}\cdot\vec{r}} = -\, ik\vec{m}\, e^{-ik\vec{m}\cdot\vec{r}},$$

then

$$\int_V \mathrm{grad}(e^{-i\vec{k}\cdot\vec{r}'}\vec{A}_o\cdot \mathrm{grad}\, n_1(\vec{r}'))\, e^{-ik\vec{m}\cdot\vec{r}'}\, dV' =$$

$$= ik\vec{m} \int_V (\vec{A}_o\cdot \mathrm{grad}\, n_1(\vec{r}'))\, e^{i\vec{k}\cdot\vec{r}'-ik\vec{m}\cdot\vec{r}'}\, dV'.$$

Consequently

$$\vec{E}_1(\vec{r}) = \frac{k^2 e^{ikr}}{2\pi r}\vec{A}_o \int_V n_1(\vec{r}')\, e^{i(\vec{k}-k\vec{m})\cdot\vec{r}'}\, dV' +$$

$$+ \frac{ike^{ikr}}{2\pi r}\vec{m} \int_V (\vec{A}_o\cdot \mathrm{grad}\, n_1(\vec{r}'))\, e^{i(\vec{k}-k\vec{m})\cdot\vec{r}'}\, dV' =$$

$$= \frac{k^2 e^{ikr}}{2\pi r} C_1\vec{A}_o + \frac{ike^{ikr}}{2\pi r} C_2\vec{m}, \tag{4.8}$$

where

$$C_1 = \int_V n_1(\vec{r}') \, e^{i(\vec{k}-k\vec{m})\cdot\vec{r}'} \, dV',$$

$$C_2 = \int_V \vec{A}_o \cdot \text{grad}\, n_1(\vec{r}') \, e^{i(\vec{k}-k\vec{m})\cdot\vec{r}'} \, dV'.$$

Both terms in the right hand side of (4.8) represent spherical waves whose amplitudes and phases depend on the refractive index fluctuations inside the volume V (through the random variables C_1 and C_2). The second term is a longitudinal alternating electric field. Transforming the expression for C_2 by using Gauss' theorem, we can show that the second term in (4.8) cancels the longitudinal component of the field contained in the first term, so that the scattered field is purely transverse [e]. Indeed, in calculating the flow of scattered energy we can simply ignore the second term in (4.8).

4.2 The mean intensity of scattering

To calculate the density of flow of the scattered energy $\vec{S} = (c/8\pi)\,\text{Re}\left(\vec{E}_1 \times \vec{H}_1^*\right)$, i.e. the average value of the density of energy flow during the period of one oscillation [f], we need the quantity $\vec{H}_1$, which can be found by using the first of the equations (4.1):

$$\vec{H}_1 = \frac{k^2 C_1}{2\pi i k} \,\text{curl}\left(\frac{e^{ikr}}{r}\vec{A}_o\right) = \frac{k^2 C_1}{2\pi i k}\vec{A}_o \times \text{grad}\left(\frac{e^{ikr}}{r}\right) =$$

$$= \frac{k^2 C_1}{2\pi i k}\left(\frac{ike^{ikr}}{r} - \frac{e^{ikr}}{r^2}\right)\vec{m} \times \vec{A}_o \sim \frac{k^2 C_1 e^{ikr}}{2\pi r}\,\vec{m} \times \vec{A}_o \,. \qquad (4.9)$$

We have neglected the rapidly decreasing term e^{ikr}/r^2. Substituting (4.8) and (4.9) into the formula for $\vec{S}$, we obtain

$$\vec{S} = \frac{ck^4}{32\pi^3 r^2} C_1 C_1^* \vec{A}_o \times (\vec{m} \times \vec{A}_o) = \frac{ck^4}{32\pi^3 r^2} C_1 C_1^* (\vec{m}\,(\vec{A}_o \cdot \vec{A}_o) - \vec{A}_o(\vec{m} \cdot \vec{A}_o)). \tag{4.10}$$

The density of energy flow in the direction $\vec{m}$ is equal to

$$S_m = \vec{S} \cdot \vec{m} = \frac{ck^4 C_1 C_1^*}{32\pi^3 r^2} (A_o^2 - (\vec{m} \cdot \vec{A}_o)^2) = \frac{ck^4 A_o^2 \sin^2 \chi}{32\pi^3 r^2} C_1 C_1^*, \tag{4.11}$$

where χ is the angle between the vectors $\vec{A}_o$ and $\vec{m}$. Substituting the expression for C_1, we find

$$S_m = \frac{ck^4 A_o^2 \sin^2 \chi}{32\pi^3 r^2} \int_V \int_V n_1(\vec{r}_1) n_1(\vec{r}_2) e^{i(\vec{k} - k\vec{m}) \cdot (\vec{r}_1 - \vec{r}_2)} dV_1 dV_2.$$

The quantity S_m is random. Its mean value is equal to

$$\overline{S}_m = \frac{ck^4 A_o^2 \sin^2 \chi}{32\pi^3 r^2} \int_V \int_V \overline{n_1(\vec{r}_1) n_1(\vec{r}_2)}\, e^{i(\vec{k} - k\vec{m}) \cdot (\vec{r}_1 - \vec{r}_2)} dV_1 dV_2. \tag{4.12}$$

Thus, $\overline{S}_m$ is expressed in terms of the spatial correlation function $B_n(\vec{r}_1, \vec{r}_2)$ of the refractive index fluctuations. We assume temporarily that the field of refractive index fluctuations is homogeneous; later we shall extend our results to the case of locally homogeneous and isotropic fields. Then $B_n(\vec{r}_1, \vec{r}_2) = B_n(\vec{r}_1 - \vec{r}_2)$ and the expression in the integrand of (4.12) depends only on the distance $\vec{r}_1 - \vec{r}_2$. Introducing the change of variables $\vec{r}_1 - \vec{r}_2 = \vec{\rho}$, $\vec{r}_1 + \vec{r}_2 = 2\vec{r}$ in (4.12), we carry out the integration with respect to $\vec{r}$, which gives as a result the volume V. Then the expression for $\overline{S}_m$ takes the form

$$\overline{S}_m = \frac{ck^4 V A_o^2 \sin^2 \chi}{4r^2} \frac{1}{8\pi^3} \int_V B_n(\vec{\rho}) e^{i[(\vec{k} - k\vec{m}) \cdot \vec{\rho}]} dV_\rho. \tag{4.13}$$

We now use the expansion (1.22) of the correlation function as a Fourier integral:

$$B_n(\vec{\rho}) = \iiint_{-\infty}^{\infty} \cos(\vec{\kappa}\cdot\vec{\rho})\, \Phi_n(\vec{\kappa})d\vec{\kappa} = \iiint_{-\infty}^{\infty} e^{-i\vec{\kappa}\cdot\vec{\rho}}\, \Phi_n(\vec{\kappa})d\vec{\kappa} . \tag{4.14}$$

Substituting this expression in the integral

$$I = \frac{1}{8\pi^3} \int_V B_n(\vec{\rho})\, e^{i\left[(\vec{k}-k\vec{m})\cdot\vec{\rho}\right]} dV_\rho ,$$

we obtain

$$I = \iiint_{-\infty}^{\infty} \Phi_n(\vec{\kappa})d\vec{\kappa}\, \frac{1}{8\pi^3} \int_V e^{i\left[(\vec{k}-k\vec{m}-\vec{\kappa})\cdot\vec{\rho}\right]} dV_\rho . \tag{4.15}$$

Let us examine the inner integral

$$F(\vec{\lambda}) = \frac{1}{8\pi^3} \int_V e^{i\vec{\lambda}\cdot\vec{\rho}} dV_\rho .$$

When the region of integration is infinite, the inner integral equals $\delta(\vec{\lambda}) = \delta(\vec{\kappa} - \vec{k} + k\vec{m})$ and therefore $I = \Phi_n(\vec{k} - k\vec{m})$. In the case of a finite volume of integration the function

$$F(\vec{\lambda}) = \frac{1}{8\pi^3} \int_V e^{i\vec{\lambda}\cdot\vec{\rho}} dV_\rho$$

has a sharp maximum in a region near the point $\lambda = 0$ and outside this region oscillates and falls off rapidly [g], while

$$\iiint_{-\infty}^{\infty} F(\vec{\lambda})d\vec{\lambda} = \int_V \delta(\vec{\rho})dV_\rho = 1.$$

Moreover, since $F(0) = V/(8\pi^3)$, the function $F(\vec{\lambda})$ is appreciably different from zero in a region of wave vector space which has a volume of order $8\pi^3/V$; of course, in each concrete case the shape of this volume and the behavior in it of the function $F(\vec{\lambda})$ depend on the dimensions and shape of the spatial volume V. Thus

$$I = \iiint_{-\infty}^{\infty} \Phi_n(\vec{\kappa})F(\vec{\kappa} - \vec{k} + k\vec{m})d\vec{\kappa} \sim \iiint_T \Phi_n(\vec{\kappa}) \frac{V}{8\pi^3} d\vec{\kappa} =$$

$$= \frac{1}{T} \iiint_T \Phi_n(\vec{\kappa})d\vec{\kappa} ,$$

where T represents the region of wave vector space with volume $T = 8\pi^3/V$ near the point $\vec{\kappa} = \vec{k} - k\vec{m}$. Therefore

$$I = \tilde{\Phi}_n(\vec{k} - k\vec{m}), \tag{4.16}$$

where $\tilde{\Phi}(\vec{\kappa})$ is the mean value of the function $\Phi(\vec{\kappa})$ obtained by averaging it over the region of wave vector space of volume $8\pi^3/V$ surrounding the point $\vec{\kappa}$; of course, this mean value should not be confused with the statistical average. Substituting the expression (4.16) in Eq. (4.13), we obtain

$$\overline{S}_m = \frac{ck^4 V\, A_o^2 \sin^2\chi}{4r^2} \tilde{\Phi}_n(\vec{k} - k\vec{m}). \tag{4.17}$$

If the function $\Phi_n(\vec{\kappa})$ does not change much in ranging over the volume $T = 8\pi^3/V$, then $\tilde{\Phi}_n(\vec{k} - k\vec{m}) \sim \Phi_n(\vec{k} - k\vec{m})$ and [h]

$$\bar{S}_m = \frac{ck^4 V A_o^2 \sin^2\chi}{4r^2} \tilde{\Phi}_n(\vec{k} - k\vec{m}). \tag{4.18}$$

Using the expression (4.17), we can find the formula for the effective scattering cross section of the volume V. Denoting by σ the effective cross section for scattering into the solid angle dΩ in the direction with unit vector $\vec{m}$, we obtain

$$d\sigma = \frac{\bar{S}_m r^2 d\Omega}{\frac{c A_o^2}{8\pi}} = 2\pi k^4 V \sin^2\chi \, \tilde{\Phi}_n(\vec{k} - k\vec{m}) d\Omega . \tag{4.19}$$

It follows from this formula that scattering at the angle $\theta(\cos\theta = \vec{k}\,\vec{m}/k)$ is determined only by a narrow portion of the turbulence spectrum near the point $\vec{\kappa} = \vec{k} - k\vec{m}$. Thus, only a small group of spectral components of the turbulence participate in the scattering at a given angle θ; these components form a spatial diffraction grating of fixed spacing $\ell(\theta)$ which is determined by the relation

$$\ell(\theta) = \frac{2\pi}{|\vec{k} - k\vec{m}|} = \frac{2\pi}{2k \sin\frac{\theta}{2}} = \frac{\lambda}{2\sin\frac{\theta}{2}} , \tag{4.20}$$

i.e., satisfies the well known Bragg condition. The directions of the vectors $\vec{k} - k\vec{m}$, $\vec{k}$ and $k\vec{m}$ are related by the "mirror reflection" condition (the "nodal planes" of the spatial diffraction grating are perpendicular to the vector $\vec{k} - k\vec{m}$). If the dimensions of the volume V are of order H, i.e. $V = H^3$, then besides the spectral components of the turbulence corresponding to the spacing $\ell(\theta) = \lambda/(2\sin\frac{\theta}{2})$, a part of the scattering at the angle θ will be contributed by spectral components corresponding to nearby periods in the interval

$$\ell_{1,2} = \frac{2\pi}{2k \sin\frac{\theta}{2} \pm \frac{2\pi}{H}} = \frac{\lambda}{2\sin\frac{\theta}{2} \pm \frac{\lambda}{H}} ,$$

about the point $\lambda/(2\sin\frac{\theta}{2})$ [i]. In every concrete case it is easy to evaluate the size of this interval, and its size is usually small compared with $\ell(\theta)$ [j]. Therefore, we shall henceforth make no distinction between functions $\Phi_n(\vec{\kappa})$ and $\tilde{\tilde{\Phi}}_n(\vec{\kappa})$.

Eq. (4.19) was obtained under the assumption that the field of refractive index fluctuations is homogeneous in the volume V. However, this result can also be extended to the case of locally homogeneous fields. In fact, since the effective cross section for scattering at a given angle really depends only on one "spectral component" of the refractive index inhomogeneities, the remaining "spectral components" can be changed as one pleases; it is only important that the quantity $\tilde{\tilde{\Phi}}_n(\vec{k} - k\vec{m})$ retain its value for given $\vec{k}$ and $\vec{m}$. Consequently, we can also consider functions $\tilde{\tilde{\Phi}}_n(\vec{\kappa})$ which have a singularity at the origin, i.e. which correspond to locally homogeneous random fields. Of course, in doing so we assume that we use Eq. (4.19) only for values of $\vec{k} - k\vec{m}$ for which $|\vec{k} - k\vec{m}| \gg 2\pi/L_o$ (L_o is the outer scale of the turbulence; see page 33), or [k]

$$\frac{\lambda}{2\sin\frac{\theta}{2}} \ll L_o. \tag{4.21}$$

4.3 Scattering by inhomogeneous turbulence

We now consider the case where the turbulence is not homogeneous inside the scattering volume and its mean characteristics change smoothly [ℓ]. The expression

$$\bar{S}_m = \frac{ck^4 A_o^2 \sin^2\chi}{32\pi^2 r^2} \int_V\int_V B_n(\vec{r}_1,\vec{r}_2)\, e^{i(\vec{k}-k\vec{m})\cdot(\vec{r}_1-\vec{r}_2)}\, dV_1 dV_2 , \tag{4.12}$$

obtained above for the density of flow of the scattered energy, does not depend on the assumption that the field of the refractive index fluctuations is homogeneous and can therefore also be applied to this case. We use the formula

$$B_n(\vec{r}_1, \vec{r}_2) = \sigma_n^2\left(\frac{\vec{r}_1 + \vec{r}_2}{2}\right) b_n(\vec{r}_1 - \vec{r}_2), \tag{4.22}$$

and introduce the coordinates $\vec{R} = \frac{1}{2}(\vec{r}_1 + \vec{r}_2)$ and $\vec{\rho} = \vec{r}_1 - \vec{r}_2$. Then Eq. (4.12) takes the form

$$S_m = \frac{ck^4 A_o^2 \sin^2\chi}{32\pi^3 r^2} \int_V \sigma_n^2(\vec{R})dV_R \int_V b_n(\vec{\rho})\, e^{i\left[(\vec{k}-k\vec{m})\cdot\vec{\rho}\right]} dV_\rho \ . \tag{4.23}$$

Using Eqs. (3.43) and (4.16), we can express the inner integral in this formula by $\tilde{\Phi}_n^{(o)}(\vec{k} - k\vec{m})$, where, as above, ~ denotes averaging over a volume $8\pi^3/V$ in wave number space. Then we have

$$S_m = \frac{ck^4 A_o^2 \sin^2\chi}{4r^2} \tilde{\Phi}_n^{(o)}(\vec{k} - k\vec{m}) \int_V \sigma_n^2(\vec{R})dV_R, \tag{4.24}$$

or, introducing $\Phi_n(\vec{\kappa},\vec{R}) = \sigma_n^2(\vec{R})\, \Phi_n^{(o)}(\vec{\kappa})$:

$$S_m = \frac{ck^4 A_o^2 \sin^2\chi}{4r^2} \int_V \tilde{\Phi}_n(\vec{k}-k\vec{m},\vec{R})dV_R. \tag{4.25}$$

Eqs. (4.24) and (4.25) are the generalization of the expression (4.17) for the case of inhomogeneous turbulence.

4.4 Analysis of various scattering theories

1. In one of the first papers devoted to the problem of the scattering of radio waves by atmospheric inhomogeneities (Booker and Gordon [27]), it was assumed that the correlation

function of the refractive index inhomogeneities has the form

$$B_n(\rho) = \overline{n_1^2}\, e^{-|\rho/r_o|} . \tag{4.26}$$

Of course, there is no serious justification for using this particular correlation function, and it is used only because it is convenient for doing calculations. As established in example a) on page 18 (Eq. (1.30)), the spectral density $\Phi(\kappa)$ corresponding to the function (4.26) has the form

$$\Phi_n(\kappa) = \frac{\overline{n_1^2}\, r_o^3}{\pi^2(1 + \kappa^2 r_o^2)^2} . \tag{4.27}$$

Substituting here $2k \sin\frac{\theta}{2}$ instead of κ, we obtain

$$d\sigma(\theta) = \frac{2}{\pi} \frac{k^4 V \overline{n_1^2} r_o^3}{\left(1 + 4k^2 r_o^2 \sin^2\frac{\theta}{2}\right)^2} \sin^2\chi \, d\Omega \tag{4.28}$$

for $d\sigma(\theta)$. Eq. (4.28) is the basic result of the paper of Booker and Gordon, and has served for a long time as the starting point for numerous experimental investigations. In these investigations, the results of measurements of refractive index inhomogeneities were analysed with the aim of determining the parameters $\overline{n_1^2}$ and r_o figuring in the correlation function (4.26); values of the order of 60 meters were usually obtained for the quantity r_o. For the usual value of k and θ, the quantity $2kr_o \sin\frac{\theta}{2}$ is much larger than unity. In this case

$$d\sigma(\theta) = \frac{V}{8\pi} \frac{\overline{n_1^2}}{r_o} \frac{\sin^2\chi}{\sin^4\frac{\theta}{2}} \, d\Omega , \tag{4.29}$$

i.e., in the Booker-Gordon theory $d\sigma(\theta)$ does not depend on the frequency and is determined by the single parameter $\overline{n_1^2} / r_o$, which characterizes the refractive index inhomogeneities of the atmosphere.

If we start from the basic formulas obtained in this chapter, it is not hard to show the fundamental defect of this series of papers. As we have already emphasized, the quantity $d\sigma(\theta)$ is proportional to $\Phi_n(\vec{k} - k\vec{m})$, i.e., it is proportional to the "intensity" of the inhomogneities with sizes satisfying the Bragg condition. From this point of view, the most natural way to determine the function $\Phi_n(\vec{\kappa})$ would be to measure it directly for the values of $\vec{\kappa}$ which may be of interest in the applications; these values of $\vec{\kappa}$ usually correspond to inhomogeneities with sizes ranging from some tens of centimeters to some tens of meters. However, in the Booker-Gordon theory and in the papers based on it, the value of the quantity $\Phi_n(\vec{\kappa})$ corresponding to comparatively small inhomogeneity sizes is determined from the outer scale r_o of the inhomogeneities and from the characteristic $\overline{n_1^2}$ of the refractive index fluctuations (which is also due to the most intense, large-scale inhomogeneities) by using the essentially arbitrary formula (4.27). We should also note that it is hopeless to evaluate small-scale fluctuations of the refractive index by using the quantities $\overline{n_1^2}$ and r_o characterizing large scale inhomogeneities, for the additional reason that the inhomogeneities of the largest scale are always inhomogeneous and anisotropic, so that their relation to the small scale inhomogeneities cannot be universal and must change as the general meteorological conditions change.

2. In some more recent papers [28], the expression

$$B_n(r) = \frac{\overline{n_1^2}}{2^{\nu-1}\,\Gamma(\nu)} \left(\frac{r}{r_o}\right)^{\nu} K_{\nu}\left(\frac{r}{r_o}\right) \qquad (4.30)$$

has been used as a correlation function. The spectral function

$$\Phi_n(\kappa) = \frac{\Gamma(\nu + \frac{3}{2})}{\pi\sqrt{\pi}\,\Gamma(\nu)} \; \frac{\overline{n_1^2}\, r_o^3}{(1 + \kappa^2 r_o^2)^{\nu + \frac{3}{2}}} \qquad (4.31)$$

corresponding to (4.30) was considered on page 19. As already shown, for $\kappa r_o \gg 1$, the function $\Phi_n(\kappa)$ coincides with the spectral density corresponding to the structure function $D_n(r) = c^2 r^{2\nu}$. Thus, for $\nu = 1/3$, the function (4.31) coincides in the region $\kappa r_o \gg 1$ with the spectral density $\Phi_n(\kappa) \sim \kappa^{-11/3}$, which expresses the theoretical size distribution of inhomogeneities in the concentration of a conservative passive additive in a developed turbulent flow. Substituting Eq. (4.31) in (4.19), we obtain

$$d\sigma(\theta) = \frac{2\Gamma(\nu + \frac{3}{2})}{\sqrt{\pi}\,\Gamma(\nu)} \frac{k^4 V \overline{n_1^2} r_o^3 \sin^2\chi}{\left(1 + 4k^2 r_o^2 \sin^2\frac{\theta}{2}\right)^{\nu + \frac{3}{2}}} d\Omega \,. \tag{4.32}$$

For $2kr_o \sin\frac{\theta}{2} \gg 1$, we obtain from this that

$$d\sigma(\theta) = \frac{\Gamma(\nu + \frac{3}{2})}{2^{2(\nu+1)}\sqrt{\pi}\,\Gamma(\nu)} \frac{\overline{n_1^2}}{r_o^{2\nu}} V k^{1-2\nu} \frac{\sin^2\chi}{(\sin\frac{\theta}{2})^{2\nu+3}} d\Omega. \tag{4.33}$$

The quantity $d\sigma(\theta)$ depends on the frequency and on the parameter $\overline{n_1^2} / r_o^{2\nu}$ which characterizes the refractive index fluctuations. Of course, Eq. (4.33) for $\nu = 1/3$ is much more justified than the expression (4.29), because the spectral density of refractive index fluctuations (4.31) used to derive it corresponds to the refractive index spectrum in a turbulent flow. How important this fact is for the problem being considered can be seen from the following example. Since the correlation functions (4.26) and (4.30) are represented by outwardly very similar curves (see Fig. 2), the parameters $\overline{n_1^2}$ and r_o determined from them will have values which are very close together. At the same time, the ratio of the quantity $d\sigma(\theta)$ calculated from Eq. (4.33) to the value of $d\sigma(\theta)$ calculated from Eq. (4.29) is equal to

$$(kr_o \sin\frac{\theta}{2})^{1 - 2\nu}$$

to within a constant factor. For $\nu = 1/3$ this quantity is equal to

$$\sqrt[3]{kr_o \sin\frac{\theta}{2}}\,.$$

Since we usually have $kr_o \sin\frac{\theta}{2} \gg 1$, Eqs. (4.29) and (4.33) will give greatly different values for $d\sigma(\theta)$. Eq. (4.33), as well as Eq. (4.29), expresses the spectral component $\Phi_n(2k \sin\frac{\theta}{2})$ which interests us in terms of the quantities r_o and $\overline{n_1^2}$ depending on the large scale inhomogeneities, and therefore it cannot be reliable enough, because the relation between the small scale and the large scale inhomogeneities just cannot be universal. We recall that for large r, or correspondingly for small κ, formulas of the type (4.30) or (4.31) describe the structure of the random field only to a very crude approximation.

3. Villars and Weisskopf [29] have made an interesting attempt to explain the scattering of electromagnetic waves by a turbulent flow. Their theory also begins by assuming that the deviation of the refractive index of the air from unity is proportional to the quantity p/T. However, Villars and Weisskopf neglect temperature fluctuations caused by turbulent mixing of the atmosphere and assume that the refractive index fluctuations of the atmosphere are caused by pressure fluctuations [m]. Pressure fluctuations p in a turbulent flow are caused by velocity fluctuations v' and are related to them by the formula

$$p \sim \rho v'^2, \tag{4.34}$$

where ρ is the density of the fluid. To explain the meaning of this relation, we recall that the Bernoulli equation $p + \rho v^2/2 = \text{const}$ is satisfied for stationary flow of a fluid. For non-stationary flow, an expression similar to (4.34) can be obtained from the equations of motion (see [30,13]). Thus, the pressure field in a turbulent field is random. Its structure function can be expressed in terms of the structure function of the velocity field by using a relation similar to (4.34), namely [30,13]:

$$\overline{[p(\vec{r}_1 + \vec{r}) - p(\vec{r}_1)]^2} = D_p(r) = \rho^2[D_{rr}(r)]^2, \tag{4.35}$$

where D_{rr} is the longitudinal structure function of the velocity field. Since for $L_o \gg r \gg \ell_o$, the structure function of the velocity field has the form $D_{rr}(r) = C(\epsilon r)^{2/3}$ (see page 32), then

$$D_p(r) = C^2\rho^2(\epsilon r)^{4/3} \qquad (\ell_o \ll r \ll L_o), \tag{4.36}$$

where ϵ is the energy dissipation rate.

It follows from the relation $n - 1 = \text{const}\ \frac{p}{T}$ that $n' \sim \frac{p'}{T}$ (since it is assumed in this paper that the temperature is constant). Thus, according to Villars and Weisskopf, the structure function of the refractive index must have the form

$$D_n(r) = \text{const}\ \rho^2\epsilon^{4/3}r^{4/3}. \tag{4.37}$$

As shown in the example on page 25, the spectral density

$$\Phi_n(\kappa) = \text{const}\ \rho^2\epsilon^{4/3}\kappa^{-13/3} \tag{4.38}$$

corresponds to the structure function (4.37). Substituting this expression into Eq. (4.19), we obtain

$$d\sigma(\theta) = \text{const}\ \rho^2\epsilon^{4/3}Vk^{-1/3}\left(\sin\frac{\theta}{2}\right)^{-13/3}\sin^2\chi\, d\Omega. \tag{4.39}$$

Villars and Weisskopf's basic assumption that refractive index fluctuations in a turbulent flow are caused by pressure fluctuations [n] does not withstand serious criticism. However, this paper is interesting in that it applies turbulence theory considerations to the problem of scattering of radio waves. This feature is expressed by the fact that Eq. (4.39) contains the parameter ϵ, which actually characterizes inhomogeneities of the sizes which cause scattering.

4. We now turn to the model which attributes the refractive index fluctuations to turbulent mixing (see Chapter 3). Assuming that the potential temperature and specific humidity are conservative and passive, we obtained in Chapter 3 the following expression for the structure function of the refractive index of the air:

$$D_n(r) = C_n^2 r^{2/3} \qquad (\ell_o \ll r \ll L_o), \tag{4.40}$$

$$D_n(r) = C_n^2 \ell_o^{2/3}\left(\frac{r}{\ell_o}\right)^2 \qquad (r \ll \ell_o). \tag{4.41}$$

The quantity C_n depends on ϵ, the energy dissipation rate in the turbulent flow, and on the rate of levelling out of the amount of refractive index inhomogeneity produced by the processes of molecular diffusion of water vapor and by the temperature conductivity. In the case where the turbulent regime and the distribution of $\bar{n}$ are stable, to calculate the quantity C_n^2 we can use the formulas (3.51) which express C_n^2 in terms of quantities characterizing the average profiles of the wind, temperature and humidity, i.e.

$$C_n^2 = a^2\left[\frac{K^2}{\left(\frac{\partial \vec{u}}{\partial z}\right)^2}\right]^{1/3} M^2 = a^2 L_o^{4/3} M^2, \tag{4.42}$$

$$M = -\frac{79 \times 10^{-6} p}{T^2}\left(1 + \frac{15,500q}{T}\right)\left(\frac{dT}{dz} + \gamma_a - \frac{7800}{1 + \frac{15,500q}{T}}\frac{dq}{dz}\right) . \tag{4.43}$$

The spectral density corresponding to the structure function (4.40) is equal to (cf. (3.52))

$$\Phi_n(\kappa) = 0.033 C_n^2 \kappa^{-11/3} \qquad \left(\frac{1}{L_o} \ll \kappa \ll \frac{1}{\ell_o}\right) . \tag{4.44}$$

Substituting this expression in Eq. (4.19), we obtain

$$d\sigma(\theta) = 0.016 V C_n^2 k^{1/3} \sin^2\chi \left(\sin\frac{\theta}{2}\right)^{-11/3} d\Omega , \tag{4.45}$$

$$\frac{1}{L_o} \ll \left(2k \sin\frac{\theta}{2}\right) \ll \frac{1}{\ell_o} .$$

An expression equivalent to Eq. (4.45) was obtained by Silverman [o,31]. Eq. (4.45) differs from all the previously considered expressions for $d\sigma(\theta)$ in the first place by the fact that to derive it we used the expression (4.44) for the spectral density of refractive index inhomogeneities corresponding to the law established in turbulence theory. In the second place, the spectral density

$$\Phi_n(\vec{k} - k\vec{m}) = \Phi_n\left(2k \sin\frac{\theta}{2}\right),$$

ertaining to the small scale inhomogeneities is now no longer described by quantities per-aining to the large scale inhomogeneities, but rather directly by the quantity C_n^2, which haracterizes the intensity of the small scale refractive index inhomogeneities.

4.5 Evaluation of the size of refractive index fluctuations from data on the scattering of radio waves in the troposphere

We now consider some concrete examples which illustrate the application of the theory ust presented. We compare the experimentally observed values of electromagnetic fields scat-ered by turbulence with the values of the same quantities inferred from Eq. (4.45). It is onvenient to carry out this comparison for the ratio of the flux density P_p of the scattered nergy to the flux density P_o which would be received at the same distance from the transmit-er to the receiver if they were located in free space. Let the distance between the trans-itter and the receiver be equal to D. If the transmitter power is E_o and the gain of its ntenna is G, then at the distance D it produces an energy flux density $P_o = GE_o/4\pi D^2$. The nergy flux density at the distance D/2, where the scattering volume is located, is $_1 = 4E_oG/4\pi D^2$. The amount of power scattered into the solid angle $d\Omega$ is $P_1 d\sigma = (4E_oG/4\pi D^2)d\sigma$. t the distance D/2 from the scattering volume, this power is distributed over an area $D/2)^2 d\Omega$, and therefore the flux density of the scattered energy is $P_p = (16E_oG/4\pi D^4)(d\sigma/d\Omega)$. hus we have

$$\frac{P_p}{P_o} = \frac{16}{D^2}\frac{d\sigma}{d\Omega} . \qquad (4.46)$$

To estimate the size of the scattering volume V, which figures in Eq. (4.19) for $d\sigma$, e use the approximate formula [p]

$$V \sim \frac{D^3\gamma^3}{8\theta} , \qquad (4.47)$$

here γ is the effective angular width of the gain pattern of the antenna. (It is assumed hat the receiving and transmitting antennas are identical and have identical gain patterns n the vertical and horizontal planes.) Using Eq. (4.47), we find

$$\frac{P_p}{P_o} = 4\pi k^4 \sin^2\chi \, \gamma^3 \, \Phi_n(2k \sin \tfrac{\theta}{2}) \, \frac{D}{\theta}$$

for P_p/P_o. In the case where the receiving and transmitting antennas are directed at the horizon, the quantity D/θ is constant and is equal to the effective radius R of the earth. Therefore we have

$$\frac{P_p}{P_o} = 4\pi R k^4 \sin^2\chi \, \gamma^3 \, \Phi_n(2k \sin \tfrac{\theta}{2}). \tag{4.48}$$

Substituting the expression

$$\Phi_n(2k \sin \tfrac{\theta}{2}) = 0.033 \, C_n^2 (2k \sin \tfrac{\theta}{2})^{-11/3} \sim 0.033 \, C_n^2 \, k^{-11/3} \, \theta^{-11/3}$$

into Eq. (4.48) and noting that $\sin^2\chi \sim 1$ for $\theta \ll 1$, we obtain

$$\frac{P_p}{P_o} = 0.76 \, C_n^2 \, R \lambda^{-1/3} \, \gamma^3 \, \theta^{-11/3}. \tag{4.49}$$

We use Eq. (4.29) to estimate the values of C_n which are necessary to explain the observed values of P_p/P_o. In Fig. 7 we show a graph of the seasonal trend of the monthly averages of the quantity P_p/P_o, which we have taken from the paper [34]. The path length was

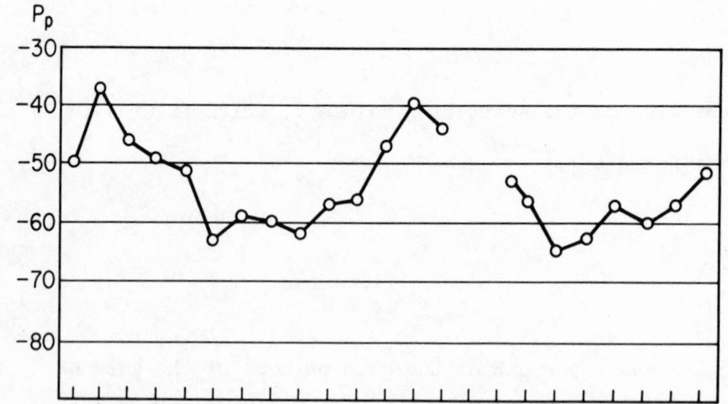

Fig. 7 Seasonal trend of mean received signal levels produced by tropospheric scattering. P_p is in decibels relative to 1 milliwatt.

300 km (188 miles), the transmitter frequency was 3600 Mcps ($\lambda = 8.17$ cm), the width of the gain patterns of the receiving and transmitting antennas was 0.012 radians, and the scattering angle was 0.048 radians. In this experiment, $\gamma < \theta$, so that we can use Eq. (4.47) and its consequence (4.49). Substituting the indicated values of λ, γ and θ into Eq. (4.49), we find that the values of C_n needed to explain the values of $10 \log (P_p/P_o)$ ranging from -67 to -93 decibels experimentally observed must lie in the range 8×10^{-8} to 4.5×10^{-9} $cm^{-1/3}$. The height of the center of the scattering volume above the earth's surface was 1.5 km, so that the values of C_n obtained pertain to this level. It should be noted that the size of the inhomogeneities responsible for the scattering is in this case $\ell(\theta) \sim \lambda/\theta = 1.7$ m. This size certainly satisfies the condition $\ell_o \ll \ell(\theta) \ll L_o$, i.e. lies in the range where the "two-thirds law" can be applied.

In order to judge whether these values are realistic, we now consider the temperature fluctuation characteristic C_T which figures in the "two-thirds law" for the temperature field:

$$D_T(\vec{r}) = \overline{[T(\vec{r} + \vec{r}_1) - T(\vec{r}_1)]^2} = C_T^2 \, r^{2/3}.$$

If we assume that the refractive index fluctuations are caused only by temperature fluctuations, then from (3.44) we can obtain the following relation between the quantities C_n and C_T:

$$C_n = \frac{79 \times 10^{-6} p}{T^2} C_T, \qquad (4.50)$$

where p is the atmospheric pressure in millibars and T is the absolute temperature. If we substitute here $p = 850$ mb and $T = 273^\circ$ K (the approximate values of these quantities at the height 1.5 km), we find that the value $C_T = 0.09$ deg $cm^{-1/3}$ corresponds to the value $C_n = 8 \times 10^{-8}$ $cm^{-1/3}$ and that the value $C_T = 0.005$ deg $cm^{-1/3}$ corresponds to the value $C_n = 4.5 \times 10^{-9}$ $cm^{-1/3}$. An analysis of the results of measurements carried out by Bullington [35] at a frequency of 3700 Mcps leads to approximately the same values of C_n and C_T, i.e. $C_T \sim 0.002$ to 0.006 deg $cm^{-1/3}$.

Direct measurements of the quantity C_T were first made by Krechmer [36]. The author of this book has also made numerous measurements in the layer of air near the earth and on a tethered balloon [37]. In the layer of air near the earth, the value of C_T varies from zero to 0.2 deg $cm^{-1/3}$ depending on the meteorological conditions, with the largest values obtained during the noon hours. In the lower troposphere (up to a height of 500 m) the size of C_T decreases compared with its value at the earth's surface, and is of the order of 0.03 deg $cm^{-1/3}$ and less [q]. Thus, it is apparent that the observed values of C_T are sufficient to explain the magnitude of the scattered signals. It should also be noted that the values of C_n obtained by analyzing the phenomena of twinkling and quivering of stellar images in telescopes have the same order of magnitude as those obtained above (see Chapter 13).

Chapter 5

THE SCATTERING OF SOUND WAVES IN A LOCALLY ISOTROPIC TURBULENT FLOW [a]

The scattering of sound waves in a turbulent flow resembles in many ways the phenomenon of scattering of electromagnetic waves. The velocity of propagation of sound waves depends both on the wind velocity and on the temperature. Since in a turbulent flow both of these quantities undergo irregular fluctuations, the velocity of sound is a random function of coordinates and time, a fact which leads to the scattering of sound waves. In this chapter we shall regard the quantity T itself as a conservative additive rather than $H = T + \gamma_a z$, since in what follows it is assumed that the results of calculations of acoustic scattering are used only in the layer of the atmosphere near the earth, where the difference between H and T is unimportant. The scattering of sound waves in a turbulent flow was first considered by Obukhov [38] in the year 1941; subsequently papers by other authors [33,32,39] have been devoted to the same problem.

The basic equation for sound propagation in a moving medium can be written in the form

$$\Delta P - \frac{1}{c^2}\left(\frac{\partial}{\partial t} + u_i \frac{\partial}{\partial x_i}\right)^2 P = 0, \tag{5.1}$$

where P is the potential of the sound wave, the u_i are the components of the velocity of motion of the medium, and c is the velocity of sound. A derivation of this equation with some simplifying assumptions is given by Andreyev and Rusakov [40]. Naturally, in using Eq. (5.1) we do not take into account the rotational component of the acoustic field. However, under atmospheric conditions, the size of this component is small compared to the potential component.

We assume that the mean flow velocity is equal to zero and that $\vec{u} = \vec{u}'$ represents the instantaneous value of the fluctuational velocity in the turbulent flow. Since the velocity fluctuations are small compared to the velocity of sound (under the conditions in the earth's atmosphere), we shall retain only the lowest power of the quantity u'/c ($u' = |\vec{u}'|$) in the equations. Squaring the operator $\frac{\partial}{\partial t} + u_i' \frac{\partial}{\partial x_i}$, we obtain

$$\Delta P - \frac{1}{c^2}\frac{\partial^2 P}{\partial t^2} = \frac{1}{c^2}\frac{\partial \vec{u}'}{\partial t}\cdot\text{grad } P + \frac{2}{c^2}\vec{u}'\cdot\text{grad }\frac{\partial P}{\partial t} \tag{5.2}$$

with an accuracy up to terms of order u'/c. The first term in the right hand side is of order no larger than $(1/c^2)\Omega\,\vec{u}'\cdot$ grad P (where Ω is the largest frequency of the fluctuations of flow velocity); the second term is of order $(1/c^2)\,\omega\,\vec{u}\cdot$grad P, where ω is the angular frequency of the sound. In the case $\Omega \ll \omega$ (and this condition is practically always met for all frequencies in the acoustic spectrum) we can neglect the first term in the right hand side of (5.2), obtaining as a result the equation

$$\Delta P - \frac{1}{c^2}\frac{\partial^2 P}{\partial t^2} = \frac{2\vec{u}'}{c^2}\cdot\text{grad }\frac{\partial P}{\partial t}\,. \tag{5.3}$$

The velocity of sound c, which figures in Eq. (5.3), is a function of temperature. For example, $c \sim \sqrt{T}$ for an ideal gas. If we denote the mean temperature in the flow by $\overline{T}$ and the temperature fluctuation by T', then we have

$$c(T) \sim c(\overline{T})\left(1 + \frac{T'}{2\overline{T}}\right). \tag{5.4}$$

In the atmosphere the quantity $T'/\overline{T}$ is of the same order as u/c. Substituting the expression (5.4) in Eq. (5.3) we obtain

$$\Delta P - \frac{1}{c^2}\frac{\partial^2 P}{\partial t^2} = \frac{2\vec{u}'}{c^2}\cdot\text{grad }\frac{\partial P}{\partial t} - \frac{1}{c^2}\frac{T'}{T}\frac{\partial^2 P}{\partial t^2}\,,$$

with an accuracy up to terms of order $T'/\overline{T}$. (Henceforth instead of $\overline{T}$ and $c(\overline{T})$ we shall write T and c, understanding these quantities to be the corresponding mean values.) Assuming that the time dependence of P is given by the factor $e^{-i\omega t}$, i.e. that $P = \Pi\, e^{-i\omega t}$, we obtain the equation

$$\Delta\Pi + k^2\,\Pi = -\,2ik\,\frac{\vec{u}}{c}\cdot\text{grad }\Pi + k^2\,\frac{T'}{T}\,\Pi\,, \tag{5.5}$$

for the amplitude potential Π, where $k = \omega/c$ is the wave number of the sound wave [b].

We shall look for a solution of Eq. (5.5) in the form of a series $\Pi = \Pi_o + \Pi_1 + \Pi_2 + \ldots$, where Π_k has the order of smallness of u'/c or T'/T raised to the power of k. Then we have

$$\Delta \Pi_o + k^2 \Pi_o = 0, \tag{5.6}$$

$$\Delta \Pi_1 + k^2 \Pi_1 = -2ik \frac{\vec{u}'}{c} \cdot \text{grad}\, \Pi_o + k^2 \frac{T'}{T} \Pi_o . \tag{5.7}$$

Π_o represents the amplitude of the acoustic wave potential incident on the scattering volume V. Assuming that the incident wave is plane, we obtain

$$\Pi_o = A_o e^{i\vec{k}\cdot\vec{r}} , \tag{5.8}$$

where $\vec{k}$ is the wave vector of the incident wave. Substituting this expression in Eq. (5.7), we obtain

$$\Delta \Pi_1 + k^2 \Pi_1 = 2k^2 \left(\frac{\vec{u}'\cdot\vec{n}}{c} + \frac{T'}{2T} \right) A_o e^{i\vec{k}\cdot\vec{r}} , \tag{5.9}$$

where $\vec{n}$ is a unit vector in the direction of $\vec{k}$ ($\vec{k} = k\vec{n}$). Eq. (5.9) has the form of Eq. (a) on page 61. Consequently, its solution at large distances from the scattering volume ($\lambda r \gg L^2$, where $L^3 = V$) is

$$\Pi_1(\vec{r}) = -\frac{1}{4\pi} \frac{e^{ikr}}{r} \int_V 2k^2 \left[\frac{\vec{n}\cdot\vec{u}'(\vec{r}')}{c} + \frac{T'(\vec{r}')}{2T} \right] A_o\, e^{i\vec{k}\cdot\vec{r}' - ik\vec{m}\cdot\vec{r}'}\, dV' , \tag{5.10}$$

where $\vec{m}$ is a unit vector directed from the center of the scattering volume to the receiving point. Thus, $\Pi_1(\vec{r})$ represents a spherical wave $\Pi_1 = Q\, e^{ikr}/r$ with random complex amplitude

$$Q = -\frac{k^2 A_o}{2\pi} \int_V \left[\frac{\vec{n}\cdot\vec{u}'(\vec{r}')}{c} + \frac{T'(\vec{r}')}{2T} \right] e^{ik(\vec{n}-\vec{m})\cdot\vec{r}'}\, dV' . \tag{5.11}$$

As is well known [14], the average value of the flux density vector of the scattered energy (taken over the period of one oscillation) is equal to

$$\vec{S} = \frac{\omega\rho}{2} \operatorname{Im}(\Pi_1^* \operatorname{grad} \Pi_1),$$

where ρ is the density of the gas. Calculating the gradient of Π_1, we obtain

$$\operatorname{grad} \Pi_1 = \operatorname{grad} Q \frac{e^{ikr}}{r} = Q \left(ik \frac{e^{ikr}}{r} - \frac{e^{ikr}}{r^2} \right) \vec{m} \sim ikQ \frac{e^{ikr}}{r} \vec{m},$$

where it is assumed that $kr \gg 1$. Therefore we have

$$\vec{S} = \frac{\omega\rho}{2} \operatorname{Im} \left(Q^* \frac{e^{-ikr}}{r} ikQ \frac{e^{ikr}}{r} \vec{m} \right) = \frac{\omega\rho k}{2r^2} QQ^* \vec{m} . \tag{5.12}$$

The quantity $\vec{S}$, which depends (via Q) on the velocity and temperature fluctuations of the flow within the scattering volume, is random. Its mean value equals [c]

$$\overline{\vec{S}} = \frac{\omega\rho k}{2r^2} \overline{QQ^*} \vec{m} = \vec{m} \frac{\rho c k^6 A_o^2}{8\pi^2 r^2} \times$$

$$\times \iint_{V\,V} \overline{\left[\frac{n_i u_i'(\vec{r}_1)}{c} + \frac{T'(\vec{r}_1)}{2T} \right] \left[\frac{n_k u_k'(\vec{r}_2)}{c} + \frac{T'(\vec{r}_2)}{2T} \right]} e^{ik(\vec{n}-\vec{m})\cdot(\vec{r}_1-\vec{r}_2)} dV_1 dV_2. \tag{5.13}$$

We assume that the random fields $\vec{u}'(\vec{r})$ and $T'(\vec{r})$ are homogeneous and isotropic; below it will be possible to extend our results to the case of locally isotropic fields as well. In this case it follows from the incompressibility condition for the turbulent flow of the fluid (valid for $u \ll c$) that [d]

$$\overline{u_i'(\vec{r}_1) T'(\vec{r}_2)} = 0.$$

Consequently, we have

$$\vec{S} = \vec{m}\,\frac{\rho c k^6 A_o^2}{8\pi^2 r^2}\left[\frac{1}{c^2}\,n_i n_k \iint_{V\,V} \overline{u_i'(\vec{r}_1)u_k'(\vec{r}_2)}\; e^{ik(\vec{n}-\vec{m})\cdot(\vec{r}_1-\vec{r}_2)}\,dV_1 dV_2 \;+\right.$$

$$\left. + \frac{1}{4T^2}\iint_{V\,V} \overline{T'(\vec{r}_1)T'(\vec{r}_2)}\; e^{ik(\vec{n}-\vec{m})\cdot(\vec{r}_1-\vec{r}_2)}\,dV_1 dV_2\right]. \qquad (5.14)$$

But

$$\overline{u_i'(\vec{r}_1)u_k'(\vec{r}_2)} = B_{ik}(\vec{r}_1 - \vec{r}_2)$$

is the correlation tensor of the velocity field, and

$$\overline{T'(\vec{r}_1)T'(\vec{r}_2)} = B_T(\vec{r}_1 - \vec{r}_2)$$

is the correlation function of the field of temperature fluctuations. Since the integrands in the right hand side of (5.14) depend only on $\vec{r}_1 - \vec{r}_2$, we can carry out one of the integrations in doing the double integrals over the volume, obtaining as a result

$$\vec{S} = \vec{m}\,\frac{\rho c k^6 A_o^2 V}{8\pi^2 r^2}\left[\frac{1}{c^2}\,n_i n_k \int_V B_{ik}(\vec{r}\,')\, e^{ik(\vec{n}-\vec{m})\cdot\vec{r}\,'}\,dV' \;+\right.$$

$$\left. + \frac{1}{4T^2}\int_V B_T(\vec{r}\,')\, e^{ik(\vec{n}-\vec{m})\cdot\vec{r}\,'}\,dV'\right]. \qquad (5.15)$$

We now use the representation of correlation functions in the form of Fourier integrals. As established in Part I, we have

$$B_T(\vec{r}) = \iiint_{-\infty}^{\infty} e^{i\vec{\kappa}\cdot\vec{r}}\, \Phi_T(\vec{\kappa})\, d\vec{\kappa}, \tag{5.16}$$

$$B_{ik}(\vec{r}) = \iiint_{-\infty}^{\infty} e^{i\vec{\kappa}\cdot\vec{r}} \left(\delta_{ik} - \frac{\kappa_i \kappa_k}{\kappa^2}\right) E(\vec{\kappa})\, d\vec{\kappa} \; . \tag{5.17}$$

Here $E(\vec{\kappa})$ is the spectral density of the energy of the turbulence in wave number space, and $\Phi_T(\vec{\kappa})$ is the spectral density of the temperature fluctuations (more exactly, the spectral density of the amount of inhomogeneity in the temperature field). Substituting the expressions (5.16) and (5.17) into the integrals in the right hand side of Eq. (5.15), we obtain

$$\int_V B_{ik}(\vec{r}\,') \, e^{-i\vec{\kappa}\cdot\vec{r}\,'} \, dV' = 8\pi^3 \overline{\overline{\left(\delta_{ik} - \frac{\kappa_i \kappa_k}{\kappa^2} E(\vec{\kappa})\right)}} \; , \tag{5.18}$$

$$\int_V B_T(\vec{r}\,') \, e^{-i\vec{\kappa}\cdot\vec{r}\,'} \, dV' = 8\pi^3 \; \overline{\overline{\Phi_T(\vec{\kappa})}}, \tag{5.19}$$

where the double overbar over a function like $F(\vec{\kappa})$ denotes the average of this function over the region in wave number space of volume $8\pi^3/V$ surrounding the point $\vec{\kappa}$. The derivation of these formulas is analogous to the derivation of Eq. (4.16). Substituting the expressions (5.18) and (5.19) into Eq. (5.15), we obtain

$$\vec{S} = \vec{m} \, \frac{\pi \rho c k^6 A_o^2 V}{r^2} \left[\frac{1}{c^2} n_i n_k \overline{\overline{\left(\delta_{ik} - \frac{k^2 (n_i - m_i)(n_k - m_k)}{k^2 (\vec{n}-\vec{m})\cdot(\vec{n}-\vec{m})}\right) E(k(\vec{n} - \vec{m}))}} + \right.$$

$$+ \frac{1}{4T^2} \overline{\overline{\Phi_T(k(\vec{n} - \vec{m}))}} \Bigg] . \tag{5.20}$$

In the case where the volume V is so large that averaging over the region $8\pi^3/V$ of wave number space does not substantially change the averaged functions, Eq. (5.20) can be simplified considerably. In this case we have

$$n_i n_k \left(\delta_{ik} - \frac{(n_i - m_i)(n_k - m_k)}{(\vec{n} - \vec{m})\cdot(\vec{n} - \vec{m})} \right) = \frac{1}{2}(1 + \vec{m}\cdot\vec{n}).$$

But $\vec{m}\cdot\vec{n} = \cos\theta$, where θ is the angle between the direction of the vector $\vec{k}$ and the vector $\vec{r}$ going from the center of the scattering volume to the observation point, i.e. the scattering angle. Therefore

$$\frac{1}{2}(1 + \vec{m}\cdot\vec{n}) = \cos^2\frac{\theta}{2},$$

and

$$\vec{S} = \vec{m}\,\frac{\pi\rho c k^6 A_o^2 V}{r^2}\left[\frac{1}{c^2} E(k(\vec{n} - \vec{m}))\cos^2\frac{\theta}{2} + \frac{1}{4T^2}\,\Phi_T(k(\vec{n} - \vec{m}))\right]. \tag{5.21}$$

Since in the case of isotropic turbulence $E(\vec{\kappa}) = E(\kappa)$ and $\Phi_T(\vec{\kappa}) = \Phi_T(\kappa)$, it follows that

$$E(k(\vec{n} - \vec{m})) = E(2k\sin\frac{\theta}{2})$$

and

$$\Phi_T(k(\vec{n} - \vec{m})) = \Phi_T(2k\sin\frac{\theta}{2}).$$

Thus we have

$$\vec{S} = \vec{m} \frac{\pi \rho c k^6 A_o^2 V}{r^2} \left[\frac{1}{c^2} E(2k \sin \frac{\theta}{2}) \cos^2 \frac{\theta}{2} + \frac{1}{4T^2} \Phi_T(2k \sin \frac{\theta}{2}) \right]. \tag{5.22}$$

Eq. (5.22) can be used to find the effective cross section for the scattering of sound in the direction θ. The acoustic power scattered into the solid angle $d\Omega$ is equal to $Sr^2 d\Omega$. The energy flux density in the incident wave $\Pi_o = A_o e^{i\vec{k}\cdot\vec{r}}$ is equal to

$$\vec{S}_o = \frac{\omega\rho}{2} \operatorname{Im} \left(A_o e^{-i\vec{k}\cdot\vec{r}} i\vec{k} A_o e^{i\vec{k}\cdot\vec{r}} \right) = \frac{1}{2} \omega\rho A_o^2 \vec{k},$$

and its absolute value is $S_o = \frac{1}{2} c\rho k^2 A_o^2$. Consequently, we have

$$d\sigma(\theta) = 2\pi k^4 V \left[\frac{1}{c^2} E(2k \sin \frac{\theta}{2}) \cos^2 \frac{\theta}{2} + \frac{1}{4T^2} \Phi_T(2k \sin \frac{\theta}{2}) \right] d\Omega. \tag{5.23}$$

Eq. (5.23) is completely analogous to Eq. (4.19), which defines the effective cross section for the scattering of electromagnetic waves. (The expression inside square brackets in Eq. (5.23) signifies the spectral density of the refractive index fluctuations.)

It follows from the expression (5.23) that the effective cross section for scattering at the angle θ depends only on spectral components of the turbulence with wave numbers $2k \sin \frac{\theta}{2}$, corresponding to "sinusoidal space diffraction gratings" with period

$$\ell(\theta) = \frac{2\pi}{2k \sin \frac{\theta}{2}} = \frac{\lambda}{2 \sin \frac{\theta}{2}} \tag{5.24}$$

satisfying the Bragg condition. This fact allows us to extend Eq. (5.23), obtained by assuming that the velocity and temperature fluctuations are homogeneous and isotropic, to the case of locally isotropic fields. In fact if $\ell(\theta) \ll L_o$, then the values of the functions $E(2k \sin \frac{\theta}{2})$ and $\Phi_T(2k \sin \frac{\theta}{2})$ are determined only by the isotropic inhomogeneities (eddies) and the anisotropy of the large scale inhomogeneities has no influence whatsoever on these values. In the case $\ell_o \ll \ell(\theta) \ll L_o$, i.e.

$$\frac{\lambda}{L_o} \ll 2 \sin\frac{\theta}{2} \ll \frac{\lambda}{\ell_o}, \tag{5.25}$$

the quantities $E(2k \sin\frac{\theta}{2})$ and $\Phi_T(2k \sin\frac{\theta}{2})$ are determined by the "two-thirds laws" for the velocity and temperature fields:

$$D_{rr} = C_V^2\, r^{2/3}, \quad D_T = C_T^2\, r^{2/3}. \tag{5.26}$$

Here $C_V^2 = C\epsilon^{2/3}$, $C_T^2 = a^2\, \overline{N}\epsilon^{-1/3}$, ϵ is the energy dissipation rate of the turbulence, and $\overline{N}$ is the rate of levelling out of the temperature inhomogeneities. In this case, we have

$$E(\kappa) = 0.061\, C_V^2\, \kappa^{-11/3}, \tag{5.27}$$

$$\Phi_T(\kappa) = 0.033\, C_T^2\, \kappa^{-11/3} \tag{5.28}$$

(see (2.20) and (3.24)). Substituting these expressions into Eq. (5.23), we obtain

$$d\sigma(\theta) = 0.030\, k^{1/3}\, V\left[\frac{C_V^2}{c^2}\cos^2\frac{\theta}{2} + 0.13\,\frac{C_T^2}{T^2}\right]\left(\sin\frac{\theta}{2}\right)^{-11/3} d\Omega\,. \tag{5.29}$$

In the layer of the atmosphere near the earth, the quantities C_V/c and C_T/T have the same order of magnitude, so that the temperature and wind fluctuations make approximately the same contribution to the scattering of sound in the atmosphere [e]. An experimental investigation of the scattering of sound in the atmosphere was carried out by Kallistratova [97]. Her results agree satisfactorily with Eq. (5.29).

Using the general formula (5.23) we can also easily find the quantity $d\sigma(\theta)$ in cases where the spectral densities of the velocity and temperature fluctuations have a form different from (5.27) and (5.28). Such expressions are given in the papers [39,41]. For example, in the case where the correlation functions of the fluctuations of wind velocity and temperature have the exponential form

$$B_{rr}(r) = \frac{1}{3} v_o^2 \exp\left(- |r|/\ell\right), \quad B_T(r) = T_o^2 \exp(- |r|/\ell), \tag{5.30}$$

the expression for $d\sigma(\theta)$ takes the form [f]

$$d\sigma(\theta) = \frac{V}{2\pi\ell} \left[\frac{v_o^2}{3c^2} 8 \sin^2\theta \left(\frac{k^2\ell^2}{1 + 4k^2\ell^2 \sin^2 \frac{\theta}{2}} \right)^3 + \frac{T_o^2}{T^2} \left(\frac{k^2\ell^2}{1 + 4k^2\ell^2 \sin^2 \frac{\theta}{2}} \right)^2 \right] d\Omega \; . \tag{5.31}$$

It is interesting to note that in this case $d\sigma(0)$ depends only on the temperature fluctuations, i.e. the wind inhomogeneities do not scatter at zero angle [g].

Part III

PARAMETER FLUCTUATIONS OF ELECTROMAGNETIC AND ACOUSTIC WAVES PROPAGATING IN A TURBULENT ATMOSPHERE

Introductory Remarks

The influence of atmospheric turbulence on the propagation of electromagnetic and acoustic waves involves more than scattering of the waves. As the waves propagate through the medium, there occur fluctuations of amplitude, phase, frequency and other wave parameters. These effects are of great importance in a host of problems in atmospheric optics, acoustics and radio meteorology. (For example, one might mention the fluctuations of frequency and angle of arrival of electromagnetic and acoustic waves, the twinkling and quivering of stellar images in telescopes, radio star scintillation, etc.) On the other hand, the study of parameter fluctuations of electromagnetic and acoustic waves can give valuable information about the structure of atmospheric turbulence (see Part IV). The most recent papers devoted to amplitude and phase fluctuations of electromagnetic waves are concerned with the phenomena of twinkling and quivering of stellar images in telescopes. In recent years, interest in this problem has increased greatly, and there already exist a large number of experimental and theoretical papers dealing with these matters.

The problem of parameter fluctuations of waves propagating in the turbulent atmosphere can be formulated as follows (with a view to obtaining a theoretical solution): Along the wave propagation path from the source to the observation point there occur refractive index fluctuations produced by the turbulence. The wave source may be situated either outside the region where the fluctuations occur or inside it. In the first case, we can replace the actual source of waves by an equivalent source located on the boundary of the region. (For example, a star located at a great distance from the earth can be replaced by a plane wave located at the boundary of the refracting atmosphere.) In the second case, we can generally disregard the part of space lying behind the wave source, since its influence on the propagating waves is negligibly small. Thus, in both cases we can assume that the source of waves lies on the boundary of the region occupied by the refractive index fluctuations. We shall always assume that the observation point lies inside the region. (If the observation point lies outside the region, the value of the field at the observation point can be determined from the values of the field at the boundary of the region occupied by the inhomogeneities.)

Just as in the problem of wave scattering by refractive index inhomogeneities, we shall assume that the field of refractive index inhomogeneities is quasi-stationary, so that we shall not be concerned with frequency fluctuations and the frequency spectrum of the amplitude and phase fluctuations of the wave. (However, the problem of the frequency spectrum of the amplitude and phase fluctuations of the wave can be approached by starting with the spatial spectrum of the fluctuations (in this regard, see Chapter 12)). The actual time changes of the refractive index field can be regarded as changes of the realizations of the random field. We shall consider that the field of refractive index fluctuations is a locally isotropic random field. Our problem will be to determine the statistical properties of the wave field at a distance L from the source of radiation (or from the boundary of the region occupied by the refractive index fluctuations).

In Part III we consider some methods for solving the problem just stated. We begin by presenting the simplest method, which is based on the equations of geometrical optics [42,43, 44,45].

Chapter 6

SOLUTION OF THE PROBLEM OF AMPLITUDE AND PHASE FLUCTUATIONS OF A PLANE MONOCHROMATIC WAVE BY USING THE EQUATIONS OF GEOMETRICAL OPTICS

6.1 Derivation and solution of the equations of geometrical optics

We consider first the problem of amplitude and phase fluctuations of short electromagnetic waves. As was shown in Part II, the process of scattering of electromagnetic waves in an inhomogeneous medium can be described by the equation (cf. (4.3))

$$\Delta \vec{E} + k^2 n^2 \vec{E} + 2\ \mathrm{grad}(\vec{E} \cdot \mathrm{grad} \log n) = 0. \tag{6.1}$$

We assume that the geometrical dimensions of all the inhomogeneities in the spatial distribution of the refractive index are much greater than the wavelength λ (i.e., that $\lambda \ll \ell_0$, where ℓ_0 is the inner scale of the turbulence). In this case we can neglect the last term of Eq. (6.1) [a]. Thus, the propagation of short waves ($\lambda \ll \ell_0$) in an inhomogeneous medium is described by the equation

$$\Delta \vec{E} + k^2 n^2(\vec{r})\vec{E} = 0. \tag{6.2}$$

The vector equation (6.2) reduces to three scalar equations, having the form

$$\Delta u + k^2 n^2(\vec{r})u = 0, \tag{6.3}$$

where u can denote any of the field components. We set $u = Ae^{iS}$, where A is the amplitude and S is the phase of the wave. Substituting this expression in Eq. (6.3) and setting the real and imaginary parts of this equation equal to zero, after first representing Eq. (6.3) in the form

$$\frac{\Delta u}{u} + k^2 n^2(\vec{r}) \equiv \Delta \log u + (\nabla \log u)^2 + k^2 n^2(\vec{r}) = 0$$

for convenience, we obtain a system of two equations equivalent to (6.3)

$$\Delta \log A + (\nabla \log A)^2 - (\nabla S)^2 + k^2 n^2(\vec{r}) = 0, \tag{6.4}$$

$$\Delta S + 2 \nabla \log A \cdot \nabla S = 0. \tag{6.5}$$

To simplify Eq. (6.4) further, we note that ∇S is of order k, e.g. (in a plane wave $S = \vec{k} \cdot \vec{r}$ and $\nabla S = \vec{k}$). Therefore the two last terms in Eq. (6.4) are of order $k^2 = 4\pi^2/\lambda^2$. Moreover, the wave amplitude A can change appreciably only in distances of the order of the dimensions of the inhomogeneities in the medium. Therefore

$$\Delta \log A + (\nabla \log A)^2 \equiv \frac{\Delta A}{A}$$

is of order no greater than $1/\ell_o^2$. Since we have assumed that $\lambda \ll \ell_o$, the first two terms of Eq. (6.4) are small compared to the last two terms and can be neglected. Thus, Eq. (6.4) takes the form

$$(\nabla S)^2 = k^2 n^2(\vec{r}). \tag{6.6}$$

We shall now use the system of equations (6.5) and (6.6), i.e. the equations of geometrical optics, to solve the problem of amplitude and phase fluctuations of a plane wave propagating in a locally isotropic turbulent flow.

Let the refractive index $n(\vec{r})$ be a random function of the coordinates, with a mean value equal to 1 [b]. We denote the deviations of $n(\vec{r})$ from unity by $n_1(\vec{r})$, i.e.

$$n(\vec{r}) = 1 + n_1(\vec{r}). \tag{6.7}$$

We assume that $|n_1(\vec{r})| \ll 1$; this condition is accurately met in all real cases. The smallness of the refractive index fluctuations allows us to use perturbation theory to solve Eqs. (6.5) and (6.6). We set $S = S_0 + S_1$ and $\log A = \log A_0 + \chi$, where $\chi = \log A/A_0$ is the "level" of the amplitude fluctuations on a logarithmic scale. Then Eqs. (6.5) and (6.6) take the form

$$(\nabla S_0)^2 + 2\nabla S_0 \cdot \nabla S_1 + (\nabla S_1)^2 = k^2 + 2k^2 n_1(\vec{r}) + k^2 n_1^2(\vec{r}), \tag{6.8}$$

$$\Delta S_0 + \Delta S_1 + 2\nabla \log A_0 \cdot \nabla S_0 + 2\nabla \log A_0 \cdot \nabla S_1 + 2\nabla\chi\cdot\nabla S_0 + 2\nabla\chi\cdot\nabla S_1 = 0. \tag{6.9}$$

Equating groups of terms of the zeroth order of smallness, we obtain

$$(\nabla S_0)^2 = k^2, \tag{6.10}$$

$$\Delta S_0 + 2\nabla \log A_0 \cdot \nabla S_0 = 0. \tag{6.11}$$

Subtracting these equations from (6.8) and (6.9), we find

$$\nabla S_1 \cdot (2\nabla S_0 + \nabla S_1) = 2k^2 n_1(\vec{r}) + k^2 n_1^2(\vec{r}), \tag{6.12}$$

$$\Delta S_1 + 2\nabla \log A_0 \cdot \nabla S_1 + 2\nabla\chi\cdot\nabla S_0 + 2\nabla\chi\cdot\nabla S_1 = 0\,. \tag{6.13}$$

In the case where $|\nabla S_1| \ll |\nabla S_0| = k$, i.e. $\lambda|\nabla S_1| \ll 2\pi$, we can neglect the term $(\nabla S_1)^2$ in Eq. (6.12). Moreover, in the right hand side of (6.12) we can omit the term $k^2 n_1^2(\vec{r})$ of the second order of smallness. Thus, the linearized equation

$$\nabla S_0 \cdot \nabla S_1 = k^2 n_1(\vec{r}) \tag{6.14}$$

is valid for $\lambda|\nabla S_1| \ll 2\pi$, i.e. when the phase changes by a small amount over the distance of a wavelength λ (note that the smallness requirement is not imposed on the value of S_1 itself). If the same condition $\lambda|\nabla S_1| \ll 2\pi$ is met, we can omit the last term in (6.13), which in this case is small compared to the third term of this equation; the result is

$$\Delta S_1 + 2 \nabla \log A_o \cdot \nabla S_1 + 2 \nabla \chi \cdot \nabla S_o = 0. \tag{6.15}$$

We now consider the amplitude and phase fluctuations of a plane wave, choosing its direction of propagation as the x-axis. Then $S_o = kx$ and $A_o = \text{const.}$ In this case, Eqs. (6.14) and (6.15) take the form

$$\frac{\partial S_1}{\partial x} = kn_1(\vec{r}), \tag{6.16}$$

$$\Delta S_1 + 2k \frac{\partial \chi}{\partial x} = 0. \tag{6.17}$$

Let the source of the plane wave be located at the plane x = 0 (this plane can also be regarded as the boundary of the region occupied by the refractive index fluctuations), and let the observation point have the coordinates (L,y,z), i.e. be located at a distance L from the source of the wave. Integrating Eq. (6.16) and (6.17), we obtain

$$S_1(L,y,z) = k \int_0^L n_1(x,y,z)dx, \tag{6.18}$$

$$\chi(L,y,z) = -\frac{1}{2k}\left[\left(\frac{\partial S_1}{\partial x}\right)_{(L,y,z)} - \left(\frac{\partial S_1}{\partial x}\right)_{(0,y,z)} + \int_0^L \left(\frac{\partial^2 S_1}{\partial y^2} + \frac{\partial^2 S_1}{\partial z^2}\right) dx\right]. \tag{6.19}$$

The quantity

$$\frac{1}{2k}\left[\left(\frac{\partial S_1}{\partial x}\right)_{(L,y,z)} - \left(\frac{\partial S_1}{\partial x}\right)_{(0,y,z)}\right] = \frac{1}{2}[n_1(L,y,z) - n_1(0,y,z)]$$

is small compared to the integral figuring in Eq. (6.19). Therefore we have approximately

$$\chi(L,y,z) = -\frac{1}{2k}\int_0^L \left[\left(\frac{\partial^2}{\partial y^2} + \frac{\partial^2}{\partial z^2}\right) k \int_0^x n_1(\xi,y,z)d\xi\right]dx =$$

$$= -\frac{1}{2}\int_0^L dx \int_0^x d\xi \left[\frac{\partial^2 n_1(\xi,y,z)}{\partial y^2} + \frac{\partial^2 n_1(\xi,y,z)}{\partial z^2}\right]. \tag{6.20}$$

Eqs. (6.18) and (6.20) express the amplitude and phase fluctuations at the point (L,y,z) in terms of the refractive index fluctuations along the propagation path.

6.2 The structure function and the spectrum of the phase fluctuations of the wave

Averaging Eqs. (6.18) and (6.20) and taking into account that $\overline{n_1} = 0$, we obtain $\overline{\chi} = \overline{S_1} = 0$. These equations allow us to express the structure (correlation) functions of the phase and amplitude fluctuations in terms of the structure function of the refractive index. For example, taking the difference of the values of S_1 at two points on the plane x = L, we obtain

$$S_1(L,y_1,z_1) - S_1(L,y_2,z_2) = k\int_0^L [n_1(x,y_1,z_1) - n_1(x,y_2,z_2)]dx. \tag{6.21}$$

We square this equation and write the square of the integral in the form of a double integral. Then performing the average, we find

$$\overline{[S_1(L,y_1,z_1) - S_1(L,y_2,z_2)]^2} =$$

$$= k^2 \int_0^L dx_1 \int_0^L dx_2 \overline{[n_1(x_1,y_1,z_1)-n_1(x_1,y_2,z_2)] \times [n_1(x_2,y_1,z_1)-n_1(x_2,y_2,z_2)]}. \tag{6.22}$$

Using the algebraic identity

$$(a - b)(c - d) = \frac{1}{2}[(a - d)^2 + (b - c)^2 - (a - c)^2 - (b - d)^2]$$

we express the integrand in terms of the structure function of the refractive index, i.e.

$$\overline{[n_1(x_1,y_1,z_1) - n_1(x_1,y_2,z_2)][n_1(x_2,y_1,z_1) - n_1(x_2,y_2,z_2)]} =$$

$$= \frac{1}{2}\overline{[n_1(x_1,y_1,z_1) - n_1(x_2,y_2,z_2)]^2} + \frac{1}{2}\overline{[n_1(x_1,y_2,z_2) - n_1(x_2,y_1,z_1)]^2} -$$

$$- \frac{1}{2}\overline{[n_1(x_1,y_1,z_1) - n_1(x_2,y_1,z_1)]^2} - \frac{1}{2}\overline{[n_1(x_1,y_2,z_2) - n_1(x_2,y_2,z_2)]^2} . \qquad (6.23)$$

Since we assume that the refractive index field is a locally isotropic random field, we have

$$\overline{[n_1(x_\alpha,y_\beta,z_\gamma) - n_1(x_\lambda,y_\mu,z_\nu)]^2} =$$

$$= D_n\left(\sqrt{(x_\alpha - x_\lambda)^2 + (y_\beta - y_\mu)^2 + (z_\gamma - z_\nu)^2}\right), \qquad (6.24)$$

where the indices $\alpha,\ldots,\mu,\ldots,\nu$ can take the values 1 and 2. Thus, the expression (6.23) is equal to

$$\frac{1}{2} D_n\left(\sqrt{(x_1 - x_2)^2 + (y_1 - y_2)^2 + (z_1 - z_2)^2}\right) +$$

$$+ \frac{1}{2} D_n\left(\sqrt{(x_1 - x_2)^2 + (y_1 - y_2)^2 + (z_1 - z_2)^2}\right) -$$

$$- \frac{1}{2} D_n\left(|x_1 - x_2|\right) - \frac{1}{2} D_n\left(|x_1 - x_2|\right) =$$

$$= D_n\left(\sqrt{(x_1 - x_2)^2 + (y_1 - y_2)^2 + (z_1 - z_2)^2}\right) - D_n\left(|x_1 - x_2|\right). \qquad (6.25)$$

Substituting (6.25) into Eq. (6.22), we obtain

$$D_S(\rho) = \overline{[S_1(L, y_1, z_1) - S_1(L, y_2, z_2)]^2} =$$

$$= k^2 \int_0^L dx_1 \int_0^L dx_2 \left[D_n\left(\sqrt{(x_1 - x_2)^2 + \rho^2}\right) - D_n\left(|x_1 - x_2|\right)\right], \qquad (6.25')$$

where $\rho = \sqrt{(y_1 - y_2)^2 + (z_1 - z_2)^2}$ is the distance between the observation points in the plane $x = L$. It is easy to convince oneself that the equality

$$\int_0^L dx_1 \int_0^L dx_2\, f(x_1 - x_2) = 2 \int_0^L (L - x) f(x) dx \qquad (6.26)$$

holds for any even function $f(x)$. Applying this relation to (6.25'), we obtain

$$D_S(\rho) = 2k^2 \int_0^L (L - x)\left[D_n\left(\sqrt{x^2 + \rho^2}\right) - D_n(x)\right] dx. \qquad (6.27)$$

The relation (6.27) can still be simplified a bit further. To do so, we should consider the fact that for $x \gg \rho$, the expression $D_n(\sqrt{x^2 + \rho^2}) - D_n(x)$ is very small. For example, if $D_n(x) = Cx^{\mu}$ $(\mu < 2)$, then

$$D_n\left(\sqrt{x^2 + \rho^2}\right) - D_n(x) \sim \frac{C\mu}{2} \rho^2 x^{\mu-2}$$

for $x \gg \rho$. The chief contribution to the integral (6.27) occurs for $x \lesssim \rho$. If $\rho \ll L$, then on the segment $x \lesssim \rho$, $L - x \sim L$ and

$$D_S(\rho) \sim 2k^2 L \int_0^L \left[D_n \left(\sqrt{x^2 + \rho^2}\right) - D_n(x)\right] dx.$$

Since the integrand is very small for $x > L$, the upper limit of integration can be replaced by ∞, and then we obtain the formula

$$D_S(\rho) = 2k^2 L \int_0^\infty \left[D_n \left(\sqrt{x^2 + \rho^2}\right) - D_n(x)\right] dx, \tag{6.28}$$

which is valid for $\rho \ll L$.

Eq. (6.28) expresses the structure function of the phase fluctuations of the wave in the plane $x = L$ in terms of the structure function $D_n(x)$ of the refractive index. From Eq. (6.28) we can obtain a relation between the spectra of the phase fluctuations and of the refractive index. As was shown in Chapter 1, a structure function given in some plane can be represented by the integral (cf. (1.49))

$$D_S(\rho) = 2 \iint_{-\infty}^{\infty} [1 - \cos(\kappa_2\eta + \kappa_3\zeta)] F_S(\kappa_2, \kappa_3, 0) d\kappa_2 d\kappa_3, \tag{6.29}$$

where $\rho^2 = \eta^2 + \zeta^2$. Here $F_S(\kappa_2, \kappa_3, 0)$ represents the two-dimensional spectral density of the structure function $D_S(\rho)$. In Chapter 1 we also derived the formula (cf. (1.48))

$$D_n \left(\sqrt{x^2 + \rho^2}\right) - D_n(x) = 2 \iint_{-\infty}^{\infty} [1 - \cos(\kappa_2\eta + \kappa_3\zeta)] F_n(\kappa_2, \kappa_3, x) d\kappa_2 d\kappa_3, \tag{6.30}$$

where $F_n(\kappa_2, \kappa_3, x)$ is related to the three dimensional spectral density $\Phi_n(\kappa_1, \kappa_2, \kappa_3)$ of the refractive index fluctuations by the relation (cf. (1.53))

$$2\pi\, \Phi_n(\kappa_1,\kappa_2,\kappa_3) = \int_{-\infty}^{\infty} F_n(\kappa_2,\kappa_3,x)\cos(\kappa_1 x)\,dx. \tag{6.31}$$

It follows from (6.31) that

$$\int_0^{\infty} F_n(\kappa_2,\kappa_3,x)\,dx = \pi\, \Phi_n(0,\kappa_2,\kappa_3). \tag{6.32}$$

We substitute the expansion (6.30) in Eq. (6.28) and change the order of integration with respect to (κ_2,κ_3) and x, i.e.

$$D_S(\rho) = 4k^2L \iint_{-\infty}^{\infty} [1 - \cos(\kappa_2\eta + \kappa_3\zeta)]\,d\kappa_2 d\kappa_3 \int_0^{\infty} F_n(\kappa_2,\kappa_3,x)\,dx.$$

Bearing in mind the relation (6.32), we find

$$D_S(\rho) = 2 \iint_{-\infty}^{\infty} [1 - \cos(\kappa_2\eta + \kappa_3\zeta)]\,2\pi k^2L\, \Phi_n(0,\kappa_2,\kappa_3)\,d\kappa_2 d\kappa_3. \tag{6.33}$$

Comparing the expansion (6.33) and Eq. (6.29), we convince ourselves that the two-dimensional spectral density $F_S(\kappa_2,\kappa_3,0)$ of the phase fluctuations is equal to

$$F_S(\kappa_2,\kappa_3,0) = 2\pi k^2L\, \Phi_n(0,\kappa_2,\kappa_3). \tag{6.34}$$

Since

$$\Phi_n(\kappa_1,\kappa_2,\kappa_3) = \Phi_n\left(\sqrt{\kappa_1^2 + \kappa_2^2 + \kappa_3^2}\right)$$

in a locally isotropic turbulent flow, then

$$\Phi_n(0,\kappa_2,\kappa_3) = \Phi_n\left(\sqrt{\kappa_2^2 + \kappa_3^2}\right)$$

and

$$F_S(\kappa_2,\kappa_3,0) = F_s\left(\sqrt{\kappa_2^2 + \kappa_3^2},\ 0\right) .$$

Writing $\kappa = \sqrt{\kappa_2^2 + \kappa_3^2}$, we finally obtain

$$F_S(\kappa,0) = 2\pi k^2 L\, \Phi_n(\kappa). \tag{6.34'}$$

6.3 Solution of the equations of geometrical optics by using spectral expansions

The relation (6.34') between the spectral densities $F_S(\kappa,0)$ and $\Phi_n(\kappa)$ is equivalent to the relation (6.28) between the structure functions of the phase fluctuations and the refractive index fluctuations. The relation (6.34') can be obtained from Eq. (6.16) by still another method, which does not require the introduction of structure functions. As was shown in Chapter 1, the locally isotropic random field $n_1(\vec{r})$ can be represented in the form of the following stochastic integral

$$n_1(x,y,z) = n_1(x,0,0) + \iint_{-\infty}^{\infty} \left(1 - e^{i(\kappa_2 y + \kappa_3 z)}\right) d\nu(\kappa_2,\kappa_3,x). \tag{6.35}$$

Since n_1 is a real quantity, we have

$$d\nu^*(-\kappa_2, -\kappa_3, x) = d\nu(\kappa_2, \kappa_3, x).$$

The random amplitudes $d\nu(\kappa_2, \kappa_3, x)$ satisfy the relation

$$\overline{d\nu(\kappa_2, \kappa_3, x)d\nu^*(\kappa_2', \kappa_3', x_1)} = \delta(\kappa_2 - \kappa_2')\delta(\kappa_3 - \kappa_3') \times$$

$$\times F_n(\kappa_2, \kappa_3, x - x')d\kappa_2 d\kappa_3 d\kappa_2' d\kappa_3' . \tag{6.36}$$

We shall look for an expansion of the phase fluctuation field $S_1(\vec{r})$ which has the same form, i.e.

$$S_1(x,y,z) = S_1(x,0,0) + \iint_{-\infty}^{\infty} \left[1 - e^{i(\kappa_2 y + \kappa_3 z)}\right] d\sigma(\kappa_2, \kappa_3, x). \tag{6.37}$$

The random amplitudes $d\sigma(\kappa_2, \kappa_3, x)$ satisfy the relation

$$\overline{d\sigma(\kappa_2, \kappa_3, x)d\sigma^*(\kappa_2', \kappa_3', x')} =$$

$$= \delta(\kappa_2 - \kappa_2')\delta(\kappa_3 - \kappa_3')F_S(\kappa_2, \kappa_3, x - x')d\kappa_2 d\kappa_3 d\kappa_2' d\kappa_3'. \tag{6.38}$$

Substituting the expansions (6.35) and (6.37) in Eq. (6.16), we obtain

$$\frac{\partial S_1(x,0,0)}{\partial x} + \iint_{-\infty}^{\infty} \left[1 - e^{i(\kappa_2 y + \kappa_3 z)}\right] \frac{\partial}{\partial x} d\sigma(\kappa_2, \kappa_3, x) =$$

$$= kn_1(x,0,0) + k \iint_{-\infty}^{\infty} \left[1 - e^{i(\kappa_2 y + \kappa_3 z)}\right] d\nu(\kappa_2,\kappa_3,x). \tag{6.39}$$

Setting $y = z = 0$, we have

$$\frac{\partial S_1(x,0,0)}{\partial x} = kn_1(x,0,0).$$

Subtracting this equation from (6.39), we obtain the equation

$$\iint_{-\infty}^{\infty} \left[1 - e^{i(\kappa_2 y + \kappa_3 z)}\right]\left[\frac{\partial}{\partial x} d\sigma(\kappa_2,\kappa_3,x) - kd\nu(\kappa_2,\kappa_3,x)\right] = 0, \tag{6.40}$$

satisfied for arbitrary y and z. Equating the integrand to zero, we obtain the relation

$$\frac{\partial}{\partial x} d\sigma(\kappa_2,\kappa_3,x) = kd\nu(\kappa_2,\kappa_3,x).$$

We integrate this equation with respect to x from 0 to L. Since $d\sigma(\kappa_2,\kappa_3,0) = 0$ (there are no fluctuations at the "input" to the turbulent region), we have [c]

$$d\sigma(\kappa_2,\kappa_3,L) = k \int_0^L dx d\nu(\kappa_2,\kappa_3,x). \tag{6.41}$$

We multiply Eq. (6.41) by its complex conjugate equation

$$d\sigma^*(\kappa_2',\kappa_3',L) = k \int_0^L dx' d\nu^*(\kappa_2',\kappa_3',x'),$$

written for the point (κ_2', κ_3') and average. Taking into account the relations (6.36) and (6.38), we obtain

$$F_s(\kappa_2, \kappa_3, 0)\delta(\kappa_2 - \kappa_2')\delta(\kappa_3 - \kappa_3')d\kappa_2 d\kappa_3 d\kappa_2' d\kappa_3' =$$

$$= k^2 \int_0^L dx \int_0^L dx' F_n(\kappa_2, \kappa_3, x - x')\delta(\kappa_2 - \kappa_2')\delta(\kappa_3 - \kappa_3')d\kappa_2 d\kappa_3 d\kappa_2' d\kappa_3'$$

whence

$$F_s(\kappa_2, \kappa_3, 0) = k^2 \int_0^L dx \int_0^L dx' F_n(\kappa_2, \kappa_3, x - x') \ . \tag{6.42}$$

The function $F_n(\kappa_2, \kappa_3, x - x')$ is even with respect to $x - x'$. Applying Eq. (6.26), we obtain

$$F_s(\kappa_2, \kappa_3, 0) = 2k^2 \int_0^L (L - x)F_n(\kappa_2, \kappa_3, x)dx \ . \tag{6.43}$$

As shown in Chapter 1, the function $F_n(\kappa_2, \kappa_3, x)$ falls off rapidly for $x > 1/\kappa$. Therefore, only the region $x \lesssim 1/\kappa$ contributes substantially to (6.43). If $1/\kappa \ll L$, the chief contribution to the integral (6.43) is obtained for $x \ll L$. In this region, $L - x \sim L$ and

$$F_s(\kappa_2, \kappa_3, 0) \sim 2k^2 L \int_0^L F_n(\kappa_2, \kappa_3, x)dx \sim$$

$$\sim 2k^2 L \int_0^\infty F_n(\kappa_2, \kappa_3, x)dx \ .$$

Applying Eq. (6.32), we obtain the previous relation

$$F_S(\kappa,0) = 2\pi k^2 L \, \Phi_n(\kappa), \tag{6.44}$$

from which follows also the equivalent relation (6.28). This spectral method of solving the problem is equivalent to the method based on structure or correlation functions, but is in many respects more convenient.

We now apply the spectral method of solution to determine the amplitude fluctuations. Above we obtained the relation (6.20), which relates the fluctuations of the "level" $\chi = \log A/A_0$ to the refractive index fluctuations $n_1(\vec{r})$. We shall look for the locally isotropic random field $\chi(\vec{r})$ in the form of an expansion

$$\chi(x,y,z) = \chi(x,0,0) + \iint_{-\infty}^{\infty} \left[1 - e^{i(\kappa_2 y + \kappa_3 z)}\right] da(\kappa_2,\kappa_3,x). \tag{6.45}$$

According to the general formula (1.46)

$$\overline{da(\kappa_2,\kappa_3,x)da^*(\kappa_2',\kappa_3',x')} = \delta(\kappa_2 - \kappa_2')\delta(\kappa_3 - \kappa_3') \times$$

$$\times F_A(\kappa_2,\kappa_3,|x - x'|)d\kappa_2 d\kappa_3 d\kappa_2' d\kappa_3', \tag{6.46}$$

where $F_A(\kappa_2,\kappa_3,|x|)$ is the two-dimensional spectral density of the field of fluctuations of the level. Substituting the expansions (6.35) and (6.45) into Eq. (6.20), we obtain

$$\chi(L,0,0) + \iint_{-\infty}^{\infty} \left[1 - e^{i(\kappa_2 y + \kappa_3 z)}\right] da(\kappa_2,\kappa_3,L) =$$

$$= -\frac{1}{2}\int_0^L dx\int_0^x d\xi \iint_{-\infty}^{\infty} (\kappa_2^2 + \kappa_3^2)\, e^{i(\kappa_2 y + \kappa_3 z)} d\nu(\kappa_2,\kappa_3,\xi). \tag{6.47}$$

Setting $y = z = 0$ in (6.47), we obtain the relation

$$X(L,0,0) = -\frac{1}{2}\int_0^L dx \int_0^x d\xi \iint_{-\infty}^{\infty} (\kappa_2^2 + \kappa_3^2) d\nu(\kappa_2,\kappa_3,\xi).$$

Subtracting this equation from Eq. (6.47), we find

$$\iint_{-\infty}^{\infty} \left[1 - e^{i(\kappa_2 y + \kappa_3 z)}\right] da(\kappa_2,\kappa_3,L) =$$

$$= \frac{1}{2}\int_0^L dx \int_0^x d\xi \iint_{-\infty}^{\infty} (\kappa_2^2 + \kappa_3^2)\left[1 - e^{i(\kappa_2 y + \kappa_3 z)}\right] d\nu(\kappa_2,\kappa_3,\xi), \tag{6.48}$$

whence

$$da(\kappa_2,\kappa_3,L) = \frac{1}{2}\int_0^L dx \int_0^x d\xi (\kappa_2^2 + \kappa_3^2) d\nu(\kappa_2,\kappa_3,\xi). \tag{6.49}$$

We multiply Eq. (6.49) by its complex conjugate, written for κ_2',κ_3',L, i.e.

$$da^*(\kappa_2',\kappa_3',L) = \frac{1}{2}\int_0^L dx' \int_0^{x'} d\xi' (\kappa_2'^2 + \kappa_3'^2) d\nu^*(\kappa_2',\kappa_3',\xi')$$

and average. Taking into account Eqs. (6.46) and (6.36), we obtain

$$F_A(\kappa_2,\kappa_3,0) = \frac{1}{4}\int_0^L dx \int_0^L dx' \int_0^x d\xi \int_0^{x'} d\xi' \kappa^4 F_n(\kappa_2,\kappa_3,\xi - \xi'), \qquad (6.50)$$

where κ^2 denotes the quantity $\kappa_2^2 + \kappa_3^2$.

Eq. (6.50), which relates the two-dimensional spectral density of the amplitude fluctuations of the wave to that of the refractive index fluctuations, can be simplified considerably. Consider the expression

$$\int_0^x d\xi \int_0^{x'} d\xi' F_n(\kappa_2,\kappa_3,\xi - \xi'). \qquad (6.51)$$

As was shown, the function $F_n(\kappa_2,\kappa_3,\xi-\xi')$ is appreciably different from zero only in the region $|\xi-\xi'| \leq 1/\kappa$, adjacent to the line $\xi = \xi'$. Therefore, in (6.51) we can replace the rectangular region of integration by a square region with side equal to the smaller of the numbers x, x', which we denote by γ; thus we have

$$\int_0^x d\xi \int_0^{x'} d\xi' F_n(\kappa_2,\kappa_3,\xi - \xi') \sim \int_0^{\gamma} d\xi \int_0^{\gamma} d\xi' F_n(\kappa_2,\kappa_3,\xi - \xi'). \qquad (6.52)$$

Since the function $F_n(\kappa_2,\kappa_3,\xi-\xi')$ is even with respect to $\xi-\xi'$, then, applying Eq. (6.26), we obtain the expression

$$2\int_0^{\gamma} (\gamma - \xi) F_n(\kappa_2,\kappa_3,\xi) d\xi. \qquad (6.53)$$

for the integral (6.51). In most of the region of integration with respect to x and x', the quantity γ is of order L. For values of κ_2,κ_3 satisfying the inequality $1/\kappa \ll L$, we can simplify the integral (6.53) further. The function $F_n(\kappa_2,\kappa_3,\xi)$ is appreciably different from zero for $\xi \lesssim 1/\kappa \ll L$. Since $\gamma \sim L$, we have $\gamma - \xi \sim \gamma$ in the region which contributes appreciably to the integral, and the integral (6.53) takes the form

$$2\gamma \int_0^{\gamma} F_n(\kappa_2,\kappa_3,\xi)d\xi \sim 2\gamma \int_0^{\infty} F_n(\kappa_2,\kappa_3,\xi)d\xi = 2\pi\gamma\, \Phi_n(0,\kappa_2,\kappa_3), \tag{6.54}$$

where Φ_n is the three-dimensional spectral density of the refractive index fluctuations. Substituting (6.54) into (6.50), we obtain

$$F_A(\kappa_2,\kappa_3,0) = \frac{\pi}{2}\kappa^4\, \Phi_n(0,\kappa_2,\kappa_3) \int_0^L dx \int_0^L dx' \min(x,x'). \tag{6.55}$$

The integral figuring in (6.55) can be calculated in an elementary fashion and equals $L^3/3$. Thus, the relation

$$F_A(\kappa,0) = \frac{\pi L^3}{6}\kappa^4\, \Phi_n(\kappa) \tag{6.56}$$

is valid for $\kappa \gg 1/L$. We have taken into account that

$$\Phi_n(0,\kappa_2,\kappa_3) = \Phi_n\left(\sqrt{\kappa_2^2+\kappa_3^2}\right) = \Phi_n(\kappa)$$

and

$$F_A(\kappa_2,\kappa_3,0) = F_A\left(\sqrt{\kappa_2^2+\kappa_3^2},0\right) = F_A(\kappa,0).$$

Eq. (6.56) relates the two-dimensional spectral density of the amplitude fluctuations of the wave to the three-dimensional spectral density of the refractive index fluctuations. It follows from this formula that the amplitude fluctuations of the wave do not depend on its frequency and are proportional to the cube of the distance traversed by the wave in the inhomogeneous medium. In a similar way, it follows from Eq. (6.44) that the phase fluctuations are proportional to the square of the frequency and to the distance traversed by the wave in the inhomogeneous medium. These results do not depend on the form of the spectral or structure (correlation) function of the refractive index inhomogeneities.

6.4 Amplitude and phase fluctuations of a wave propagating in a locally isotropic turbulent flow

We use Eqs. (6.44) and (6.56) to calculate the amplitude and phase fluctuations of a wave propagating in a locally isotropic turbulent flow. As was shown above (see page 58), in this case the structure function of the refractive index has the form

$$D_n(r) = \begin{cases} C_n^2\, r^{2/3} & \text{for } r \gg \ell_o, \\ C_n^2\, \ell_o^{2/3}\left(\frac{r}{\ell_o}\right)^2 & \text{for } r \ll \ell_o. \end{cases} \qquad (6.57)$$

The spectral density $\Phi_n(\kappa)$ corresponding to (6.57) equals $0.033\, C_n^2\, \kappa^{-11/3}$ for $\kappa \ll 1/\ell_o$ and quickly falls off to zero for $\kappa \sim 1/\ell_o$. The way $\Phi_n(\kappa)$ falls off for $\kappa \sim 1/\ell_o$ is related to the form of the structure function $D_n(r)$ in the region $r \sim \ell_o$ and at present has not yet been ascertained exactly. We can adduce different spectral functions $\Phi_n(\kappa)$ which correspond to the form (6.57) of the structure function for small and large r. One such function was introduced on page 48, i.e.

$$\Phi_n(\underline{\kappa}) = \begin{cases} 0.033\, C_n^2\, \kappa^{-11/3} & \text{for } \kappa < \kappa_m, \\ 0 & \text{for } \kappa > \kappa_m, \end{cases} \qquad (6.58)$$

where κ_m is connected with ℓ_o by the relation

$$\kappa_m \ell_o = 5.48 . \tag{6.59}$$

Substituting the spectral density (6.58) into Eqs. (6.44) and (6.56) for the spectral densities of the amplitude and phase fluctuations, we obtain

$$F_S(\kappa,0) = \begin{cases} 0.21\ k^2 L C_n^2 \kappa^{-11/3} & \text{for } \kappa < \kappa_m, \\ 0 & \text{for } \kappa > \kappa_m, \end{cases} \tag{6.60}$$

$$F_A(\kappa,0) = \begin{cases} 0.017\ L^3 C_n^2 \kappa^{1/3} & \text{for } \kappa < \kappa_m, \\ 0 & \text{for } \kappa > \kappa_m. \end{cases} \tag{6.61}$$

The spectral density of the phase fluctuations has a non-integrable singularity at zero. Consequently, the field of phase fluctuations in the plane $x = L$ is a locally isotropic random field and is characterized by a structure function rather than by a correlation function. Using the formula (see page 23)

$$D(\rho) = 4\pi \int_0^\infty [1 - J_o(\kappa\rho)] F(\kappa,0) \kappa d\kappa, \tag{6.62}$$

we obtain

$$D_S(\rho) = 4\pi(0.21) k^2 L C_n^2 \int_0^{\kappa_m} [1 - J_o(\kappa\rho)] \kappa^{-8/3} d\kappa \tag{6.63}$$

for the structure function $D_S(\rho)$. For $\kappa_m \rho \ll 1$, $1 - J_o(\kappa\rho) \sim \kappa^2\rho^2/4$ over the whole region of variation of κ, and the integral reduces to the formula

$$D_S(\rho) = 3.44\ k^2 L C_n^2 \rho^2 \ell_o^{-1/3} \qquad (\rho \ll \ell_o). \tag{6.64}$$

(We have used the relation (6.59) to express κ_m in terms of ℓ_o.) For $\kappa_m\rho \gg 1$, the integration in (6.63) can be extended to ∞, as a result of which we obtain [d]

$$D_S(\rho) = 2.91\, k^2 L C_n^2 \rho^{5/3}. \tag{6.65}$$

A formula similar to (6.65) was first obtained by Krasilnikov [42,44].

We now turn to the amplitude fluctuations. The spectral density (6.61) of the amplitude fluctuations is finite for $\kappa = 0$. Therefore, the field of amplitude fluctuations in the plane $x = L$ is homogeneous and isotropic and the fluctuations have a correlation function $B_A(\rho)$. Using the formula (see page 24)

$$B_A(\rho) = 2\pi \int_0^\infty J_o(\kappa\rho) F_A(\kappa,0)\kappa d\kappa, \tag{6.66}$$

we obtain

$$B_A(\rho) = 2\pi(0.017) L^3 C_n^2 \int_0^{\kappa_m} J_o(\kappa\rho)\kappa^{4/3} d\kappa. \tag{6.67}$$

The value of the correlation function $B_A(\rho)$ at $\rho = 0$ gives the mean square fluctuation of the logarithm of the wave amplitude:

$$\overline{\chi^2} = \overline{\left(\log \frac{A}{A_o}\right)^2} = 2\pi(0.017) L^3 C_n^2 \int_0^{\kappa_m} \kappa^{4/3} d\kappa,$$

i.e.

$$\overline{\left(\log \frac{A}{A_o}\right)^2} = 2.46\, C_n^2 L^3 \ell_o^{-7/3} \tag{6.68}$$

(the value of κ_m is expressed in terms of ℓ_o). Thus, the mean square fluctuation of the logarithm of the amplitude depends on the dimensions of the smallest inhomogeneities of the refractive index [e] (on the inner scale of turbulence ℓ_o) and is proportional to the characteristic C_n^2 of the structure function of the refractive index fluctuations. According to (6.67) and (6.68), the correlation function of the fluctuations of the logarithm of the amplitude of the wave in the plane x = L, normalized to unity, is equal to

$$b_A(\rho) = \frac{B_A(\rho)}{B_A(0)} = \frac{7}{3} \int_0^1 J_0(\kappa_m \rho \xi)\xi^{4/3} d\xi, \tag{6.69}$$

where $\xi = \kappa/\kappa_m$. The function (6.69) is shown in Fig. 8. The correlation distance of the amplitude fluctuations in the plane x = L agrees in order of magnitude with the inner scale of turbulence ℓ_o.

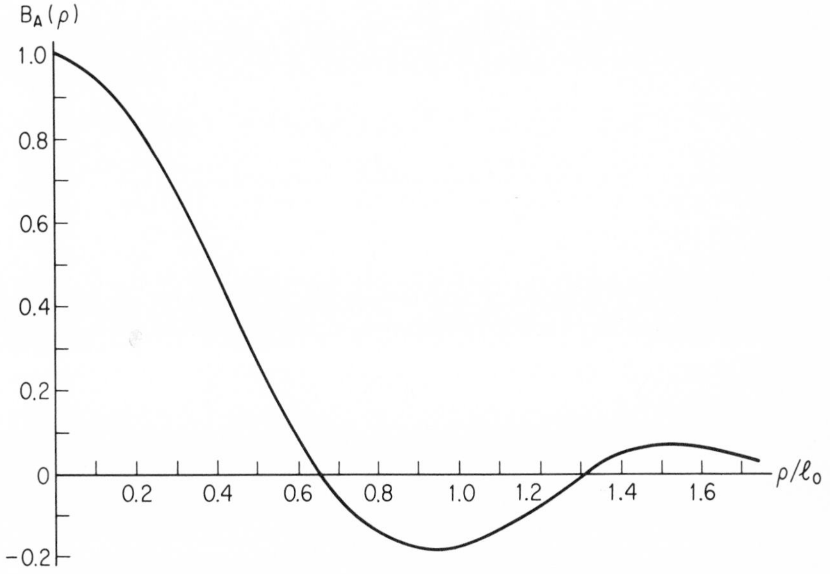

Fig. 8 The correlation coefficient of fluctuations of the logarithm of the amplitude in the plane x = L under the condition $\sqrt{\lambda L} \ll \ell_o$ [f].

6.5 A consequence of the law of conservation of energy

It is appropriate to indicate an important property of the function $B_A(\rho)$. It follows from Eq. (6.61) that $F_A(0,0) = 0$. Since the correlation function is the Fourier transform of its spectral density, we have

$$F_A(\kappa,0) = F_A(\kappa_2,\kappa_3,0) = \frac{1}{(2\pi)^2} \iint\limits_{-\infty}^{\infty} \cos(\kappa_2\eta + \kappa_3\zeta)B_A(\eta,\zeta)d\eta d\zeta,$$

and it follows from the equality $F(0,0) = 0$ that

$$\iint\limits_{-\infty}^{\infty} B_A(\eta,\zeta)d\eta d\zeta = 2\pi \int\limits_0^{\infty} B_A(\rho)\rho d\rho = 0. \tag{6.70}$$

Eq. (6.70) is a consequence of the law of energy conservation which itself follows from Eq. (6.17):

$$\Delta S_1 + 2k \frac{\partial X}{\partial x} = 0. \tag{6.17}$$

In fact, suppose that the region T containing the refractive index fluctuations is bounded by the planes $x = 0$, $x = L$ and some "lateral" surface located at a finite distance from the origin of coordinates, and suppose that $n_1 = 0$ outside of T. Moreover, suppose that the region T is imbedded in the region T_1 bounded by the planes $x = -\epsilon$ and $x = L + \epsilon$. We integrate Eq. (6.17) (which can be written in the form div grad $S_1 + 2k \frac{\partial X}{\partial x} = 0$) over the region T_1. Applying Gauss' theorem, we obtain

$$\oint \operatorname{grad}_n S_1 d\vec{\sigma} + 2k \iint\limits_{x=L+\epsilon} X dydz - 2k \iint\limits_{x=-\epsilon} X dydz = 0, \tag{6.71}$$

where $d\sigma$ is an element of surface bounding the region T. Since the quantity S_1 is constant outside the region T (see Eq. (6.16)), then grad $S_1 = 0$ on the boundary of the region T_1, and the surface integral vanishes, i.e.

$$\oint \operatorname{grad}_n S_1 d\vec{\sigma} = 0.$$

However, the values of X on the planes x = L and x = L + ϵ coincide. Since there are no amplitude fluctuations at the "input" to the region occupied by the inhomogeneities, we have

$$\iint_{x=-\epsilon} \chi \, dydz = 0.$$

Then it follows from Eq. (6.71) that

$$\iint_{-\infty}^{\infty} \chi(L,y,z)dydz = 0. \tag{6.72}$$

We multiply Eq. (6.72) by (L,y',z') and average. As a result we obtain the relation

$$\iint_{-\infty}^{\infty} \overline{\chi(L,y,z)\chi(L,y',z')}\, dydz = \iint_{-\infty}^{\infty} B_A(\eta,\zeta)d\eta d\zeta = 0 \tag{6.73}$$

($\eta = y - y'$, $\zeta = z - z'$), which agrees with (6.70). Thus, the relation (6.70) must be satisfied independently of the form of the structure function or the spectrum of the refractive index fluctuations. It follows from Eq. (6.73) that the correlation function of the fluctuations of any quantity X which satisfies a conservation law of the type (6.72) must change its sign at least once.

6.6 Amplitude and phase fluctuations of sound waves

We now consider the problem of amplitude and phase fluctuations of sound waves. As was shown in Chapter 5, the amplitude Π of the acoustic wave potential satisfies the equation

$$\Delta \Pi + \frac{\omega^2}{c^2}\Pi + 2i\frac{\omega}{c}\frac{\vec{u}}{c}\cdot\nabla\Pi = 0. \tag{6.74}$$

Dividing this equation by Π and taking into account the identity

$$\frac{\Delta \Pi}{\Pi} = \Delta \log \Pi + (\nabla \log \Pi)^2 ,$$

we obtain the equation

$$\Delta \log \Pi + (\nabla \log \Pi)^2 + \frac{\omega^2}{c^2} + 2i \frac{\omega}{c} \frac{\vec{u}}{c} \cdot \nabla \log \Pi = 0. \qquad (6.75)$$

We set $\Pi = Ae^{iS}$ or $\log \Pi = \log A + iS$. Substituting this expression in (6.75) and equating the real and imaginary parts to zero, we obtain two equations

$$\frac{\Delta A}{A} - (\nabla S)^2 + \frac{\omega^2}{c^2} - 2 \frac{\omega}{c} \frac{\vec{u}}{c} \cdot \nabla S = 0, \qquad (6.76)$$

$$\Delta S + 2 \nabla \log A \cdot \nabla S + \frac{2\omega}{c} \frac{\vec{u}}{c} \cdot \nabla \log A = 0. \qquad (6.77)$$

Since $|\nabla S| \sim k = 2\pi/\lambda$, then as $\lambda \rightarrow 0$ we can neglect the term $\Delta A/A$ in Eq. (6.76) (see page 94). Thus, Eq. (6.76) takes the form

$$(\nabla S)^2 = \frac{\omega^2}{c^2} - 2 \frac{\omega}{c} \frac{\vec{u}}{c} \cdot \nabla S. \qquad (6.78)$$

The velocity of sound c figuring in Eqs. (6.77) and (6.78) is a function of the temperature T. Suppose the temperature T undergoes fluctuations T' about a mean temperature T_o, i.e. $T = T_o + T'$. Since the velocity of sound in the air is proportional to $\sqrt{T}$, we have

$$c \sim c_o\left(1 + \frac{T'}{2T_o}\right) \qquad \text{or} \qquad \frac{1}{c^2} \sim \frac{1}{c_o^2}\left(1 - \frac{T'}{T_o}\right), \qquad (6.79)$$

where $c_o = c(T_o)$ is the mean value of the velocity of sound. We shall regard T'/T_o and $\vec{u}/c_o$ as quantities of the first order of smallness, and we set $\log A = \log A_o + \chi$, $S = S_o + S_1$, where χ and S_1 are the fluctuations of the logarithmic amplitude and phase of the wave. Substituting these values of $\log A$, S and c in Eqs. (6.78) and (6.77), we obtain

$$(\nabla S_o)^2 + (2\nabla S_o + \nabla S_1)\cdot\nabla S_1 =$$

$$= k^2\left(1 - \frac{T'}{T_o}\right) - \frac{2\omega}{c_o}\left(1 - \frac{T'}{T_o}\right)\frac{\vec{u}}{c_o}\cdot(\nabla S_o + \nabla S_1), \tag{6.80}$$

$$\Delta S_o + \Delta S_1 + 2(\nabla \log A_o + \nabla X)\cdot(\nabla S_o + \nabla S_1) +$$

$$+ \frac{2\omega}{c_o}\left(1 - \frac{T'}{T_o}\right)\frac{\vec{u}}{c_o}\cdot(\nabla \log A_o + \nabla X) = 0, \tag{6.81}$$

where $k = \omega/c_o$. The quantities S_o and $\log A_o$ of the zeroth order of smallness satisfy the equations

$$(\nabla S_o)^2 = k^2,$$

$$\Delta S_o + 2\nabla \log A_o \cdot \nabla S_o = 0.$$

Assuming that the unperturbed wave is plane, we set A_o = const and

$$\nabla S_o = k\vec{m}, \tag{6.82}$$

where $\vec{m}$ is a unit vector in the direction of propagation of the unperturbed wave. Equating to zero the terms of the first order of smallness in (6.80) and (6.81), we obtain the equations

$$2\nabla S_o \cdot \nabla S_1 = -k^2\frac{T'}{T_o} - 2k^2\frac{\vec{u}\cdot\vec{m}}{c_o}, \tag{6.83}$$

$$2\nabla S_o \cdot \nabla X + \Delta S_1 = 0, \tag{6.84}$$

for the validity of which it is necessary that the conditions

$$|\nabla S_o| \gg |\nabla S_1| \text{ or } \lambda|\nabla S_1| \ll 2\pi \qquad (6.85)$$

be satisfied (see page 95). Eq. (6.84) agrees with Eq. (6.15), which was obtained for electromagnetic waves (recall that $\nabla \log A_o = 0$). Eq. (6.83) can be written in the form

$$\nabla S_o \cdot \nabla S_1 = k^2(-\frac{T'}{2T_o} - \vec{m} \cdot \frac{\vec{u}}{c_o}).$$

This equation agrees with Eq. (6.14) if we set

$$n_1 = -\frac{T'}{2T_o} - \vec{m}\cdot\frac{\vec{u}}{c_o} = -\frac{T'}{2T_o} - \frac{m_i u_i}{c_o}. \qquad (6.86)$$

All subsequent results can be obtained from the corresponding formulas for electromagnetic waves if in them we take n_1 to be the expression (6.86).

By using (6.86), the structure function $D_n(r)$ of the refractive index can be expressed in terms of the temperature structure function $D_T(r) = C_T^2 r^{2/3}$ [g] and the wind velocity structure function $D_{ik}(r)$, i.e.

$$D_n(r) = \overline{[n_1(\vec{r}_1) - n_1(\vec{r}_2)]^2} = \frac{1}{4T_o^2} D_T(r) + \frac{1}{c_o^2} m_i m_k D_{ik}(\vec{r}_1, \vec{r}_2) +$$

$$+ \frac{1}{T_o c_o} m_i \overline{[T'(\vec{r}_1) - T'(\vec{r}_2)][u_1(\vec{r}_1) - u_1(\vec{r}_2)]} \qquad (\vec{r} = \vec{r}_1 - \vec{r}_2).$$

But the cross correlation function of the fluctuations of temperature and wind velocity vanishes in a locally isotropic field (see note [c] to Chapter 5), so that the last term drops out of the equation. Since

$$D_{ik}(\vec{r}) = D_{tt}\delta_{ik} + (D_{rr} - D_{tt})n_i n_k, \qquad (6.87)$$

where $\vec{n}$ is a unit vector directed along $\vec{r}$, we have

$$m_i m_k D_{ik} = D_{tt} + (D_{rr} - D_{tt})\cos^2\alpha, \qquad (6.88)$$

where $\cos\alpha = \vec{m}\cdot\vec{n}$. In a locally isotropic turbulent flow, $D_{rr} = C_v^2 r^{2/3}$ and $D_{tt} = \frac{4}{3} C_v^2 r^{2/3}$. Thus we have

$$m_i m_k D_{ik} = \frac{1}{3} C_v^2 (4 - \cos^2\alpha) r^{2/3}$$

and

$$D_n(r) = \left[\frac{C_T^2}{4T_o^2} + \frac{1}{3}\frac{C_v^2}{c_o^2}(4 - \cos^2\alpha)\right] r^{2/3}. \tag{6.89}$$

Thus, it follows that the structure function of the refractive index of sound waves depends on the angle between the direction of wave propagation and the direction of the line joining the observation points. The expression (6.89) goes under the integral sign in Eq. (6.28) and in the analogous formula for the correlation function of the amplitude fluctuations of the wave. However, in most of the region of integration $\cos\alpha \approx 1$ for $\rho \ll L$. Therefore, we can write approximately

$$D_n(r) = \left[\frac{C_T^2}{4T_o^2} + \frac{C_v^2}{c_o^2}\right] r^{2/3} = C_n^2 r^{2/3}. \tag{6.90}$$

Thus, the amplitude and phase fluctuations of a plane sound wave are approximately described by the same final formulas as the corresponding fluctuations of an electromagnetic wave, if we take C_n^2 to be the expression

$$C_n^2 = \frac{C_T^2}{4T_o^2} + \frac{C_v^2}{c_o^2}. \tag{6.91}$$

An exact calculation based on Eq. (6.89) gives the same formula (6.65) for the structure function of the phase fluctuations of a sound wave as for the fluctuations of an electromagnetic wave, but with a value of the numerical coefficient which is changed by a few percent [46]. The expression for the amplitude fluctuations of a sound wave agrees with Eq. (6.68) to an even higher degree of accuracy.

6.7 Limits of applicability of geometrical optics

The theory of amplitude and phase fluctuations of electromagnetic and acoustic waves which we have just considered was based on the equations of geometrical optics, which are valid when the condition

$$\lambda \ll \ell_0 \tag{6.92}$$

is satisfied. However it is easy to see that in some cases this condition is not sufficient for the solution obtained on the basis of geometrical optics to remain valid when diffraction effects are taken into account. We can convince ourselves of this by using the following simple argument [47].

Let an obstacle with geometrical dimensions ℓ be located on the propagation path of a plane wave. At a distance L from this obstacle we obtain its image (shadow) with the same dimensions ℓ. At the same time, diffraction of the wave by the obstacle will occur. The angle of divergence of the diffracted (scattered) wave will be of order $\theta \sim \lambda/\ell$. At a distance L from the obstacle the size of the diffracted bundle will be of order $\theta L \sim \lambda L/\ell$. Clearly, in order for the geometrical shadow of the obstacle not to be appreciably changed, it is necessary for the relation $\frac{\lambda L}{\ell} \ll \ell$ or $\sqrt{\lambda L} \ll \ell$ to hold. When there is a whole set of obstacles with different geometrical sizes, it is obviously necessary that this relation be satisfied for the smallest obstacles, which have the size ℓ_0. Applying a similar argument to the problem under consideration, we convince ourselves that the solutions we have obtained are valid only in the case where the inequality

$$\sqrt{\lambda L} \ll \ell_0 \tag{6.93}$$

is satisfied, where ℓ_0 is the inner scale of the turbulence. In other words, the theory of amplitude and phase fluctuations based on the equations of geometrical optics is valid only for limited distances L satisfying the condition

$$L \ll L_{cr} = \frac{\ell_0^2}{\lambda} . \tag{6.94}$$

A more detailed analysis shows that the conditions (6.92) and (6.93) are sufficient for agreement of the amplitudes and phases of the solutions obtained by using the equations of geometrical optics and those obtained by using the wave equation [48,49]. We shall also arrive at the same conclusion in Chapter 7.

Chapter 7

CALCULATION OF AMPLITUDE AND PHASE FLUCTUATIONS OF A PLANE MONOCHROMATIC WAVE FROM THE WAVE EQUATION USING THE METHODS OF "SMALL" AND "SMOOTH" PERTURBATIONS

7.1 Solution of the wave equation by the method of small perturbations

As we have already seen in Chapter 6, even when the condition $\lambda \ll \ell_o$ is met, the solution of the problem of amplitude and phase fluctuations of a wave which we obtained using the equations of geometrical optics becomes unsuitable for large distances L, which exceed the critical distance $L_{cr} = \ell_o^2/\lambda$. At large distances one can no longer neglect the diffraction of the wave by refractive index inhomogeneities, regardless of the smallness of the diffraction angle. In order to take account of diffraction effects in solving the problem of parameter fluctuations of a wave traversing an inhomogeneous medium, it is necessary to start from the wave equation (6.3), i.e.

$$\Delta u + k^2 n^2(\vec{r})u = 0. \tag{7.1}$$

Setting

$$n(\vec{r}) = 1 + n_1(\vec{r}) \tag{7.2}$$

as in Chapter 6, and assuming that $|n_1(\vec{r})| \ll 1$, we apply the method of small perturbations to solve Eq. (7.1). To do so, we look for a solution in the form of the sum of an unperturbed wave u_o, which satisfies the equation $\Delta u_o + k^2 u_o = 0$, and a small perturbation u_1, i.e.

$$u = u_o + u_1. \tag{7.3}$$

Substituting (7.2) and (7.3) into Eq. (7.1), and taking into account that $\Delta u_o + k^2 u_o = 0$, we obtain

$$\Delta u_1 + k^2 u_1 + 2n_1 k^2 (u_o + u_1) + k^2 n_1^2 (u_o + u_1) = 0. \tag{7.4}$$

The last term in the equation is of order n_1^2 and can be omitted. If we assume that $|u_1| \ll |u_o|$, or more precisely that $|u_1/u_o| \lesssim n_1$, then in Eq. (7.4) we can also neglect the term $n_1(\vec{r})u_1$. Then we obtain the equation

$$\Delta u_1 + k^2 u_1 = - 2k^2 n_1(\vec{r}) u_o, \tag{7.5}$$

which is valid when the condition

$$|u_1| \ll |u_o|, \tag{7.6}$$

which expresses the smallness of the fluctuations of the field, is satisfied.

Let the unperturbed wave u_o have the form

$$u_o = A_o e^{iS_o}, \tag{7.7}$$

where A_o and S_o are its amplitude and phase. To find the amplitude and phase of the perturbed wave $u = u_o + u_1$, we set $u = Ae^{iS}$. Then $\log u = \log A + iS$ and by (7.3) and (7.7), we have

$$\log u = \log A + iS = \log(u_o + u_1) = \log u_o + \log \left(1 + \frac{u_1}{u_o}\right) .$$

Since $|u_1/u_o| \ll 1$, then

$$\log \left(1 + \frac{u_1}{u_o}\right) \sim \frac{u_1}{u_o}$$

and

$$\log A + iS = \log A_o + iS_o + \frac{u_1}{u_o} .$$

Separating the real and imaginary parts of the last equation, we find

$$\log \frac{A}{A_o} = \chi = \mathrm{Re}\,\frac{u_1}{u_o}, \tag{7.8}$$

$$S - S_o = S_1 = \mathrm{Im}\,\frac{u_1}{u_o}. \tag{7.9}$$

7.2 The equations of the method of smooth perturbations

The equation (7.5) and the formulas (7.8) and (7.9) just obtained are valid in the case of small amplitude and phase fluctuations, i.e. when $|\chi| \ll 1$ and $|S_1| \ll 1$. These conditions are much more stringent than the condition $\lambda |\nabla S_1| \ll 2\pi$, which was needed in order to apply the method of small perturbations to the equations of geometrical optics. In order to avoid this restriction, it is natural to try to apply the method of small perturbations to the equation

$$\frac{\Delta u}{u} + k^2 n^2(\vec{r}) = \Delta \log u + (\nabla \log u)^2 + k^2 n^2(\vec{r}) = 0, \tag{7.10}$$

which contains only derivatives of log u, rather than directly to Eq. (7.1) [a].

We set $\log u = \log A + iS = \psi$ ($\mathrm{Re}\,\psi = \log A$, $\mathrm{Im}\,\psi = S$). Then we have

$$\Delta \psi + (\nabla \psi)^2 + k^2(1 + n_1(\vec{r}))^2 = 0. \tag{7.11}$$

We then set $\psi = \psi_o + \psi_1$; ψ_o satisfies the equation

$$\Delta \psi_o + (\nabla \psi_o)^2 + k^2 = 0. \tag{7.12}$$

Substituting $\psi = \psi_o + \psi_1$ in Eq. (7.11) and taking into account (7.12), we obtain

$$\Delta \psi_1 + \nabla \psi_1 \cdot (2\nabla \psi_o + \nabla \psi_1) + 2k^2 n_1(\vec{r}) + k^2 n_1^2(\vec{r}) = 0. \tag{7.13}$$

In Eq. (7.13) we can omit the term $k^2 n_1^2(\vec{r})$ which is of the second order of smallness. In the case where $|\nabla \psi_1| \ll |\nabla \psi_o|$, or more precisely where $|\nabla \psi_1| \lesssim n_1 |\nabla \psi_o|$, we can also neglect the term $(\nabla \psi_1)^2$ in (7.13). Finally we obtain the equation

$$\Delta \psi_1 + 2 \nabla \psi_o \cdot \nabla \psi_1 + 2k^2 n_1(\vec{r}) = 0, \tag{7.14}$$

which is valid when the conditions

$$|n_1(\vec{r})| \ll 1, \qquad |\nabla \psi_1| \ll |\nabla \psi_o| \tag{7.15}$$

are met. Since $|\nabla \psi_o| \sim k = 2\pi/\lambda$, the second condition (7.15) can be written in the form

$$\lambda |\nabla \psi_1| \ll 2\pi$$

and expresses the smallness of the change of ψ_1 over distances of the order of a wavelength.

By using the substitution $\psi_1 = e^{-\psi_o} w$, Eq. (7.14) can be reduced to the form

$$\Delta w + k^2 w + 2k^2 n_1(\vec{r}) e^{\psi_o} = 0. \tag{7.16}$$

Since $e^{\psi_o} = u_o$, Eq. (7.16) coincides with Eq. (7.5) obtained by the method of small perturbations. Consequently, $w = u_1$ and $\psi_1 = e^{-\psi_o} w = u_1/u_o$. We now find expressions for the amplitude and phase fluctuations of the wave. Since

$$\psi = \log A + iS \qquad \text{and} \qquad \psi_o = \log A_o + iS_o ,$$

we have

$$\psi_1 = \psi - \psi_o = \log \frac{A}{A_o} + i(S - S_o) = \chi + iS_1 .$$

Therefore

$$\log \frac{A}{A_o} = \chi = \operatorname{Re} \psi_1 = \operatorname{Re} \frac{u_1}{u_o} , \tag{7.17}$$

$$S - S_o = S_1 = \operatorname{Im} \psi_1 = \operatorname{Im} \frac{u_1}{u_o} . \tag{7.18}$$

Eq. (7.16) and the formulas (7.17) and (7.18) agree formally with Eq. (7.5) and the formulas (7.8) and (7.9). However, for the validity of these expressions the conditions $\lambda|\nabla S_1| \ll 2\pi$ and $\lambda|\nabla \chi| \ll 1$ have to be met, rather than requiring the smallness of the perturbations χ and S themselves. As we shall see below, the inequality $|\chi| < |S_1|$ is usually satisfied. Therefore, when the inequality $\lambda|\nabla S_1| \ll 2\pi$ is satisfied, the inequality $\lambda|\nabla \chi| \ll 1$ is satisfied also. Thus, to apply the method of solving the wave equation presented above, the conditions [b]

$$|n_1| \ll 1, \quad \lambda|\nabla S_1| \ll 2\pi \tag{7.19}$$

must be met; these conditions are the same as those for applying the method of small perturbations to the equations of geometrical optics. As is well known, the solution of Eq. (7.16) has the form

$$w(\vec{r}) = \frac{k^2}{2\pi} \int_V n_1(\vec{r}\,')u_o(\vec{r}\,') \frac{e^{ik|\vec{r} - \vec{r}\,'|}}{|\vec{r} - \vec{r}\,'|} dV'. \tag{7.20}$$

(The integration in (7.20) extends over the region where $n_1(\vec{r})$ is different from zero.) For the quantity $\psi_1 = w(\vec{r})/u_o(\vec{r})$, we obtain

$$\psi_1(\vec{r}) = \frac{k^2}{2\pi u_o(\vec{r})} \int_V n_1(\vec{r}\,')u_o(\vec{r}\,') \frac{e^{ik|\vec{r} - \vec{r}\,'|}}{|\vec{r} - \vec{r}\,'|} dV' . \tag{7.21}$$

The function (7.21) is the general solution of Eq. (7.14) for any function ψ_o which satisfies the equation $\nabla \psi_o + (\nabla \psi_o)^2 + k^2 = 0$.

We now consider the problem of fluctuations of a plane monochromatic wave, confining ourselves to the case where the wavelength λ is small compared to the inner scale of turbulence ℓ_o. We locate the origin of coordinates on the boundary of the region occupied by the refractive index inhomogeneities, and we direct the x-axis along the direction of propagation of the incident wave. Then $u_o(\vec{r}) = A_o e^{ikx}$ and Eq. (7.21) takes the form

$$\psi_1(\vec{r}) = \frac{k^2}{2\pi} \int_V n_1(\vec{r}\,')e^{-ik(x-x')} \frac{e^{ik|\vec{r} - \vec{r}\,'|}}{|\vec{r} - \vec{r}\,'|} dV'. \tag{7.22}$$

In the case where $\lambda \ll \ell_o$, Eq. (7.22) can be greatly simplified. In this case, the angle of scattering of the waves by refractive index inhomogeneities is of order no greater than $\theta_o = \lambda/\ell_o$ and is thus small. Therefore, the value of $\psi_1(\vec{r})$ can only be appreciably affected by the inhomogeneities included in a cone with vertex at the observation point, with axis directed towards the wave source, and with angular aperture $\theta_o = \lambda/\ell_o \ll 1$. In most of this region

$$|x - x'| \gg \sqrt{(y - y')^2 + (z - z')^2}.$$

Therefore we have

$$|\vec{r} - \vec{r}\,'| = \sqrt{(x - x')^2 + (y - y')^2 + (z - z')^2} =$$

$$= (x - x') \sqrt{1 + \frac{(y - y')^2 + (z - z')^2}{(x - x')^2}} \sim$$

$$\sim (x - x') \left[1 + \frac{(y - y')^2 + (z - z')^2}{2(x - x')^2}\right] = (x - x') + \frac{(y - y')^2 + (z - z')^2}{2(x - x')}.$$

Substituting this expansion in $e^{ik|\vec{r}-\vec{r}\,'|}$ and retaining only the first term of the expansion in the denominator of (7.22), we obtain the approximate formula

$$\psi_1(\vec{r}) = \frac{k^2}{2\pi} \int_V n_1(\vec{r}\,') \frac{\exp\left(ik \frac{(y - y')^2 + (z - z')^2}{2(x - x')}\right)}{x - x'} dV'. \tag{7.23}$$

It is not hard to show that the function (7.23) is the exact solution of the equation

$$\frac{\partial^2\psi_1}{\partial y^2} + \frac{\partial^2\psi_1}{\partial z^2} + 2ik\frac{\partial\psi_1}{\partial x} + 2k^2 n_1(r) = 0, \tag{7.24}$$

obtained from Eq. (7.14) by omitting the term $\partial^2\psi_1/\partial x^2$. We note that by retaining only the first two terms of the expansion

$$k|\vec{r} - \vec{r}'| = k(x - x') + k\rho^2/2(x - x') + k\rho^4/8(x - x')^3 + \ldots$$

we change the phase of (7.21) by an amount of order $k\rho^4/(x - x')^3$. Since $\rho \sim \theta L \sim \lambda L/\ell_0$ and $(x - x') \sim L$ in the important region of integration, then the error permitted here is small if

$$L \ll \ell_0^4/\lambda^3. \tag{7.25}$$

Since $\lambda \ll \ell_0$, the quantity ℓ_0^4/λ^3 is much larger than the distance $L_{cr} = \ell_0^2/\lambda$, which determines the limits of applicability of geometrical optics.

7.3 Solution of the equations of the method of "smooth" perturbations by using spectral expansions

We shall begin with Eq. (7.24) in order to solve the problem of amplitude and phase fluctuations of a sufficiently short ($\lambda \ll \ell_0$) plane wave. We use a method of solving Eq. (7.24) which is based on the use of spectral expansions (just like the way we solved the equations of geometrical optics in Chapter 6). In a turbulent medium, $n_1(\vec{r})$ is a locally isotropic random field. To represent $n_1(\vec{r})$, we apply the representation (6.35):

$$n_1(x,y,z) = n_1(x,0,0) + \iint_{-\infty}^{\infty} \left[1 - e^{i(\kappa_2 y + \kappa_3 z)}\right] d\nu(\kappa_2,\kappa_3,x). \tag{7.26}$$

We shall look for the same kind of expansion for $\psi_1(\vec{r})$, i.e.

$$\psi_1(\vec{r}) = \psi_1(x,0,0) + \iint_{-\infty}^{\infty} \left[1 - e^{i(\kappa_2 y + \kappa_2 z)}\right] d\varphi(\kappa_2,\kappa_3,x). \tag{7.27}$$

Substituting the expansions (7.26) and (7.27) into Eq. (7.24), we obtain

$$\iint_{-\infty}^{\infty} (\kappa_2^2 + \kappa_3^2) e^{i(\kappa_2 y + \kappa_3 z)} d\varphi(\kappa_2,\kappa_3,x) + 2ik \frac{d\psi_1(x,0,0)}{dx} +$$

$$+ 2ik \iint_{-\infty}^{\infty} \left[1 - e^{i(\kappa_2 y + \kappa_3 z)}\right] \frac{\partial}{\partial x} d\varphi(\kappa_2,\kappa_3,x) + 2k^2 n_1(x,0,0) +$$

$$+ 2k^2 \iint_{-\infty}^{\infty} \left[1 - e^{i(\kappa_2 y + \kappa_3 z)}\right] d\nu(\kappa_2,\kappa_3,x) = 0. \tag{7.28}$$

Setting $y = z = 0$ in this equation and writing $\kappa_2^2 + \kappa_3^2 = \kappa^2$, we obtain

$$\iint_{-\infty}^{\infty} \kappa^2 d\varphi(\kappa_2,\kappa_3,x) + 2ik \frac{d\psi_1(x,0,0)}{dx} + 2k^2 n_1(x,0,0) = 0. \tag{7.29}$$

We subtract Eq. (7.29) from Eq. (7.28), i.e.

$$\iint_{-\infty}^{\infty} - \kappa^2 \left[1 - e^{i(\kappa_2 y + \kappa_3 z)}\right] d\varphi(\kappa_2,\kappa_3,x) +$$

$$+ 2ik \iint\limits_{-\infty}^{\infty} \left[1 - e^{i(\kappa_2 y + \kappa_3 z)}\right] \frac{\partial}{\partial x} d\varphi(\kappa_2,\kappa_3,x) +$$

$$+ 2k^2 \iint\limits_{-\infty}^{\infty} \left[1 - e^{i(\kappa_2 y + \kappa_3 z)}\right] d\nu(\kappa_2,\kappa_3,x) = 0. \qquad (7.30)$$

It follows from Eq. (7.30) that the random amplitudes $d\nu(\kappa_2,\kappa_3,x)$ and $d\varphi(\kappa_2,\kappa_3,x)$ are related by the differential equation

$$2ik \frac{\partial}{\partial x} d\varphi(\kappa_2,\kappa_3,x) - \kappa^2 d\varphi(\kappa_2,\kappa_3,x) + 2k^2 d\nu(\kappa_2,\kappa_3,x) = 0. \qquad (7.31)$$

The solution of this equation which goes to zero for $x = 0$ (the fluctuations of the field vanish at the boundary of the region filled with the refractive index inhomogeneities) has the form

$$d\varphi(\kappa_2,\kappa_3,x) = ik \int\limits_0^x dx' \exp\left[- \frac{i\kappa^2(x - x')}{2k}\right] d\nu(\kappa_2,\kappa_3,x'). \qquad (7.32)$$

(The integration in (7.32) is carried out with respect to x'; see note [c] to Chapter 6.)

We now find the relations between the spectral amplitudes of the field S_1 of the phase fluctuations of the wave and the field $\log(A/A_0)$ of the fluctuations of logarithmic amplitude of the wave. Using the formula $X = \text{Re}\ \psi_1$ and the expansion (7.27), we obtain

$$X(\vec{r}) = \text{Re}\ \psi_1(x,0,0) + \text{Re} \iint\limits_{-\infty}^{\infty} \left[1 - e^{i(\kappa_2 y + \kappa_3 z)}\right] d\varphi(\kappa_2,\kappa_3,x) =$$

$$= \text{Re}\,\psi_1(x,0,0) + \frac{1}{2}\iint_{-\infty}^{\infty}\left[1 - e^{i(\kappa_2 y + \kappa_3 z)}\right]d\varphi(\kappa_2,\kappa_3,x) +$$

$$+ \frac{1}{2}\iint_{-\infty}^{\infty}\left[1 - e^{-i(\kappa_2 y + \kappa_3 z)}\right]d\varphi^*(\kappa_2,\kappa_3,x).$$

Changing variables from κ_2,κ_3 to $-\kappa_2,-\kappa_3$ in the last integral, we find

$$\chi(\vec{r}) = \text{Re}\,\psi_1(x,0,0) +$$

$$+ \iint_{-\infty}^{\infty}\left[1 - e^{i(\kappa_2 y + \kappa_3 z)}\right]\frac{d\varphi(\kappa_2,\kappa_3,x) + d\varphi^*(-\kappa_2,-\kappa_3,x)}{2}\,. \tag{7.33}$$

In a completely analogous way, we obtain for $S_1 = \text{Im}\,\psi_1$ the formula

$$S_1(\vec{r}) = \text{Im}\,\psi_1(x,0,0) +$$

$$+ \iint_{-\infty}^{\infty}\left[1 - e^{i(\kappa_2 y + \kappa_3 z)}\right]\frac{d\varphi(\kappa_2,\kappa_3,x) - d\varphi^*(-\kappa_2,-\kappa_3,x)}{2i}\,. \tag{7.34}$$

Denoting the spectral amplitudes of the random fields $\chi(\vec{r})$ and $S_1(\vec{r})$ by $da(\kappa_2,\kappa_3,x)$ and $d\sigma(\kappa_2,\kappa_3,x)$ (as in Chapter 6) and using (7.33) and (7.34), we obtain

$$da(\kappa_2,\kappa_3,x) = \frac{d\varphi(\kappa_2,\kappa_3,x) + d\varphi^*(-\kappa_2,-\kappa_3,x)}{2} , \tag{7.35}$$

$$d\sigma(\kappa_2,\kappa_3,x) = \frac{d\varphi(\kappa_2,\kappa_3,x) - d\varphi^*(-\kappa_2,-\kappa_3,x)}{2i} . \tag{7.36}$$

Substituting the expression (7.32) for $d\varphi(\kappa_2,\kappa_3,x)$ into these formulas, we obtain

$$da(\kappa_2,\kappa_3,x) = k \int_0^x dx' \sin\left[\frac{\kappa^2(x - x')}{2k}\right] d\nu(\kappa_2,\kappa_3,x') , \tag{7.37}$$

$$d\sigma(\kappa_2,\kappa_3,x) = k \int_0^x dx' \cos\left[\frac{\kappa^2(x - x')}{2k}\right] d\nu(\kappa_2,\kappa_3,x') . \tag{7.38}$$

The physical meaning of Eq. (7.32) or of the equivalent Eqs. (7.37) and (7.38) is transparent. Inhomogeneities of the wave field characterized by the wave number κ (i.e. by geometrical dimensions $\ell = 2\pi/\kappa$) are "made up" by the superposition of refractive index inhomogeneities $d\nu(\kappa_2,\kappa_3,x')$ characterized by the same wave number κ (i.e. having the same geometrical dimensions $\ell = 2\pi/\kappa$). Moreover, the refractive index inhomogeneities with dimensions ℓ which are located at a distance $x - x'$ from the observation point appear with weight $\sin(\pi\Lambda^2/\ell^2)$ or $\cos(\pi\Lambda^2/\ell^2)$, where $\Lambda^2 = \lambda(x - x')$ is the square of the radius of the first Fresnel zone. In other words, the weight of a refractive index inhomogeneity depends on the relation between its dimensions and the dimensions of the Fresnel zone. Using the relations (7.37) and (7.38) between the random spectral amplitudes of the refractive index and of the fluctuations X and S_1, we can find the relations between the spectral densities of the corresponding structure or correlation functions. We multiply Eq. (7.37) by its complex conjugate $da^*(\kappa_2',\kappa_3',x)$, i.e.

$$da^*(\kappa_2',\kappa_3',x) = k \int_0^x dx'' \sin\left[\frac{\kappa'^2(x - x'')}{2k}\right] d\nu^*(\kappa_2',\kappa_3',x'').$$

Averaging, we obtain

$$\overline{da(\kappa_2,\kappa_3,x)da^*(\kappa_2',\kappa_3',x)} = k^2 \int_0^x dx' \int_0^x dx'' \sin\left[\frac{\kappa^2(x - x')}{2k}\right] \times$$

$$\times \sin\left[\frac{\kappa'^2(x - x'')}{2k}\right] \overline{d\nu(\kappa_2,\kappa_3,x')d\nu^*(\kappa_2',\kappa_3',x'')}. \tag{7.39}$$

But according to the general formula (6.36), we have

$$\overline{d\nu(\kappa_2,\kappa_3,x)d\nu^*(\kappa_2',\kappa_3',x)} =$$

$$= \delta(\kappa_2 - \kappa_2')\delta(\kappa_3 - \kappa_3')F_n(\kappa_2,\kappa_3,x' - x'')d\kappa_2 d\kappa_3 d\kappa_2' d\kappa_3' \tag{7.40}$$

and

$$\overline{da(\kappa_2,\kappa_3,x)da^*(\kappa_2',\kappa_3',x)} =$$

$$= \delta(\kappa_2 - \kappa_2')\delta(\kappa_3 - \kappa_3')F_A(\kappa_2,\kappa_3,0)d\kappa_2 d\kappa_3 d\kappa_2' d\kappa_3', \tag{7.41}$$

where $F_n(\kappa_2,\kappa_3,x' - x'')$ is the two-dimensional spectral function of the refractive index and $F_A(\kappa_2,\kappa_3,0)$ is the two-dimensional spectral density of the structure or correlation function of the fluctuations of χ in the plane x = const. Substituting (7.40) and (7.41) into Eq. (7.39), we obtain

$$F_A(\kappa_2,\kappa_3,0) = k^2 \int_0^x\int_0^x \sin\left[\frac{\kappa^2(x - x')}{2k}\right] \sin\left[\frac{\kappa^2(x - x'')}{2k}\right] \times$$

$$\times F_n(\kappa_2,\kappa_3,x' - x'')dx'dx'' . \tag{7.42}$$

Similarly, from Eq. (7.38) we can obtain the relation

$$F_S(\kappa_2,\kappa_3,0) = k^2 \int_0^x\int_0^x \cos\left[\frac{\kappa^2(x - x')}{2k}\right] \cos\left[\frac{\kappa^2(x - x'')}{2k}\right] \times$$

$$\times F_n(\kappa_2,\kappa_3,x' - x'')dx'dx'' . \tag{7.43}$$

The relations (7.42) and (7.43) can be greatly simplified. First of all we note that $F_n(\kappa_2,\kappa_3,x' - x'') = F_n(\kappa_2,\kappa_3, x'' - x')$. Then, in (7.42) and (7.43) we introduce new variables of integration $\xi = x' - x''$ and $2\eta = x' + x''$. The integration with respect to η can be carried out explicitly, since F_n does not depend on η. As a result, we arrive at the formulas

$$F_A(\kappa_2,\kappa_3,0) =$$

$$= \int_0^L \left\{k^2(L - \xi) \cos\frac{\kappa^2\xi}{2k} + \frac{k^3}{\kappa^2} \sin\frac{\kappa^2\xi}{2k} - \frac{k^3}{\kappa^2} \sin\frac{\kappa^2(2L - \xi)}{2k}\right\} F_n(\kappa_2,\kappa_3,\xi)d\xi, \tag{7.44}$$

$$F_S(\kappa_2,\kappa_3,0) =$$

$$= \int_0^L \left\{k^2(L - \xi) \cos\frac{\kappa^2\xi}{2k} - \frac{k^3}{\kappa^2} \sin\frac{\kappa^2\xi}{2k} + \frac{k^3}{\kappa^2} \sin\frac{\kappa^2(2L - \xi)}{2k}\right\} F_n(\kappa_2,\kappa_3,\xi)d\xi. \tag{7.45}$$

(Here we denote the coordinate x of the observation point by L.) As has already been repeatedly pointed out, the function $F_n(\kappa_2,\kappa_3,\xi)$ falls off very rapidly to zero for $\kappa\xi \gtrsim 1$. Therefore, the important contribution to the values of the integrals (7.44) and (7.45) occurs for $\xi \lesssim \frac{1}{\kappa}$. In the region $\xi \lesssim \frac{1}{\kappa}$, we have $\frac{\kappa^2\xi}{k} \lesssim \frac{\kappa}{k}$. We assumed above that the wavelength λ is much less than the inner scale of turbulence ℓ_o. But $\ell_o \sim 1/\kappa_m$, where κ_m is the largest wave number for which $F_n(\kappa,\xi)$ still differs from zero. Therefore we have $1/k \ll 1/\kappa_m$ and $\kappa/k < \kappa_m/k \ll 1$. Thus, $\kappa^2\xi/2k \ll 1$ in the important region of integration and we can write

$$\cos\frac{\kappa^2\xi}{2k} \sim 1,\ \sin\frac{\kappa^2\xi}{2k} \sim \frac{\kappa^2\xi}{2k},\quad \frac{\sin\kappa^2(2L-\xi)}{2k} \sim \sin\frac{\kappa^2 L}{k}.$$

We shall be interested in the structure (or correlation) functions of χ and S_1 only for values of the arguments which are small compared to L. This means that in (7.44) and (7.45) we consider only values of κ which satisfy the condition $1/\kappa \ll L$. Since $\xi \lesssim 1/\kappa$ in the important region of integration, then within this region we have $\xi \ll L$. Taking all these simplifications into account, we obtain

$$F_A(\kappa_2,\kappa_3,0) \sim \int_0^L \left(k^2L - \frac{k^3}{\kappa^2}\sin\frac{\kappa^2 L}{k}\right) F_n(\kappa_2,\kappa_3,\xi)d\xi, \tag{7.46}$$

$$F_S(\kappa_2,\kappa_3,0) \sim \int_0^L \left(k^2L + \frac{k^3}{\kappa^2}\sin\frac{\kappa^2 L}{k}\right) F_n(\kappa_2,\kappa_3,\xi)d\xi. \tag{7.47}$$

Since the function $F_n(\kappa_2,\kappa_3,\xi)$ falls off rapidly to zero for large ξ, the integration in (7.46) and (7.47) can be extended to infinity, without appreciably changing the values of the integrals. Since

$$\int_0^\infty F_n(\kappa_2,\kappa_3,\xi)d\xi = \pi\,\Phi_n(0,\kappa_2,\kappa_3),$$

where $\Phi_n(\vec{\kappa})$ is the three-dimensional spectral density of the refractive index structure function (see Eq. (1.53)). Eqs. (7.46) and (7.47) take the form

$$F_A(\kappa_2,\kappa_3,0) = \pi k^2 L \left(1 - \frac{k}{\kappa^2 L} \sin \frac{\kappa^2 L}{k}\right) \Phi_n(0,\kappa_2,\kappa_3) , \tag{7.48}$$

$$F_S(\kappa_2,\kappa_3,0) = \pi k^2 L \left(1 + \frac{k}{\kappa^2 L} \sin \frac{\kappa^2 L}{k}\right) \Phi_n(0,\kappa_2,\kappa_3) . \tag{7.49}$$

In the case where the refractive index field is a locally isotropic random field, we have

$$\Phi_n(\kappa_1,\kappa_2,\kappa_3) = \Phi\left(\sqrt{\kappa_1^2 + \kappa_2^2 + \kappa_3^2}\right) .$$

Therefore, recalling that

$$\kappa^2 = \kappa_2^2 + \kappa_3^2 , \; F_A(\kappa_2,\kappa_3,0) = F_A(\kappa,0) , \; F_S(\kappa_2,\kappa_3,0) = F_S(\kappa,0),$$

we have $\Phi_n(0,\kappa_2,\kappa_3) = \Phi_n(\kappa)$, and Eqs. (7.48) and (7.49) finally become

$$F_A(\kappa,0) = \pi k^2 L \left(1 - \frac{k}{\kappa^2 L} \sin \frac{\kappa^2 L}{k}\right) \Phi_n(\kappa) , \tag{7.50}$$

$$F_S(\kappa,0) = \pi k^2 L \left(1 + \frac{k}{\kappa^2 L} \sin \frac{\kappa^2 L}{k}\right) \Phi_n(\kappa) . \tag{7.51}$$

Eqs. (7.50) and (7.51) relate the two-dimensional spectral density of the structure (correlation) functions of the amplitude and phase fluctuations of the wave in the plane $x = L$ to the three-dimensional spectral density of the structure (correlation) function of the refractive index. Using Eqs. (1.50) and (1.51) we can go from the spectral densities $F_A(\kappa,0)$ and $F_S(\kappa,0)$ to the structure (correlation) functions of the amplitude and phase of the wave in the plane $x = L$, i.e.

$$D_A(\rho) = \overline{|X(L,y,z) - X(L,y',z')|^2} = 4\pi \int_0^\infty [1 - J_0(\kappa\rho)] F_A(\kappa,0)\kappa d\kappa, \tag{7.52}$$

$$D_S(\rho) = \overline{|S_1(L,y,z) - S_1(L,y',z')|^2} = 4\pi \int_0^\infty [1 - J_0(\kappa\rho)] F_S(\kappa,0)\kappa d\kappa, \tag{7.53}$$

where $\rho^2 = (y - y')^2 + (z - z')^2$.

7.4 Qualitative analysis of the solutions

Using Eqs. (7.50) and (7.51), we can draw some general conclusions about the character of the amplitude and phase fluctuations of the wave. It follows from Eqs. (7.50) and (7.51) that the phase fluctuations are always larger than the fluctuations of logarithmic amplitude [c]. As $\kappa \to 0$, we have

$$1 - \frac{k}{\kappa^2 L} \sin \frac{\kappa^2 L}{k} \to \frac{1}{6} \frac{\kappa^4 L^2}{k^2} .$$

Therefore $F_A(0,0) = 0$ if $\Phi_n(\kappa)$ goes to infinity at $\kappa = 0$ no faster than κ^{-4}. This implies the existence of the correlation function

$$B_A(\rho) = 2\pi \int_0^\infty J_0(\kappa\rho) F_A(\kappa,0)\kappa d\kappa, \tag{7.54}$$

of the amplitude fluctuations, which satisfies the equation (see p. 114)

$$\int_0^\infty B_A(\rho)\rho d\rho = 0. \tag{7.55}$$

Eq. (7.55) is a consequence of the law of energy conservation (see the analogous equation (6.70)).

We now consider the general character of the behavior of the correlation function of the amplitude fluctuations. It follows from Eq. (7.50) that the two-dimensional spectral density of the correlation function $B_A(\rho)$ is the product of two functions: the three-dimensional spectral density $\Phi_n(\kappa)$ of the structure function of the refractive index fluctuations and the function $\left(1 - \frac{k}{\kappa^2 L}\right) \sin^2 \frac{\kappa^2 L}{k}$. In the general case, $\Phi_n(\kappa)$ has the form shown in Fig. 9.

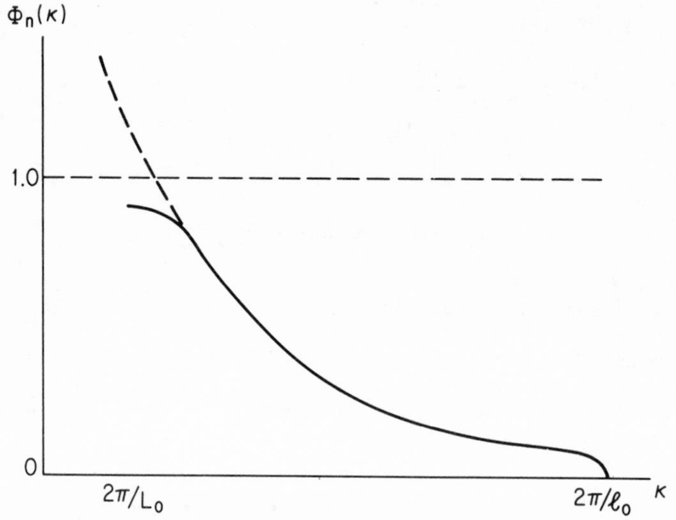

Fig. 9 General form of the spectral density of the refractive index fluctuations.

In the region of small scales which are much less than ℓ_o, i.e. for $\kappa \gg 2\pi/\ell_o$, the function $\Phi_n(\kappa)$ is equal to zero or is negligibly small. For smaller values of κ, lying between $2\pi/L_o$ and $2\pi/\ell_o$ (L_o is the outer scale of turbulence), $\Phi_n(\kappa)$ grows as κ decreases (since the refractive index fluctuations which are larger in size are related to the large scale inhomogeneities). In the case where the refractive index fluctuations obey the "two-thirds law", $\Phi_n(\kappa)$ is proportional to $\kappa^{-11/3}$ in this region, but in the general case its appearance in this region can be different. For $\kappa < 2\pi/L_o$, the growth of $\Phi_n(\kappa)$ slows down; this is connected with the fact that the refractive index fluctuations are finite. Strictly speaking, in this range of sizes the function $\Phi_n(\kappa)$ loses its meaning, since the structure function $D_n(\vec{r}_1, \vec{r}_2)$ then depends on each of the arguments $\vec{r}_1$ and $\vec{r}_2$ separately, and it is impossible to represent it in the form of a spectral expansion of the type (1.41). The function $f(\kappa) = \left(1 - \frac{k}{\kappa^2 L}\right) \sin \frac{\kappa^2 L}{k}$ is approximately equal to $\frac{1}{6} \frac{\kappa^4 L^2}{k^2}$ for $\frac{\kappa^2 L}{k} \ll 1$. For $\kappa = \sqrt{\frac{\pi k}{L}} = \sqrt{\frac{2\pi^2}{\lambda L}}$, the function $f(\kappa)$ is equal unity, and for large values of κ, $f(\kappa)$ approaches unity, undergoing smaller and smaller oscillations. The characteristic scale of this function is the quantity $\kappa_o \sim \frac{2\pi}{\sqrt{\lambda L}}$. For $\kappa \ll \kappa_o$, $f(\kappa) \sim \frac{1}{6}\frac{\kappa^4 L^2}{k^2}$, and for $\kappa \gg \kappa_o$, $f(\kappa) \sim 1$. Depending on the size of the parameter $\kappa_o = \frac{2\pi}{\sqrt{\lambda L}}$, the following relative positions of the points κ_o, $\frac{2\pi}{\ell_o}$ and $\frac{2\pi}{L_o}$ are possible:

$$1)\ \frac{1}{\sqrt{\lambda L}} > \frac{1}{\ell_o}\ ,\quad 2)\ \frac{1}{L_o} < \frac{1}{\sqrt{\lambda L}} < \frac{1}{\ell_o}\ ,\quad 3)\ \frac{1}{\sqrt{\lambda L}} < \frac{1}{L_o}\ .$$

We consider first the case where $\frac{1}{\sqrt{\lambda L}} \gg \frac{1}{\ell_o}$. In this case the relative position of the curves $\Phi_n(\kappa)$ and $f(\kappa)$ is shown in Fig. 10.

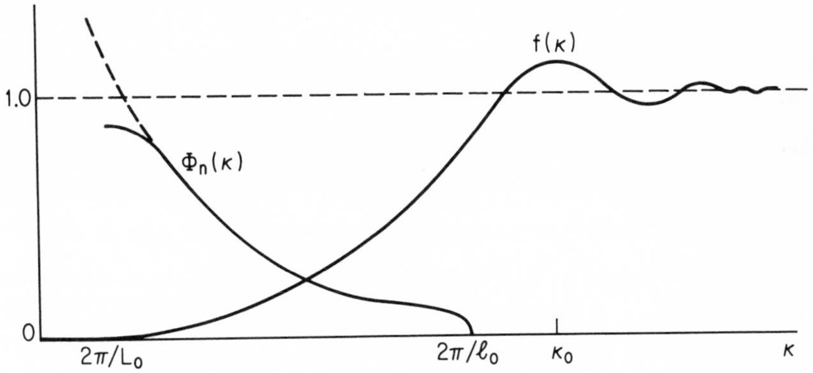

Fig. 10 Relative position of the curves $\Phi_n(\kappa)$ and $(1 - \frac{k}{\kappa^2 L}\sin\frac{\kappa^2 L}{k})$ in the case $\sqrt{\lambda L} \ll \ell_o$.

For all values of $\kappa < 2\pi/\ell_o$, the function $f(\kappa)$ is approximately equal to $\frac{1}{6}\frac{\kappa^4 L^2}{k^2}$. Therefore, we have

$$F_A(\kappa,0) = \frac{1}{6}\pi L^3 \kappa^4 \Phi_n(\kappa) \tag{7.56}$$

and

$$F_S(\kappa,0) = 2\pi k^2 L\, \Phi_n(\kappa)\ , \tag{7.57}$$

since in this case $1 + \frac{k}{\kappa^2 L}\sin\frac{\kappa^2 L}{k} \sim 2$. Eqs. (7.56) and (7.57) are valid when the condition $\sqrt{\lambda L} \ll \ell_o$ is met, and agree with Eqs. (6.44) and (6.56), which were obtained in Chapter 6 by using the equations of geometrical optics. In the case under consideration (see Fig. 10) the product of the functions $\Phi_n(\kappa)$ and $f(\kappa)$ has a maximum near the point $2\pi/\ell_o$ and is equal to zero (or negligibly small) for $\kappa > 2\pi/\ell_o$. Thus, in the case where $\sqrt{\lambda L} \ll \ell_o$, the spectrum of the correlation function of the amplitude fluctuations is concentrated near the point $2\pi/\ell_o$ (i.e., in this case refractive index inhomogeneities with scales of the order ℓ_o have the greatest influence on the amplitude fluctuations). It follows from general properties of the Fourier transform that the correlation function $B_A(\rho)$ has a characteristic scale (correlation distance) of order ℓ_o. This general conclusion is illustrated by the example given in Chapter 6 (see Fig. 8).

We now consider the case where the system of inequalities $\frac{1}{L_o} \ll \frac{1}{\sqrt{\lambda L}} \ll \frac{1}{\ell_o}$ or $\ell_o \ll \sqrt{\lambda L} \ll L_o$ holds. In this case the relative position of the curves $\Phi_n(\kappa)$ and $f(\kappa)$ is shown in Fig. 11.

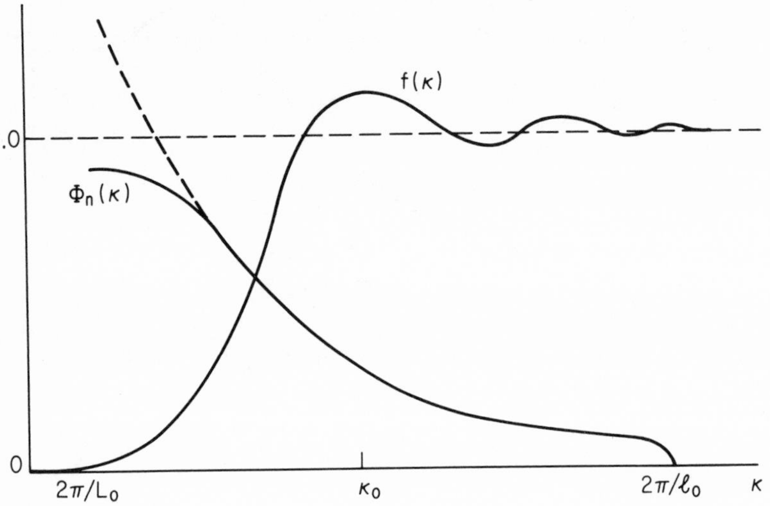

Fig. 11 Relative position of the curves $\Phi_n(\kappa)$ and $(1 - \frac{k}{\kappa^2 L} \sin \frac{\kappa^2 L}{k})$ in the case $\ell_o \ll \sqrt{\lambda L} \ll L_o$.

The product of $\Phi_n(\kappa)$ and $f(\kappa)$ has a maximum near the point $2\pi/\sqrt{L\lambda}$ and goes to zero for $\kappa \gtrsim 2\pi/\ell_o$. The behavior of the function $\Phi_n(\kappa)$ for $\kappa < 2\pi/\ell_o$ has almost no effect on the character of the function $F_A(\kappa,0) = \pi k^2 L f(\kappa)\Phi_n(\kappa)$, since in this region the function $f(\kappa)$ is near zero. Thus, in the case where $\ell_o \ll \sqrt{\lambda L} \ll L_o$, the spectrum of the correlation function of amplitude fluctuations is concentrated near the point $2\pi/\sqrt{\lambda L}$ (i.e., the refractive index inhomogeneities with scales of order $\sqrt{\lambda L}$ make the largest contribution to the amplitude fluctuations of the wave). It follows from this that the correlation function of the amplitude fluctuations in the plane $x = L$ has a characteristic scale (correlation distance) of order $\sqrt{\lambda L}$. Below we shall give a concrete example of such a correlation function.

Finally, we consider the third case, where the condition $\frac{1}{\sqrt{\lambda L}} \ll \frac{1}{L_0}$ or $\sqrt{\lambda L} \gg L_0$ is met. The relative position of the curves $\Phi_n(\kappa)$ and $f(\kappa)$ in this case is shown in Fig. 12. As can be seen from the figure, in the case under consideration the chief contribution to the spectrum of the correlation function of the amplitude fluctuations is made by large scale inhomogeneities in the interval $(L_0, \sqrt{\lambda L})$. However, it must be pointed out at once that in the range of scales exceeding L_0, the refractive index field is not a locally homogeneous and isotropic random field. Therefore, strictly speaking, for such scales the structure function of the refractive index field depends on the coordinates of both points of observation, and for it one cannot define a spectral density $\Phi_n(\vec{\kappa})$ of one argument, even a vector argument. The same thing obviously applies as well to the spectral densities $F_A(\kappa,0)$ and $F_S(\kappa,0)$ of the amplitude and phase fluctuations of the wave, since the latter are proportional to $\Phi_n(\kappa)$. The functions $F_A(\kappa,0)$ and $F_S(\kappa,0)$ have meaning only in the region $\kappa \gtrsim 2\pi/L_0$. Therefore, one can speak of the structure functions $D_A(\rho)$ and $D_S(\rho)$ of the amplitude and phase fluctuations of the wave only for $\rho \lesssim L_0$. For large values of ρ, this function begins to depend not only on the distance ρ between the observation points, but also on the location of these points in the plane $x = L$.

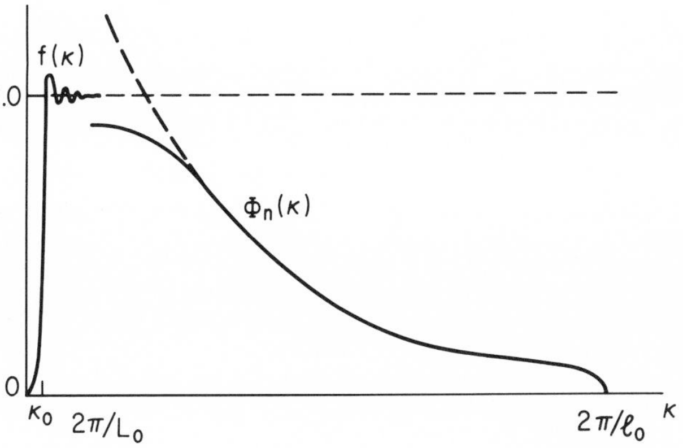

Fig. 12 The relative position of the curves $\Phi_n(\kappa)$ and $(1 - \frac{k}{\kappa^2 L} \sin \frac{k^2 L}{\kappa})$ in the case $\sqrt{\lambda L} \gg L_0$.

Let us examine the form of the spectral densities $F_A(\kappa,0)$ and $F_S(\kappa,0)$ for $\kappa > 2\pi/L_0$. In this region the function $f(\kappa) = 1 - \frac{k}{\kappa^2 L} \sin \frac{\kappa^2 L}{k} \sim 1$ and $1 + \frac{k}{\kappa^2 L} \sin \frac{\kappa^2 L}{k} \sim 1$. Therefore, we have

$$F_A(\kappa,0) \sim F_S(\kappa,0) = \pi k^2 L\, \Phi_n(\kappa) \qquad (\kappa \gtrsim \frac{2\pi}{L_0}). \tag{7.58}$$

Thus, for $\sqrt{\lambda L} \gg L_0$, the two-dimensional spectral densities of the structure functions of the amplitude and phase fluctuations of the wave are equal to one another in the range $\kappa \gtrsim 2\pi/L_0$ and proportional to the three-dimensional spectral density of the structure function of the refractive index fluctuations. Consequently, in the region $\rho \lesssim L_0$, the structure functions $D_A(\rho)$ and $D_S(\rho)$ are equal to

$$D_S(\rho) = D_A(\rho) \sim 4\pi^2 k^2 L \int_0^\infty [1 - J_0(\kappa\rho)]\, \Phi_n(\kappa)\kappa d\kappa \,. \tag{7.59}$$

In this case, the fluctuations of the amplitude and phase of the wave are proportional to the distance L traversed by the wave in the turbulent medium.

In the region $\rho \gtrsim L_0$, the form of the structure functions D_A and D_S depends in an essential way on the character of the largest scale components of the turbulence, which are not homogeneous and isotropic and therefore cannot be universal. We can only assert that, since $F_A(0,0) = 0$, the mean square amplitude fluctuation of the wave is always finite and does not depend on refractive index inhomogeneities with scales larger than $\sqrt{\lambda L}$.

If we assume that the random refractive index field is statistically homogeneous and isotropic for all scales (such an assumption is made in many papers, despite the fact that it is not adequately justified, because it considerably simplifies the solution of the problem), then we can draw further conclusions about the character of the amplitude and phase fluctuations of the wave. In this case, the fields of the amplitude and phase fluctuations of the wave in the plane $x = L$ are also homogeneous and isotropic, so that they have correlation functions

$$B_A(\rho) = 2\pi \int_0^\infty J_0(\kappa\rho) F_A(\kappa,0)\kappa d\kappa \,, \tag{7.60}$$

$$B_S(\rho) = 2\pi \int_0^\infty J_0(\kappa\rho) F_S(\kappa,0)\kappa d\kappa \,. \tag{7.61}$$

Substituting the expressions (7.50) and (7.51) for $F_A(\kappa,0)$ and $F_S(\kappa,0)$ into Eqs. (7.60) and (7.61), we obtain

$$B_A(\rho) = 2\pi^2 k^2 L \int_0^\infty J_0(\kappa\rho)\left(1 - \frac{k}{\kappa^2 L} \sin \frac{\kappa^2 L}{k}\right) \Phi_n(\kappa)\kappa d\kappa \,. \tag{7.62}$$

$$B_S(\rho) = 2\pi^2 k^2 L \int_0^\infty J_0(\kappa\rho)\left(1 + \frac{k}{\kappa^2 L} \sin \frac{\kappa^2 L}{k}\right) \Phi_n(\kappa)\kappa d\kappa \, . \tag{7.63}$$

As can be seen from Fig. 12, for $\sqrt{\lambda L} \gg L_o$, the function $(1 \mp \frac{k}{\kappa^2 L} \sin \frac{\kappa^2 L}{k}) \Phi_n(\kappa)$ coincides with $\Phi_n(\kappa)$ over almost all of the region of integration, with the exception of a small piece of the spectrum where $\kappa < 2\pi/\sqrt{\lambda L}$. Since the integral over the segment $0 < \kappa < 2\pi/\sqrt{\lambda L}$ is small compared to the integral over the whole range of κ, we have approximately

$$B_A(\rho) = B_S(\rho) = 2\pi^2 k^2 L \int_0^\infty J_0(\kappa\rho) \Phi_n(\kappa)\kappa d\kappa \, . \tag{7.64}$$

However, it should be noted that if we discard the quantity $\frac{k}{\kappa^2 L} \sin \frac{\kappa^2 L}{k}$ in Eq. (7.62), we obtain the expression $\pi k^2 L \, \Phi_n(\kappa)$ for the spectral density of the correlation function of the amplitude fluctuations of the wave, an expression which does not go to zero at $\kappa = 0$. Therefore, the expression for $B_A(\rho)$ which was obtained using Eq. (7.64) will not in general satisfy the relation (7.55), which is a consequence of the law of conservation of energy; this can sometimes lead to physically meaningless conclusions.

In the case being considered, the functions $B_n(r)$ and $\Phi_n(\kappa)$ are connected by the relation (1.25), i.e.

$$\Phi_n(\kappa) = \frac{1}{2\pi^2 \kappa} \int_0^\infty B_n(r) \sin(\kappa r) r dr \, .$$

Substituting this expression into Eq. (7.64) and changing the order of integration, we find

$$B_A(\rho) = B_S(\rho) = k^2 L \int_0^\infty B_n(r) r dr \int_0^\infty J_0(\kappa\rho) \sin(\kappa r) d\kappa \, .$$

Taking into consideration that [53]

$$\int_0^{\infty} J_0(\kappa\rho)\sin(\kappa r)d\kappa = \begin{cases} 0 & \text{for } r^2 < \rho^2 , \\ \dfrac{1}{\sqrt{r^2 - \rho^2}} & \text{for } r^2 > \rho^2 , \end{cases}$$

we obtain the formula

$$B_A(\rho) = B_S(\rho) = k^2 L \int_0^{\infty} B_n\left(\sqrt{\rho^2 + x^2}\right) dx \qquad (\sqrt{\lambda L} \gg L_0) , \tag{7.65}$$

which relates the correlation functions of the amplitude and phase fluctuations of the wave in the plane $x = L$ to the correlation function of the refractive index fluctuations. Setting $\rho = 0$ in Eq. (7.65), we obtain an expression for the mean square amplitude and phase fluctuations of the wave:

$$\overline{\chi^2} = \overline{S_1^2} = k^2 L \int_0^{\infty} B_n(x)dx . \tag{7.66}$$

The quantity

$$L_n = \frac{1}{B_n(0)} \int_0^{\infty} B_n(x)dx = \frac{1}{\overline{n_1^2}} \int_0^{\infty} B_n(x)dx , \tag{7.67}$$

which agrees in order of magnitude with the outer scale of turbulence, is called the integral scale of turbulence [d]. Substituting (7.67) into (7.66), we obtain the formula

$$\overline{\chi^2} = \overline{S_1^2} = \overline{n_1^2}\, k^2 L L_n . \tag{7.68}$$

It follows from Eq. (7.68) that for $\sqrt{\lambda L} \gg L_0$, the size of the amplitude and phase fluctuations of the wave is determined by two parameters of the turbulence: $\overline{n_1^2}$, the size of the mean square refractive index fluctuations, and L_n, the integral scale of the turbulence.

The correlation distance of the amplitude and phase fluctuations of the wave in the plane $x = L$ can be characterized by the "integral scale" of these fluctuations, i.e.

$$L_S = L_A = \frac{1}{B_A(0)} \int_0^\infty B_A(\rho)d\rho = \frac{k^2L}{B_A(0)} \int_0^\infty\int_0^\infty B_n\left(\sqrt{x^2 + \rho^2}\right) dxd\rho \, . \tag{7.69}$$

Going over to polar coordinates in (7.69), we find

$$L_S = L_A = \frac{\pi k^2 L}{2B_A(0)} \int_0^\infty B_n(r)rdr. \tag{7.70}$$

Finally, setting $B_A(0) = k^2LL_nB_n(0)$, we obtain the formula

$$L_S = L_A = \frac{\pi}{2L_n} \int_0^\infty \frac{B_n(r)}{B_n(0)} rdr \, . \tag{7.71}$$

Since $B_n(r)$ is appreciably different from zero only in the interval $(0,L_n)$, we have

$$\int_0^\infty \frac{B_n(r)}{B_n(0)} rdr \sim L_n^2 \, ,$$

so that

$$L_S = L_A \sim L_n \sim L_o \, . \tag{7.72}$$

Thus, for $\sqrt{\lambda L} \gg L_o$, the correlation distance of the amplitude and phase fluctuations in the plane $x = L$ agrees in order of magnitude with the outer scale of turbulence [e].

Summarizing the results of our qualitative analysis of the character of the amplitude and phase fluctuations of the wave, we come to the conclusion that the following cases can occur, depending on the size of the parameter $\sqrt{\lambda L}$:

1) $\sqrt{\lambda L} \ll \ell_0$. The amplitude fluctuations of the wave do not depend on the frequency an grow with the distance like L^3, while the phase fluctuations are proportional to the square of the frequency and to the distance L. The correlation distance of the amplitude fluctuations o the wave in the plane $x = L$ is of order ℓ_0.

2) $\ell_0 \ll \sqrt{\lambda L} \ll L_0$. The form of the correlation function of the amplitude fluctuations depends on the concrete form of the spectral density $\Phi_n(\kappa)$ of the refractive index fluctuation The correlation distance of the amplitude fluctuations of the wave in the plane $x = L$ is of order $\sqrt{\lambda L}$.

3) $\sqrt{\lambda L} \gg L_0$. The fields of amplitude and phase fluctuations in the plane $x = L$ are no locally isotropic random fields. For $\rho \lesssim L_0$, we have $D_A(\rho) = D_S(\rho)$. The amplitude and phase fluctuations are proportional to the square of the frequency and to the distance L.

4) $\sqrt{\lambda L} \gg L_0$ and the field of refractive index fluctuations is homogeneous and isotropi Here the correlation functions of the amplitude and phase fluctuations of the wave in the plan $x = L$ coincide. The correlation distance of the amplitude and phase fluctuations of the wave in this plane agrees with L_0 in order of magnitude.

In all the cases considered, the largest wave numbers which participate in the spectral expansions of the amplitude and phase fluctuations of the wave are of order $2\pi/\ell_0$. It follows from this that the correlation and structure functions of the amplitude and phase fluctuations of the wave change quite slowly over a distance of order ℓ_0. In particular, the function $D_S(\rho)$ has a square law character in a region of order ℓ_0 near the origin, and in the same region $B_A(\rho)$ has the form $B_A(0)(1 - a\,\rho^2/\ell_0^2 + \dots)$.

Eqs. (7.50) and (7.51) obtained above relate the spectral densities of the amplitude and phase fluctuations of the wave to the spectral density of the refractive index fluctuations. Using these formulas, we can obtain relations relating the correlation function of the fluctuations of logarithmic amplitude and the structure function of the phase fluctuations of the wave to the structure function of the refractive index fluctuations. Such relations have been obtained in [54,55], but their form is much more complicated (the formulas contain double integrals) than the form of Eqs. (7.50) and (7.51). This fact greatly hampers the application of these formulas both for the purposes of qualitative study of solutions and for practical calculations with various concrete correlation functions. Eqs. (7.50) and (7.51) for the spectral densities $F_A(\kappa,0)$ and $F_S(\kappa,0)$ are much more convenient.

We now consider an example. Let the field of refractive index fluctuations be statistically homogeneous and isotropic and let it be described by the correlation function [f]

$$B_n(r) = \overline{n_1^2}\, e^{-r^2/a^2} . \tag{7.73}$$

The spectral density corresponding to the function (7.73) is equal to (see page 18)

$$\Phi_n(\kappa) = \frac{\overline{n_1^2}\, a^3}{8\pi\sqrt{\pi}}\, e^{-\kappa^2 a^2/4} . \tag{7.74}$$

The functions (7.73) and (7.74) are simple enough to permit complete calculation of the correlation functions of the amplitude and phase fluctuations. However, one should remark that these functions are characterized by only one scale a, which can be regarded with equal justification as both the inner and the outer scale of the turbulence [g]. Therefore, results obtained by using these functions are in many respects not sufficiently general. Moreover, as we established in Chapter 1, the refractive index fluctuations in a turbulent atmosphere are quite accurately described by the "two-thirds law", and not by the correlation function (7.73). Therefore, the present example is of a purely illustrative character and the formulas obtained below can be used only to the extent that their form does not depend on the form of the correlation function of the refractive index (for example, the dependence of $\overline{\chi^2}$ on L for $\sqrt{\lambda L} \ll a$ and $\sqrt{\lambda L} \gg a$ has a universal character, which does not depend on $B_n(r)$).

Substituting the function (7.74) into Eqs. (7.50) and (7.51), we obtain

$$F_A(\kappa,0) = \frac{1}{8\sqrt{\pi}}\, \overline{n_1^2}\, a^3 k^2 L \left(1 - \frac{k}{\kappa^2 L} \sin \frac{\kappa^2 L}{k}\right) \exp\left(-\frac{\kappa^2 a^2}{4}\right) , \tag{7.75}$$

$$F_S(\kappa,0) = \frac{1}{8\sqrt{\pi}}\, \overline{n_1^2}\, a^3 k^2 L \left(1 + \frac{k}{\kappa^2 L} \sin \frac{\kappa^2 L}{k}\right) \exp\left(-\frac{\kappa^2 a^2}{4}\right) . \tag{7.76}$$

The mean square fluctuation of logarithmic amplitude is equal to (see (7.54))

$$\overline{\chi^2} = 2\pi \int_0^\infty F_A(\kappa,0)\kappa d\kappa =$$

$$= \frac{\sqrt{\pi}}{4} \overline{n_1^2} a^3 k^2 L \int_0^\infty \left(1 - \frac{k}{\kappa^2 L} \sin \frac{\kappa^2 L}{k}\right) \exp\left(-\frac{\kappa^2 a^2}{4}\right) \kappa d\kappa. \quad (7.77$$

The integral figuring in (7.77) can be calculated in an elementary way and equals

$$\frac{2}{a^2}\left(1 - \frac{\arctan D}{D}\right), \text{ where } D = \frac{4L}{ka^2} .$$

Thus we have

$$\overline{\chi^2} = \frac{\sqrt{\pi}}{2} \overline{n_1^2} ak^2 L\left(1 - \frac{\arctan D}{D}\right) , \quad (7.78$$

and completely analogously

$$\overline{S_1^2} = \frac{\sqrt{\pi}}{2} \overline{n_1^2} ak^2 L\left(1 + \frac{\arctan D}{D}\right) . \quad (7.79$$

Eqs. (7.78) and (7.79) were obtained in the paper of Obukhov [51] without using spectral expa sions of the fluctuations. The quantity D figuring in (7.78) and (7.79) (the so-called wave parameter) is proportional to the square of the ratio of $\sqrt{\lambda L}$ (the radius of the first Fresn zone) to a (the average size of the inhomogeneities). Depending on the value of this paramete the following limiting cases can occur:

a) $D \ll 1$ or $L \ll \frac{\pi a^2}{2\lambda} = L_{cr}$. Then $\frac{1}{D} \arctan D \sim 1 - \frac{D^2}{3}$ and Eqs. (7.78) and (7.79) take the form

$$\overline{\chi^2} = \frac{8\sqrt{\pi}}{3} \overline{n_1^2} \frac{L^3}{a^3} ,$$

$$\overline{S_1^2} = \sqrt{\pi} \overline{n_1^2} ak^2 L .$$

hese formulas, which are valid for $L \ll L_{cr}$, correspond to geometrical optics.

b) In the opposite case, where $D \gg 1$ or $L \gg L_{cr}$, the quantity $\frac{1}{D}$ arc tan $D \ll 1$ and

$$\overline{\chi^2} = \overline{S_1^2} = \frac{\sqrt{\pi}}{2} \overline{n_1^2} k^2 aL , \tag{7.80}$$

hich corresponds to the case considered above, where $\sqrt{\lambda L} \gg L_o$.

Using the relations

$$B_A(\rho) = \frac{\sqrt{\pi}}{4} \overline{n_1^2} k^2 a^3 L \int_0^\infty J_o(\kappa\rho) \left(1 - \frac{k}{\kappa^2 L} \sin \frac{\kappa^2 L}{k}\right) e^{-\kappa^2 a^2/4} \kappa d\kappa , \tag{7.81}$$

$$B_S(\rho) = \frac{\sqrt{\pi}}{4} \overline{n_1^2} k^2 a^3 L \int_0^\infty J_o(\kappa\rho) \left(1 + \frac{k}{\kappa^2 L} \sin \frac{\kappa^2 L}{k}\right) e^{-\kappa^2 a^2/4} \kappa d\kappa , \tag{7.82}$$

e can also determine the correlation functions of the amplitude and phase fluctuations of the ave. The integrals appearing in (7.81) and (7.82) can be expressed in terms of the integral xponential function Ei(z), so that Eqs. (7.81) and (7.82) take the form

$$B_A(\rho) = \frac{\sqrt{\pi}}{2} \overline{n_1^2} k^2 aL \left\{ \exp\left[-\frac{\rho^2}{a^2} - \left(\frac{\rho^2}{ka^3}\right)^2\right] + \frac{1}{D} \operatorname{Im} \operatorname{Ei}\left(\frac{i\frac{\rho^2}{a^2}}{D - i}\right)^2 \right\} , \tag{7.83}$$

$$B_S(\rho) = \frac{\sqrt{\pi}}{2} \overline{n_1^2} k^2 aL \left\{ \exp\left[-\frac{\rho^2}{a^2} - \left(\frac{\rho^2}{ka^3}\right)^2\right] - \frac{1}{D} \operatorname{Im} \operatorname{Ei}\left(\frac{i\frac{\rho^2}{a^2}}{D - i}\right)^2 \right\} . \tag{7.84}$$

Eqs. (7.83) and (7.84) were obtained by Chernov [56]. As $\rho \to 0$, these expressions reduce to Eqs. (7.78) and (7.79). We must bear in mind that as $z \to 0$, the function $Ei(z)$ has a logarithmic singularity with $\text{Im}\, Ei(z) \to \arg z$. An analysis of Eqs. (7.83) and (7.84) leads to the conclusion that both for $D \ll 1$ and for $D \gg 1$ the correlation distance of the amplitude and phase fluctuations of the wave is of order a [56]. However, this result is caused by the special choice of the form of the correlation function of the refractive index fluctuation i.e. the Gaussian curve (7.73). As we have shown above, when the condition $\sqrt{\lambda L} \ll \ell_0$ is met, the correlation distance of the amplitude fluctuations in the plane $x = L$ agrees in order of magnitude with ℓ_0, in the case where $\sqrt{\lambda L} \gg L_0$, it is of order L_0, while in the intermediate case it equals $\sqrt{\lambda L}$. However, since the values of ℓ_0 and L_0 are of the same order of magnitude for a Gaussian correlation function, i.e. $\ell_0 \sim L_0 \sim a$ [g] then in the present case the correlation distance of the amplitude fluctuations of the wave in the plane $x = L$ is of order a for any value of the parameter $\sqrt{\lambda L}$ (i.e. both for $D \ll 1$ and for $D \gg 1$).

7.5 Amplitude and phase fluctuations of a wave propagating in a locally isotropic turbulent medium

We now consider another, much more realistic example. Let the refractive index field be locally homogeneous and let it be described by the structure function

$$D_n(r) = \begin{cases} C_n^2\, r^{2/3} & \text{for } \ell_0 \ll r \ll L_0\,, \\ C_n^2\, \ell_0^{2/3} \left(\frac{r}{\ell_0}\right)^2 & \text{for } r \ll \ell_0\,. \end{cases} \tag{7.85}$$

In the region of values of r exceeding L_0, the form of the structure function $D_n(r)$ is not universal. However, this indeterminacy does not affect the correlation function of the amplitude fluctuations. In fact, as we have already seen above (see Figs. 10,11), in the case where $\sqrt{\lambda L} \ll L_0$, the behavior of the spectral density $\Phi_n(\kappa)$ for $\kappa < 2\pi/L_0$ has almost no influence on the calculation of the correlation function of the amplitude fluctuations of the wave. Thus, if we restrict ourselves to values of L which satisfy the condition $\sqrt{\lambda L} \ll L_0$, we can specify the form of the function $D_n(r)$ for $r \gtrsim L_0$ in an arbitrary way (it is only necessary that $D_n(r)$ does not grow faster than r for $r > L_0$). In particular, we can assume that for $r \gtrsim L_0$, $D_n(r)$ preserves the same form as for $\ell_0 \ll r \ll L_0$, i.e., we can omit the condition $r \ll L_0$ in Eq. (7.85). A similar situation also occurs in the case of the structure function of the phase fluctuations of the wave. Inhomogeneities with dimensions much larger than ρ have little effect on the value of $D_S(\rho)$. Therefore, if ρ is restricted by the condition $\rho \ll L_0$, the form of the structure function $D_n(r)$ for $r \gtrsim L_0$ has no important bearing, and we can also omit the condition $r \ll L_0$ in Eq. (7.85).

As we have seen above, the structure function (7.85) can be associated with the spectral density

$$\Phi_n(\kappa) = \begin{cases} 0.033\, C_n^2\, \kappa^{-11/3} & \text{for } \kappa < \kappa_m, \\ 0 & \text{for } \kappa > \kappa_m, \end{cases} \tag{7.86}$$

where $\kappa_m = 5.48/\ell_0$. Substituting (7.86) into Eqs. (7.50) and (7.51), we obtain the following expressions

$$F_A(\kappa,0) = \begin{cases} 0.033\pi C_n^2 k^2 L \left(1 - \dfrac{k}{\kappa^2 L} \sin \dfrac{\kappa^2 L}{k}\right) \kappa^{-11/3} & \text{for } \kappa < \kappa_m, \\ 0 & \text{for } \kappa > \kappa_m, \end{cases} \tag{7.87}$$

$$F_S(\kappa,0) = \begin{cases} 0.033\pi C_n^2 k^2 L \left(1 + \dfrac{k}{\kappa^2 L} \sin \dfrac{\kappa^2 L}{k}\right) \kappa^{-11/3} & \text{for } \kappa < \kappa_m, \\ 0 & \text{for } \kappa > \kappa_m. \end{cases} \tag{7.88}$$

We shall find the correlation and structure functions corresponding to these spectral densities in the separate cases where $\sqrt{\lambda L} \ll \ell_0$ and $\sqrt{\lambda L} \gg \ell_0$. For $\sqrt{\lambda L} \ll \ell_0$, $\kappa^2 L/k < \kappa_m^2 L/k \ll 1$ and Eqs. (7.87) and (7.88) reduce to Eqs. (6.61) and (6.60), which correspond to geometrical optics. The correlation and structure functions of the amplitude and phase fluctuations of the wave in this case were studied in Chapter 6.

We now consider the case where $\sqrt{\lambda L} \gg \ell_o$. In this case, in order to calculate the structure functions of the amplitude and phase, it is necessary to use the unsimplified formulas (7.87) and (7.88). For $D_A(\rho)$ we obtain the expression

$$D_A(\rho) = 4\pi^2(0.033)C_n^2k^2L\int_0^{\kappa_m}[1 - J_o(\kappa\rho)]\left(1 - \frac{k}{\kappa^2L}\sin\frac{\kappa^2L}{k}\right)\kappa^{-8/3}\,d\kappa\,. \qquad (7.8$$

First we consider the behavior of the function $D_A(\rho)$ for $\rho \ll \ell_o$. In this case $\kappa_m\rho \ll 1$ and the approximate equality $1 - J_o(\kappa\rho) \sim \frac{1}{4}\kappa^2\rho^2$ is valid in the whole range of integration $(0,\kappa_$ Consequently, for $\rho \ll \ell_o$ we have

$$D_A(\rho) = \frac{1}{2}\pi^2(0.033)C_n^2k^{13/6}L^{5/6}\rho^2\int_0^{\kappa_m^2L/k}\left(1 - \frac{\sin x}{x}\right)x^{-5/6}\,dx\,. \qquad (7.9$$

Since we are considering the case where $\sqrt{\lambda L} \gg \ell_o$, then $\kappa_m^2L/k \gg 1$ and the integral appeari in (7.90) is approximately equal to $6(\kappa_m^2L/k)^{1/6}$ [h]. Consequently, for $\rho \ll \ell_o$

$$D_A(\rho) = 1.72C_n^2k^2L\,\ell_o^{-1/3}\,\rho^2, \qquad (7.9$$

i.e., for small ρ, the structure function of the amplitude fluctuations has a parabolic character, and therefore for $\rho \ll \ell_o$, the correlation function of the amplitude fluctuations of the wave has the form $B_A(\rho) \sim B_A(0)(1 - \alpha\rho^2)$ (see page 146). For $\rho \gg \ell_o$, the integration (7.89) can be extended to infinity. This only influences the form of the function $D_A(\rho)$ for small ρ, but we have considered this case separately (Eq. (7.91)). We obtain the formula

$$B_A(\rho) = 2\pi^2(0.033)C_n^2k^2L\int_0^{\infty}J_o(\kappa\rho)\left(1 - \frac{k}{\kappa^2L}\sin\frac{\kappa^2L}{k}\right)\kappa^{-8/3}\,d\kappa \qquad (7.9$$

for the correlation function $B_A(\rho)$. First we find the mean square fluctuation of logarithmic amplitude, i.e.

$$\overline{\chi^2} = B_A(0) = 2\pi^2(0.033)C_n^2 k^2 L \int_0^\infty \left(1 - \frac{k}{\kappa^2 L} \sin \frac{\kappa^2 L}{k}\right) \kappa^{-8/3} d\kappa . \tag{7.93}$$

Calculating the integral appearing in this formula [i], we obtain

$$\overline{\chi^2} = 0.31 \, C_n^2 \, k^{7/6} \, L^{11/6} \qquad (\sqrt{\lambda L} \gg \ell_0) . \tag{7.94}$$

As we have seen above (see page 146), the dependence of the quantity $\overline{\chi^2}$ on L has the form $\overline{\chi^2} \sim L^3$ in the case $\sqrt{\lambda L} \ll \ell_0$ and the form $\overline{\chi^2} \sim L$ in the case $\sqrt{\lambda L} \gg L_0$. For $\ell_0 \ll \sqrt{\lambda L} \ll L_0$, the exponent α in the formula $\overline{\chi^2} \sim L^\alpha$ has an intermediate value, determined by the form of the structure function of the refractive index fluctuations. If $D_n(r) \sim r^\mu$, the quantity α has the value $(\mu + 3)/2$; for $0 < \mu < 1$, we have $1.5 < \alpha < 2$.

The correlation coefficient $b_A(\rho) = B_A(\rho)/B_A(0)$ of the amplitude fluctuations of the wave in the plane $x = L$, determined by Eqs. (7.92) and (7.94), can be found by numerical integration [j]. By integrating along the contour consisting of the circumference of an infinitely large circle and the rays $\mathrm{Re}\,\kappa = \mathrm{Im}\,\kappa$, $\mathrm{Im}\,\kappa = 0$, we can reduce the integral appearing in (7.92) to a form suitable for numerical integration. The function $b_A(\rho)$ obtained as a result of the numerical integration is shown in Fig. 13. The correlation distance of the amplitude fluctuations of the wave agrees in order of magnitude with the radius $\sqrt{\lambda L}$ of the first Fresnel zone. As was to be expected (see Eq. (7.55)), the function $b_A(\rho)$ takes on negative values, since the relation

$$\int_0^\infty b_A(\rho)\rho d\rho = 0$$

must be satisfied [k].

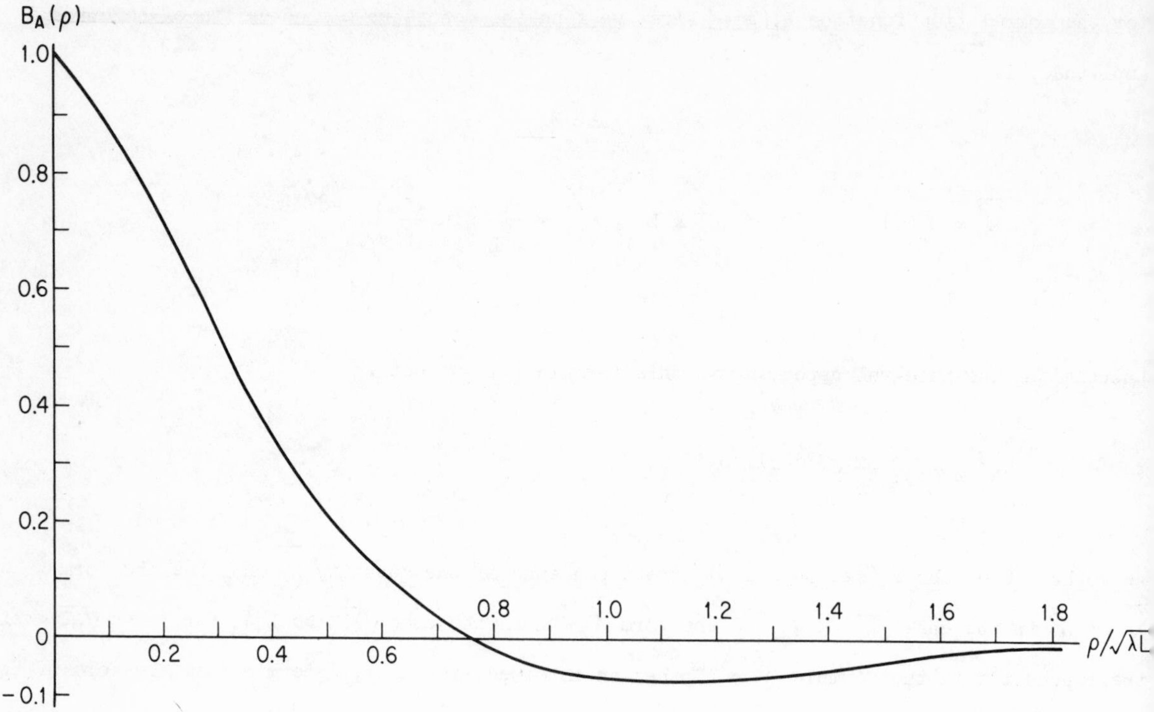

Fig. 13 The correlation coefficient of the fluctuations of logarithmic amplitude in the plane $x = L$, with the condition $\ell_o \ll \sqrt{\lambda L} \ll L_o$.

We now turn to the calculation of the structure function of the phase fluctuations of the wave. Adding Eqs. (7.52) and (7.53), we obtain the formula

$$D_A(\rho) + D_S(\rho) = 8\pi^2 k^2 L \int_0^\infty [1 - J_o(\kappa\rho)] \Phi_n(\kappa)\kappa d\kappa \ . \tag{7.95}$$

It follows from this that

$$D_A(\rho) + D_S(\rho) = 8\pi^2 (0.033) k^2 L C_n^2 \int_0^{\kappa_m} [1 - J_o(\kappa\rho)]\kappa^{-8/3} \, d\kappa \ , \tag{7.96}$$

in the case where $\Phi_n(\kappa)$ is determined by Eq. (7.86). Let $\rho \ll \ell_o$ or $\kappa_m \rho \ll 1$. Then $1 - J_o(\kappa\rho) \sim \frac{1}{4} \kappa^2 \rho^2$ and

$$D_A(\rho) + D_S(\rho) = 3.44\, k^2 L C_n^2\, \ell_o^{-1/3}\, \rho^2 \qquad (\rho \ll \ell_o) \tag{7.97}$$

(κ_m is expressed in terms of ℓ_o by using the relation $\kappa_m \ell_o = 5.48$). For $\kappa_m \rho \gg 1$, the integration in (7.96) can be extended to infinity and then (see note [d] to Chapter 6)

$$D_A(\rho) + D_S(\rho) = 2.91\, k^2 L C_n^2\, \rho^{5/3}\ . \tag{7.98}$$

Eqs. (7.97) and (7.98) allow us to find the function $D_S(\rho)$ if we know the function $D_A(\rho)$. For small values of ρ (Eq. (7.91)), $D_A(\rho) = 1.72\, C_n^2\, k^2 L\, \ell_o^{-1/3}\, \rho^2$. Substituting this value of $D_A(\rho)$ into Eq. (7.97), we obtain

$$D_S(\rho) = D_A(\rho) = 1.72\, C_n^2\, \ell_o^{-1/3}\, k^2 L \rho^2\ , \qquad (\rho \ll \ell_o). \tag{7.99}$$

For $\rho \gg \ell_o$, we can find $D_A(\rho)$ from the relation

$$D_A(\rho) = 2B_A(0) - 2B_A(\rho) = 2\, \overline{X^2}\, (1 - b_A(\rho)).$$

Substituting this expression into (7.98) and using Eq. (7.94), we obtain

$$D_S(\rho) = 2.91\, k^2 L\, C_n^2\, \rho^{5/3} - 0.62\, C_n^2\, L^{11/6}\, k^{7/6} [1 - b_A(\rho)]\ . \tag{7.100}$$

For $\rho \gg \sqrt{\lambda L}$, and actually even for $\rho \sim \sqrt{\lambda L}$, the second term in (7.100) is small compared to the first and

$$D_S(\rho) = 2.91\, k^2 L\, C_n^2\, \rho^{5/3}\ , \qquad (\rho \gtrsim \sqrt{\lambda L}). \tag{7.101}$$

For values of ρ small compared to $\sqrt{\lambda L}$, the second term is of the same order of magnitude as the first. If we use the asymptotic expansion of $b_A(\rho)$ for $\ell_o \ll \rho \ll \sqrt{\lambda L}$ given in note [j], then we obtain a formula of the form (7.101), but with a numerical coefficient which is half as large, i.e.

$$D_S(\rho) = 1.46\, k^2 L\, C_n^2\, \rho^{5/3} \qquad (\ell_o \ll \rho \ll \sqrt{\lambda L}). \qquad (7.102)$$

Eq. (7.101), which is valid under the condition $\sqrt{\lambda L} \gg \ell_o$, agrees with Eq. (6.65) which is valid when the condition $\sqrt{\lambda L} \ll \ell_o$ is met. Thus, the character of the phase fluctuations of the wave does not change when L goes through the critical value $L_{cr} \sim \ell_o^2/\lambda$. However, in thes[e] two cases the amplitude fluctuations are described by different formulas.

7.6 Relation between amplitude and phase fluctuations and wave scattering

As we have seen above, Eq. (7.21), which determines the size of the field fluctuations, can be obtained both by using the equation

$$\Delta u_1 + k^2 u_1 = -2k^2 n_1(\vec{r}) u_o,$$

which determines the wave scattering, and by using the equation

$$\Delta \psi_1 + 2 \nabla \psi_o \cdot \nabla \psi_1 + 2k^2 n_1(\vec{r}) = 0,$$

which describes the amplitude and phase fluctuations of the wave. In deriving Eq. (7.21) by the first method, we added together the incident wave u_o and the wave u_1 scattered by the inhomogeneities of the medium. The scattered waves, arriving at the observation point with random values of amplitude and phase, are added to the "unperturbed" wave and produce amplitud[e] and phase fluctuations of the total wave. The relation between the amplitude and phase fluctuations of the wave and the scattering of the waves can be pursued in more detail. As we hav[e] shown above, $\overline{\chi^2} = B_A(0)$, the mean square amplitude fluctuation of the wave, can be expressed in terms of the function $\Phi_n(\kappa)$ by using Eqs. (7.50) and (7.54), i.e.

$$\overline{\chi^2} = B_A(0) = 2\pi^2 k^2 L \int_0^\infty \left(1 - \frac{k}{\kappa^2 L} \sin \frac{\kappa^2 L}{k}\right) \Phi_n(\kappa)\kappa d\kappa \; . \tag{7.103}$$

The function $\Phi_n(\kappa)$ also determines the effective scattering cross section of the volume V into the solid angle $d\Omega$ (see page 68), i.e.

$$d\sigma(\theta) = 2\pi^2 k^4 V \, \Phi_n(2k \sin \frac{\theta}{2}) d\Omega \; , \tag{7.104}$$

where we have omitted the factor $\sin^2\chi$ which depends on the polarization of the incident wave. Introducing $d\sigma_o$, the effective scattering cross section of the unit volume, we have

$$d\sigma_o(\theta) = 2\pi k^4 \Phi_n(2k \sin \frac{\theta}{2}) d\Omega \; . \tag{7.105}$$

We make the change of variable

$$\kappa = 2k \sin \frac{\theta}{2} \tag{7.106}$$

in the integral (7.103). The variable κ in Eq. (7.103) ranges from 0 to ∞. At the same time, the quantity $2k \sin \frac{\theta}{2}$ can only take values from 0 to 2k for real θ. The value of the function $\Phi_n(\kappa)$ is zero or negligibly small for $\kappa > \kappa_m$. Therefore, in the case $\kappa \gg \kappa_m$ considered in this section, the upper limit of integration in (7.103) can be replaced by any number which is much larger than κ_m, in particular by $2k/\sqrt{2}$, corresponding to the value $\theta = \pi/2$. Substituting (7.106) into (7.103), we obtain the formula

$$\overline{\chi^2} = 2\pi^2 k^2 L \int_0^{\pi/2} \left[1 - \frac{\sin(4kL \sin^2 \frac{\theta}{2})}{4kL \sin^2 \frac{\theta}{2}}\right] \Phi_n(2k \sin \frac{\theta}{2}) k^2 \sin\theta d\theta \; . \tag{7.107}$$

If now we use Eq. (7.105), then we can eliminate the function Φ_n from Eq. (7.107) by expressing it in terms of $d\sigma_o/d\Omega$, i.e.

$$\overline{\chi^2} = \pi L \int_o^{\pi/2} \left[1 - \frac{\sin(4kL \sin^2 \frac{\theta}{2})}{4kL \sin^2 \frac{\theta}{2}} \right] \frac{d\sigma_o(\theta)}{d\Omega} \sin\theta \, d\theta \, . \tag{7.108}$$

The quantity $d\sigma_o(\theta)/d\Omega$ is equal to the effective scattering cross section at the angle θ into the solid angle $d\Omega = \sin\theta \, d\theta \, d\varphi$. We denote by $d\sigma_1(\theta)$ the effective scattering cross section into the solid angle $d\Omega_1 = 2\pi \sin\theta \, d\theta$ bounded by the cones of aperture θ and $\theta + d\theta$. Since $d\sigma_o(\theta)$ does not depend on φ, then $d\sigma_o/d\varphi = d\sigma_1(\theta)/2\pi$ and $d\sigma_o(\theta)\sin\theta d\theta/d\varphi\sin\theta d\theta = d\sigma_1(\theta)/2\pi$. Eq. (7.108) takes the final form

$$\overline{\chi^2} = \frac{1}{2} L \int_o^{\pi/2} \left[1 - \frac{\sin(4kL \sin^2 \frac{\theta}{2})}{4kL \sin^2 \frac{\theta}{2}} \right] d\sigma_1(\theta) \, . \tag{7.109}$$

The expression just obtained has a simple physical meaning. The amplitude fluctuations of the wave are caused by the superposition of the scattered waves (the quantity $d\sigma_1(\theta)$ in the integrand). The factor

$$1 - \frac{\sin(4kL \sin^2 \frac{\theta}{2})}{4kL \sin^2 \frac{\theta}{2}}$$

depends on the ratio between the dimensions of the Fresnel zone and the dimensions of the scattering inhomogeneities. In fact, as shown above, the quantity $\ell(\theta)$, the size of the inhomogeneities which scatter at the angle θ, is equal to $\ell(\theta) = \lambda/(2 \sin \frac{\theta}{2})$, i.e. $2 \sin \frac{\theta}{2} = \frac{\lambda}{\ell(\theta)}$.

Therefore, the quantity

$$4kL\sin^2\frac{\theta}{2} = \frac{2\pi}{\lambda} L \frac{\lambda^2}{\ell^2(\theta)} = 2\pi \frac{\lambda L}{\ell^2(\theta)}$$

is proportional to the square of the ratio of the radius of the first Fresnel zone to the size of $\ell(\theta)$. The function

$$1 - \frac{\sin(2\pi\lambda L/\ell^2(\theta))}{2\pi\lambda L/\ell^2(\theta)}$$

has a maximum for $\ell(\theta) \sim \sqrt{\lambda L}$. Thus, in forming the amplitude fluctuations of the wave, "fullest" use is made of the energy scattered by the inhomogeneities whose dimensions are close to the radius of the first Fresnel zone. In the case where all the inhomogeneities are "large" compared to $\sqrt{\lambda L}$, they act like coherent scatterers, and the effects of the different Fresnel zones spanned by the inhomogeneities cancel one another out to a considerable extent. In this case

$$1 - \frac{\ell^2(\theta)}{2\pi\lambda L}\sin\left(\frac{2\pi\lambda L}{\ell^2(\theta)}\right) = 1 - \frac{\sin(4kL\sin^2\frac{\theta}{2})}{4kL\sin^2\frac{\theta}{2}} \sim \frac{1}{6}\cdot 16k^2L^2\sin^4\frac{\theta}{2} ,$$

and (7.109) reduces to the formula

$$\overline{\chi^2} = \frac{4}{3} k^2L^3 \int_0^{\pi/2} \sin^4\frac{\theta}{2}\, d\sigma_1(\theta) , \tag{7.110}$$

which corresponds to geometrical optics. In the opposite case, where the radius of the first Fresnel zone is much larger than the largest scale refractive index inhomogeneities, there are a large number of incoherent scatterers inside each zone, and their effects add up like energy. In this case $\sqrt{\lambda L}/\ell(\theta) \gg 1$, and Eq. (7.109) takes the especially simple form

$$\overline{\chi^2} = \frac{1}{2} L \int_0^{\pi/2} d\sigma_1(\theta) = \frac{1}{2} \sigma L \; . \qquad (7.111)$$

Here σ is the effective scattering cross section of a unit volume or the scattering coefficient (σ has the dimensions of cm^{-1}). This quantity determines the attenuation of the wave due to scattering in going a unit distance.

Eq. (7.111) and the similar formula for phase fluctuations of the wave can be obtained without recourse to the expression (7.104) defining the effective scattering cross section [39]. To do this, we divide the whole region traversed by the wave in the inhomogeneous medium into volume elements V_k, whose linear dimensions are much larger than the correlation distance L_o of the refractive index fluctuations. The field at a point M is the sum of the field u_o of the incident wave and of the fields u_k scattered by the volumes V_k in the direction of the point M, i.e.

$$u = u_o + \sum_k u_k \; . \qquad (7.112)$$

We represent the field u_o in the form $u_o = A_o \exp(iS_o)$ and the fields u_k in the form $A_k \exp(iS_k)$. Since the volumes V_k are separated from one another by distances which are much larger than L_o, the waves u_k scattered by them will be statistically independent. We assume that the fluctuations of the field are small, i.e. that [ℓ]

$$\left| \sum u_k \right| \ll \left| u_o \right| \; .$$

Then we have

$$\log u = \log u_o + \log \left(1 + \sum \frac{u_k}{u_o} \right) \sim \log u_o + \sum \frac{u_k}{u_o} \; .$$

Separating the real and imaginary parts of this equation, we obtain

$$\log A = \log A_o + \sum \frac{A_k}{A_o} \cos(S_k - S_o) , \tag{7.113}$$

$$S = S_o + \sum \frac{A_k}{A_o} \sin(S_k - S_o) . \tag{7.114}$$

From this we obtain

$$\overline{\chi^2} = \overline{\left(\log \frac{A}{A_o}\right)^2} = \overline{\sum \sum \frac{A_i A_k}{A_o^2} \cos(S_i - S_o) \cos(S_k - S_o)} , \tag{7.115}$$

$$\overline{S_1^2} = \overline{(S - S_o)^2} = \overline{\sum \sum \frac{A_i A_k}{A_o^2} \sin(S_i - S_o) \sin(S_k - S_o)} \tag{7.116}$$

for the mean square fluctuations. Because of the statistical independence of the waves scattered by the different volumes V_k, only the terms with $i = k$ are different from zero in the double sums. Therefore we have

$$\overline{\chi^2} = \overline{\sum \frac{A_k^2}{A_o^2} \cos^2(S_k - S_o)} , \quad \overline{S_1^2} = \overline{\sum \frac{A_k^2}{A_o^2} \sin^2(S_k - S_o)} . \tag{7.117}$$

It can be shown that the quantities A_k and $S_k - S_o$ are statistically independent [60]. Therefore

$$\overline{A_k^2 \cos^2(S_k - S_o)} = \overline{A_k^2}\ \overline{\cos^2(S_k - S_o)} = \frac{1}{2} \overline{A_k^2}$$

since the mean square value of the cosine is equal to 1/2 when its argument is uniformly distributed in the interval $(0, 2\pi)$. Similarly

$$\overline{A_k^2 \sin^2(S_k - S_o)} = \frac{1}{2}\,\overline{A_k^2}$$

so that

$$\overline{X^2} = \overline{S_1^2} = \frac{1}{2} \sum \frac{\overline{A_k^2}}{A_o^2} . \tag{7.118}$$

The quantity $\overline{A_k^2(\theta_k)}$ represents the mean square modulus of the scattered field produced at the point M by the scattering volume V_k (the angle of scattering is denoted by θ_k). The flux of scattered energy is proportional to the quantity $\overline{A_k^2}\, r^2\, d\Omega$, where r is the distance from the center of the volume V_k to the point M. The density of the energy flux of the primary wave u_o incident on V_k, which we denote by $V_k d\sigma_o(\theta_k)$, is equal to

$$V_k d\sigma_o(\theta_k) = \frac{\overline{A_k^2}}{A_o^2}\, r^2\, d\Omega ,$$

so that

$$\frac{\overline{A_k^2}}{A_o^2} = \frac{V_k}{r^2}\,\frac{d\sigma_o(\theta_k)}{d\Omega} .$$

Substituting this expression in (7.118), we obtain

$$\overline{X^2} = \overline{S_1^2} = \frac{1}{2} \sum \frac{d\sigma_o(\theta_k)}{d\Omega}\,\frac{V_k}{r^2} . \tag{7.119}$$

Going from summation to integration in this formula, we have

$$\overline{X^2} = \overline{S_1^2} = \frac{1}{2} \int_V \frac{d\sigma_o(\theta)}{d\Omega}\,\frac{dV}{r^2} . \tag{7.120}$$

If we locate the origin of spherical coordinates at the observation point M, the polar angle will equal the scattering angle θ and $dV = r^2 d\Omega dr$. Therefore

$$\overline{\chi^2} = \overline{S_1^2} = \frac{1}{2} \int_0^L dr \int \frac{d\sigma_0(\theta)}{d\Omega} d\Omega = \frac{1}{2} \sigma L , \tag{7.121}$$

and we again arrive at Eq. (7.111). Since we assumed that the field at the point M is proportional to A_k and does not depend on the dimensions of the scattering volume V_k, we have hereby assumed that the linear dimensions of the volume V_k are much smaller than the radius of the first Fresnel zone, i.e. that $L_0 \ll V_k^{1/3} \ll \sqrt{\lambda L}$. Therefore, Eq. (7.21), and Eq. (7.111) as well, is valid when the condition $\sqrt{\lambda L} \gg L_0$ is met.

With this we finish our study of the problem of parameter fluctuations of a plane monochromatic wave. In Part IV, we shall consider some applications of the theory presented above (calculation of the frequency spectrum of the fluctuations, dependence of the fluctuations on parameters of the receiving apparatus) and we shall compare the theory with experimental data.

Chapter 8

PARAMETER FLUCTUATIONS OF A WAVE PROPAGATING IN A TURBULENT MEDIUM WITH SMOOTHLY VARYING CHARACTERISTICS

Until now we have considered the case of a locally isotropic refractive index field, and it has been assumed everywhere that the structure C_n^2 does not vary along the entire propagation path of the wave. However, in practice one must almost always deal with inhomogeneous turbulence. As already noted, the "two-thirds law" obtained in Part I is valid only in the case where the distance between the two observation points does not exceed the outer scale of turbulence L_o, i.e., it is valid in a region with dimensions of the order L_o. If we place our pair of observation points in another region with dimensions of the order L_o', which does not intersect the first region, then the "two-thirds law" holds for it as well, but this time with another value $C_n'^2$ of the structure constant. Therefore, we can assume that C_n is a very smooth function of the coordinates, which changes appreciably only in distances of the order L_o [59] (see Chapter 3). Thus

$$D_n(\vec{r}_1,\vec{r}_2) = C_n^2\left(\frac{\vec{r}_1 + \vec{r}_2}{2}\right) |\vec{r}_1 - \vec{r}_2|^{2/3} , \tag{8.1}$$

where $|\vec{r}_1 - \vec{r}_2| \ll L_o$, and $C_n^2(\vec{r})$ changes appreciably only when $\vec{r}$ changes by an amount of order L_o. For small values of $|\vec{r}_1 - \vec{r}_2|$, we have

$$D_n(\vec{r}_1,\vec{r}_2) = C_n^2\left(\frac{\vec{r}_1 + \vec{r}_2}{2}\right) \ell_o^{2/3} \left(\frac{|\vec{r}_1 - \vec{r}_2|}{\ell_o}\right)^2 \qquad (|\vec{r}_1 - \vec{r}_2| \ll \ell_o), \tag{8.2}$$

as before.

The concept of the spectral density $\Phi_n(\vec{\kappa})$ corresponding to (8.1) and (8.2) was introduced in Chapter 3. We can immediately write down an expression for $\Phi_n(\vec{\kappa})$, by changing the constant C_n^2 in Eq. (7.86) to the function $C_n^2(\vec{r})$. Then we have [a]

$$\Phi_n(\vec{\kappa},\vec{r}) = C_n^2(\vec{r})\ \Phi_n^{(o)}(\vec{\kappa}) , \tag{8.3}$$

where

$$\Phi_n^{(o)}(\vec{\kappa}) = \begin{cases} 0.033\ \kappa^{-11/3} & \text{for } \kappa < \kappa_m , \\ & \\ 0 & \text{for } \kappa > \kappa_m . \end{cases} \tag{8.4}$$

In the more general case, where we shall not use the "two-thirds law", but some other correlation or structure function, we shall always assume that $\Phi_n(\vec{\kappa},\vec{r})$ can be represented in the form (8.3), but with another function $\Phi_n^{(o)}(\vec{\kappa})$. In analogy to (8.3), we can also write the two-dimensional spectral density $F_n(\kappa_2,\kappa_3,|x' - x''|,\frac{\vec{r}' + \vec{r}''}{2})$ (see Chapter 3):

$$F_n\left(\kappa_2,\kappa_3,\ |x' - x''|,\ \frac{\vec{r}' + \vec{r}''}{2}\right) = C_n^2\left(\frac{\vec{r}' + \vec{r}''}{2}\right) f_n(\kappa_2,\kappa_3,\ |x' - x''|) . \tag{8.5}$$

As before, the functions F_n and Φ_n are connected by the relation (1.53). In particular, we have

$$\int_0^\infty f_n(\kappa_2,\kappa_3,\xi)d\xi = \pi\ \Phi_n^{(o)}(0,\kappa_2,\kappa_3) . \tag{8.6}$$

We now consider how to solve the problem of amplitude and phase fluctuations of a plane wave propagating in a medium with a smoothly varying "intensity" of turbulence. To solve this problem we shall start with Eq. (7.24) and we shall use the same kind of two-dimensional spectral expansions of the refractive index fluctuations as in solving the problem for a homogeneous medium. In deriving Eqs. (7.26)-(7.43), we never used the assumption that $F_n(\kappa_2,\kappa_3,x',x'')$ depends only on $x' - x''$. Therefore Eqs. (7.42)-(7.43) continue to hold in the case where $F_n(\kappa_2,\kappa_3,x',x'')$ has the form (8.5), i.e.

$$F_A(\kappa_2,\kappa_3,0) = k^2 \int_0^L\int_0^L \sin\left[\frac{\kappa^2(L - x')}{2k}\right] \sin\left[\frac{\kappa^2(L - x'')}{2k}\right] \times$$

$$\times F_n\left(\kappa_2,\kappa_3, |x' - x''|, \frac{\vec{r}' + \vec{r}''}{2}\right) dx'dx'' =$$

$$= \frac{k^2}{2} \iint_D \left[\cos\frac{\kappa^2\xi}{2k} - \cos\frac{\kappa^2(L - \eta)}{k}\right] C_n^2(\vec{r}) f_n(\kappa, |\xi|) d\eta d\xi \ , \tag{8.7}$$

where $\xi = x' - x''$, $2\eta = x' + x''$, $2\vec{r} = \vec{r}' + \vec{r}''$. The region of integration D is a rhombus with vertices at the points (0,0), (L,L/2), (0,L), (-L,L/2). Similarly, we have

$$F_S(\kappa_2,\kappa_3,0) = \frac{k^2}{2} \iint_D \left[\cos\frac{\kappa^2\xi}{2k} + \cos\frac{\kappa^2(L - \eta)}{k}\right] \times$$

$$\times C_n^2(\vec{r}) f_n(\kappa, |\xi|) d\eta d\xi \ . \tag{8.8}$$

Bearing in mind that the integrands are even with respect to ξ, we need carry out the integration only in the right hand half of the region D. Then we obtain

$$F_A(\kappa_2,\kappa_3,0) = k^2 \int_0^{L/2} C_n^2(\vec{r}) d\eta \int_0^{2\eta} f_n(\kappa,\xi)\left[\cos\frac{\kappa^2\xi}{2k} - \cos\frac{\kappa^2(L - \eta)}{k}\right] d\xi \ +$$

$$+ k^2 \int_{L/2}^{L} C_n^2(\vec{r}) d\eta \int_0^{2(L - \eta)} f_n(\kappa,\xi)\left[\cos\frac{\kappa^2\xi}{2k} - \cos\frac{\kappa^2(L - \eta)}{k}\right] d\xi \ . \tag{8.9}$$

In the important region of integration with respect to ξ, we have $\kappa\xi \lesssim 1$ (since $f_n(\kappa,\xi) \to 0$ for $\kappa\xi \gg 1$; see page 23). Therefore, $\kappa^2\xi/k \lesssim \kappa/k \ll 1$ in this region. Consequently, $\cos \kappa^2\xi/2k \sim 1$ and the inner integrals in (8.9) are approximately equal to

$$\left[1 - \cos \frac{\kappa^2(L - \eta)}{k}\right] \int_0^{2\eta} f_n(\kappa,\xi)d\xi$$

and

$$\left[1 - \cos \frac{\kappa^2(L - \eta)}{k}\right] \int_0^{2(L - \eta)} f_n(\kappa,\xi)d\xi \; .$$

However, in the larger part of the region of integration both 2η and $2(L - \eta)$ have the order of magnitude L. Therefore, we have approximately

$$\int_0^{2\eta} f_n(\kappa,\xi)d\xi \sim \int_0^{\infty} f_n(\kappa,\xi)d\xi = \pi\, \Phi_n^{(o)}(\kappa)$$

and

$$\int_0^{2(L - \eta)} f_n(\kappa,\xi)d\xi \sim \pi\, \Phi_n^{(o)}(\kappa) \; ,$$

i.e., both inner integrals in (8.9) are approximately equal to

$$\pi\left[1 - \cos \frac{\kappa^2(L - \eta)}{k}\right] \Phi_n^{(o)}(\kappa) = 2\pi \sin^2\left[\frac{\kappa^2(L - \eta)}{2k}\right] \Phi_n^{(o)}(\kappa) \; .$$

Thus we obtain

$$F_A(\kappa_2,\kappa_3,0) \sim 2\pi k^2 \int_0^{L} C_n^2(\vec{r})\, \Phi_n^{(o)}(\kappa) \sin^2\left[\frac{\kappa^2(L - \eta)}{2k}\right]d\eta \; , \qquad (8.10)$$

$$F_S(\kappa_2,\kappa_3,0) \sim 2\pi k^2 \int_0^L C_n^2(\vec{r})\, \Phi_n^{(o)}(\kappa)\, \cos^2\left[\frac{\kappa^2(L-\eta)}{2k}\right] d\eta \, . \tag{8.11}$$

It follows from Eq. (8.10) that the contribution to $F_A(\kappa_2,\kappa_3,0)$ of inhomogeneities located near the observation point is zero [b], since the integrand vanishes for $\eta = L$.

We now consider the correlation function of the amplitude fluctuations of the wave in the plane $x = L$. According to the general formula (1.51), we have

$$B_A(\rho) = 2\pi \int_0^\infty J_o(\kappa\rho) F_A(\kappa, 0) \kappa d\kappa \; ,$$

i.e.

$$B_A(\rho) = 4\pi^2 k^2 \int_0^L C_n^2(\vec{r}) d\eta \int_0^\infty J_o(\kappa\rho) \Phi_n^{(o)}(\kappa) \; \sin^2\left[\frac{\kappa^2(L-\eta)}{2k}\right] \kappa d\kappa \; , \tag{8.12}$$

$$B_A(0) = \overline{\left(\log \frac{A}{A_o}\right)^2} = 4\pi^2 k^2 \int_0^L C_n^2(\vec{r}) d\eta \int_0^\infty \Phi_n^{(o)}(\kappa) \; \sin^2\left[\frac{\kappa^2(L-\eta)}{2k}\right] \kappa d\kappa \, . \tag{8.13}$$

Eqs. (8.12) and (8.13) solve the problem of amplitude fluctuations of the wave. Consider the case where the refractive index fluctuations obey the "two-thirds law". In this case $\Phi_n^{(o)}(\vec{\kappa})$ is given by Eq. (8.4) and

$$\overline{\chi^2} = \overline{\left(\log \frac{A}{A_o}\right)^2} = 4\pi^2 (0.033) k^2 \int_0^L C_n^2(\vec{r}) d\eta \int_0^{\kappa_m} \kappa^{-11/3} \sin^2\left[\frac{\kappa^2(L-\eta)}{2k}\right] \kappa d\kappa \, . \tag{8.13}$$

For $\kappa_m^2 L/k \ll 1$ (geometrical optics), we obtain

$$\overline{\chi^2} = 4\pi^2(0.033)k^2 \int_0^L C_n^2(\vec{r})d\eta \int_0^{\kappa_m} \kappa^{-11/3} \frac{\kappa^4(L-\eta)^2}{4k^2} \kappa d\kappa =$$

$$= 7.37\, \ell_o^{-7/3} \int_0^L C_n^2(\vec{r})(L-\eta)^2 d\eta. \tag{8.14}$$

(We have used the relation $\kappa_m \ell_o = 5.48$, see page 49). For $\kappa_m^2 L/k \gg 1$, i.e. $\sqrt{\lambda L} \gg \ell_o$, the integration in (8.13) can be extended to infinity, and then [c]

$$\overline{\chi^2} = 0.56\, k^{7/6} \int_0^L C_n^2(\vec{r})(L-x)^{5/6} dx\ . \tag{8.15}$$

In the case C_n^2 = const, Eqs. (8.14) and (8.15) imply Eqs. (6.68) and (7.94) for homogeneous turbulence. It is convenient to change Eqs. (8.14) and (8.15) somewhat, by locating the origin of coordinates at the observation point. Then we have

$$\overline{\chi^2} = 7.37\, \ell_o^{-7/3} \int_0^L C_n^2(\vec{r}) x^2 dx \qquad (\sqrt{\lambda L} \ll \ell_o) \tag{8.16}$$

and

$$\overline{\chi^2} = 0.56\, k^{7/6} \int_0^L C_n^2(\vec{r}) x^{5/6} dx \qquad (\sqrt{\lambda L} \gg \ell_o)\ . \tag{8.17}$$

When the wave source is located at infinity, we can set $L = \infty$ in Eqs. (8.16) and (8.17). Then, in estimating the quantity $\sqrt{\lambda L}$, it suffices to take the distance in which C_n^2 essentially falls to zero instead of L.

We now consider the phase fluctuations of the wave. Adding (8.10) and (8.11), we obtain

$$F_A(\kappa_2,\kappa_3,0) + F_S(\kappa_2,\kappa_3,0) = 2\pi k^2 \Phi_n^{(o)}(\kappa) \int_0^L C_n^2(\vec{r})d\eta \ , \tag{8.18}$$

and

$$D_A(\rho) + D_S(\rho) = 8\pi^2 k^2 \int_0^L C_n^2(r)d\eta \int_0^\infty [1 - J_o(\kappa\rho)] \Phi_n^{(o)}(\kappa)\kappa d\kappa \ . \tag{8.19}$$

Eq. (8.19) replaces Eq. (7.95) for the case of homogeneous turbulence. When $\Phi_n^{(o)}(\kappa)$ is given by Eq. (8.4), we obtain an expression similar to (7.98), i.e.

$$D_A(\rho) + D_S(\rho) = 2.91 \ k^2\rho^{5/3} \int_0^L C_n^2(\vec{r})dx \ . \tag{8.20}$$

It follows from (8.20) (see the derivation of Eqs. (7.101) and (7.102)), that in the region $\sqrt{\lambda L} \gg \ell_o$, we have

$$D_S(\rho) = 1.46 \ k^2\rho^{5/3} \int_0^L C_n^2(\vec{r})dx \qquad (\ell_o \ll \rho \ll \sqrt{\lambda L}\ ), \tag{8.21}$$

$$D_S(\rho) = 2.91 \ k^2\rho^{5/3} \int_0^L C_n^2(\vec{r})dx \qquad (\rho \gtrsim \sqrt{\lambda L}) \ . \tag{8.22}$$

The integration in Eqs. (8.16) - (8.22) is carried out along the "ray" from the observation point to the source. Comparing Eqs. (8.16) and (8.17) with Eqs. (8.21) and (8.22), we can easily discover an important difference between them. In fact, all the inhomogeneities, regardless of their distance from the observation point, have the same effect on the phase fluctuations [d]. However, the inhomogeneities which are furthest away from the observation point have the greatest effect on the amplitude fluctuations of the wave [b].

Let us consider an example. In analyzing the twinkling and quivering of stellar images, we encounter a very nonuniform distribution in height of the refractive index fluctuations. Usually, the strongest fluctuations are observed near the surface of the earth, and the fluctuations become weaker as the height increases. In this case, the lower layers of the atmosphere will make the largest contribution to the integral

$$\int_0^\infty C_n^2(z)dz$$

which determines $D_S(\rho)$. However, higher layers will make the basic contribution to the integral

$$\int_0^\infty C_n^2(z)z^{5/6}dz$$

which determines the amplitude fluctuations of the wave. For example, let

$$C_n^2 = C_{no}^2 e^{-z/z_o} . \qquad (8.23)$$

Then (assuming that $\sqrt{\lambda z_o} \gg \ell_o$), we have

$$\overline{\chi^2} = 0.56 k^{7/6} C_{no}^2 z_o^{11/6} \Gamma(\tfrac{11}{6}) = 0.53 C_{no}^2 k^{7/6} z_o^{11/6} , \qquad (8.24)$$

$$D_S(\rho) = 2.91 k^2 \rho^{5/3} C_{no}^2 z_o . \qquad (8.25)$$

If C_n^2 is given in the form

$$C_n^2(z) = C_{no}^2 \frac{1}{1+\left(\frac{z}{z_o}\right)^2} , \qquad (8.26)$$

then

$$\overline{\chi^2} = 0.56 k^{7/6} C_{no}^2 z_o^{11/6} \int_0^\infty \frac{x^{5/6}dx}{1+x^2} = \frac{0.56\pi}{2\sin\frac{\pi}{12}} C_{no}^2 k^{7/6} z_o^{11/6} ,$$

or

$$\overline{\chi^2} = 3.4\, C_{no}^2\, k^{7/6}\, z_o^{11/6}, \tag{8.27}$$

$$D_S(\rho) = 2.91\, \frac{\pi}{2}\, k^2\, \rho^{5/3}\, C_{no}^2\, z_o = 4.57\, C_{no}^2\, k^2\, \rho^{5/3}\, z_o\,. \tag{8.28}$$

Eqs. (8.24), (8.27) and Eqs. (8.25), (8.28) have the same structure, but they have quite different values of the numerical coefficients.

Chapter 9

AMPLITUDE FLUCTUATIONS OF A SPHERICAL WAVE

In addition to the problem of the amplitude and phase fluctuations of a plane monochromatic wave considered in Chapter 8, in many cases it is of interest to consider the problem of fluctuations in a spherical wave [60]. To solve this problem, we shall start with Eq. (7.21), which gives the solution of Eq. (7.14) for the case of an arbitrary unperturbed wave, i.e.

$$\Delta \psi_1 + 2 \nabla \psi_0 \cdot \nabla \psi_1 + 2k^2 n_1(\vec{r}) = 0 , \tag{9.1}$$

$$\psi_1(\vec{r}) = \frac{k^2}{2\pi u_0(\vec{r})} \int_V n_1(\vec{r}\,')u_0(\vec{r}\,') \frac{e^{ik|\vec{r} - \vec{r}\,'|}}{|\vec{r} - \vec{r}\,'|} dV' . \tag{9.2}$$

Let $u_0(\vec{r})$ represent a spherical wave propagating from the origin of coordinates, i.e.

$$u_0(\vec{r}) = \frac{Qe^{ikr}}{r} , \tag{9.3}$$

where Q is some constant. Then we have

$$\psi_1(\vec{r}) = \frac{k^2 r}{2\pi} \int_V n_1(\vec{r}\,') \frac{e^{ik(r' - r)}}{r'} \frac{e^{ik|\vec{r} - \vec{r}\,'|}}{|\vec{r} - \vec{r}\,'|} dV' . \tag{9.4}$$

As in Chapter 8, we assume that $\lambda \ll \ell_0$, where ℓ_0 is the inner scale of the turbulence. Then, a substantial contribution is made to the integral (9.4) only by the region of integration contained inside a cone of aperture $\theta \sim \lambda/\ell_0 \ll 1$, whose vertex lies at the observation point and whose axis (which we assume to be the x-axis) is directed from the wave source to the observation point. Inside of this cone, we have

$$|x'| \gg |y'|,\ |z'| \text{ and } |x-x'| \gg |y-y'|,\ |z-z'| \ .$$

In this case, the expansions

$$r' \sim x' + \frac{y'^2 + z'^2}{2x'}, \quad |\vec{r} - \vec{r}'| \sim x - x' + \frac{(y - y')^2 + (z - z')^2}{2(x - x')}$$

are valid. In addition to the values of the field at the point $\vec{r} = (x,0,0)$, we shall also be interested in values of the field at points for which $\sqrt{y^2 + z^2}$ is not zero but is much less than the distance x to the wave source. Therefore, the field $u_o = \frac{Q}{r} e^{ikr}$ of the incident wave can also be represented in the form

$$u_o = \frac{Q}{x} \exp\left[ik\left(x + \frac{y^2 + z^2}{2x}\right)\right] .$$

Substituting all these expansions into Eq. (9.4), we obtain

$$\psi_1(\vec{r}) = \frac{k^2 x}{2\pi} \int_V n_1(x',y',z') \times$$

$$\times \frac{\exp\left\{-ik \dfrac{2xx'(yy' + zz') - x'^2(y^2 + z^2) - x^2(y'^2 + z'^2)}{2xx'(x - x')}\right\}}{x'(x - x')} dx'dy'dz' \ . \qquad (9.5)$$

We assume that the random field $n_1(x',y',z')$ is a homogeneous and isotropic random field and can be represented in the form of a stochastic Fourier-Stieltjes integral:

$$n_1(x',y',z') = \iint_{-\infty}^{\infty} \exp\left[i\left(\kappa_2' y' + \kappa_3' z'\right)\right] d\nu(\kappa_2',\kappa_3',x') \ , \qquad (9.6)$$

where the quantities $d\nu(\kappa_2,\kappa_3,x')$ satisfy the previous relation (7.40), i.e.

$$\overline{d\nu(\kappa_2,\kappa_3,x)d\nu^*(\kappa_2',\kappa_3',x')} =$$

$$= \delta(\kappa_2 - \kappa_2')\delta(\kappa_3 - \kappa_3')F_n(\kappa_2,\kappa_3,|x - x'|)d\kappa_2 d\kappa_3 d\kappa_2' d\kappa_3' \;. \tag{9.7}$$

(We have assumed that the field $n_1(\vec{r})$ is homogeneous and isotropic in order to simplify the solution of the problem. However, in what follows, it will not be difficult to extend the solution obtained to the case of a locally homogeneous and isotropic field $n_1(\vec{r})$ as well.) We shall look for the function $\psi_1(x,y,z)$ in the form of the same kind of expansion, i.e.

$$\psi_1(x,y,z) = \iint_{-\infty}^{\infty} \exp\left[i\left(\kappa_2' y + \kappa_3' z\right) \right] d\varphi(\kappa_2',\kappa_3',x) \;. \tag{9.8}$$

Substituting the expansions (9.6) and (9.8) into Eq. (9.5), we obtain

$$\iint_{-\infty}^{\infty} \exp\left[i\left(\kappa_2' y + \kappa_3' z\right)\right] d\varphi(\kappa_2',\kappa_3',x) = \frac{k^2 x}{2\pi} \times$$

$$\times \int dV' \frac{\exp\left(-ik\,\dfrac{2xx'(yy' + zz') - x'^2(y^2 + z^2) - x^2(y'^2 + z'^2)}{2xx'(x - x')}\right)}{x'(x - x')} \times$$

$$\times \iint_{-\infty}^{\infty} \exp\left[i\left(\kappa_2' y' + \kappa_3' z'\right)\right] d\nu(\kappa_2',\kappa_3',x'). \tag{9.9}$$

We multiply this equation by $\frac{1}{4\pi^2} e^{-i(\kappa_2 y + \kappa_3 z)}$ and integrate with respect to y and z between the limits $-\infty$ and ∞. Bearing in mind that $(1/2\pi) \int_{-\infty}^{\infty} \exp(i\lambda z)dz = \delta(\lambda)$ and that the symbol equality

$$d\kappa_2 d\kappa_3 \iint_{-\infty}^{\infty} \delta(\kappa_2 - \kappa_2')\delta(\kappa_3 - \kappa_3')d\varphi(\kappa_2',\kappa_3',x) = d\varphi(\kappa_2,\kappa_3,x) ,$$

holds [a], we obtain

$$d\varphi(\kappa_2,\kappa_3,x) = d\kappa_2 d\kappa_3 \frac{k^2 x}{8\pi^3} \iint_{-\infty}^{\infty} \exp\left[-i(\kappa_2 y + \kappa_3 z)\right]dydz \quad \times$$

$$\times \quad \int dV' \frac{\exp\left(-ik \dfrac{2xx'(yy' + zz') - x'^2(y^2 + z^2) - x^2(y'^2 + z'^2)}{2xx'(x - x')}\right)}{x'(x - x')} \quad \times$$

$$\times \quad \iint_{-\infty}^{\infty} \exp\left[i \left(\kappa_2' y' + \kappa_3' z'\right) \right]d\nu(\kappa_2',\kappa_3',x') . \tag{9.10}$$

The integration with respect to the variables y' and z' in (9.10) can be extended between the limits $-\infty$ and ∞ , since in the region where the values of y' and z' are large, the integrand oscillates rapidly and the integral over this region is near zero. Changing the order of integration in (9.10) and also changing x to L (the distance to the wave source), we obtain

$$d\varphi(\kappa_2,\kappa_3,L) = d\kappa_2 \, d\kappa_3 \frac{k^2 L}{8\pi^3} \int_0^L \frac{dx'}{x'(L - x')} \iint_{-\infty}^{\infty} d\nu(\kappa_2',\kappa_3',x') \quad \times$$

$$\times \iiiint_{-\infty}^{\infty} \exp\left[i\left(\kappa_2'y' + \kappa_3'z' - \kappa_2 y - \kappa_3 z\right)\right] \times$$

$$\times \exp\left[-ik \frac{2Lx'(yy' + zz') - x'^2(y^2 + z^2) - L^2(y'^2 + z'^2)}{2Lx'(L - x')}\right] dydzdy'dz'. \qquad (9.11)$$

The inner fourfold integral can be simply evaluated by contour integration in the complex plane and is easily seen to equal

$$\frac{8\pi^3 L(L - x')}{ikx'} \exp\left[\frac{-iL(L - x')(\kappa_2^2 + \kappa_3^2)}{2kx'}\right] \delta\left(\kappa_2' - \kappa_2 \frac{L}{x'}\right) \delta\left(\kappa_3' - \kappa_3 \frac{L}{x'}\right) . \qquad (9.12)$$

Substituting (9.12) in Eq. (9.11) and carrying out the integration with respect to κ_2' and κ_3', we obtain a simple formula connecting the spectral amplitudes of the field fluctuations and those of the refractive index fluctuations:

$$d\varphi(\kappa_2, \kappa_3, L) = -ik \int_0^L dx \exp\left[-\frac{iL(L - x)(\kappa_2^2 + \kappa_3^2)}{2kx}\right] d\nu\left(\kappa_2 \frac{L}{x}, \kappa_3 \frac{L}{x}, x\right) . \qquad (9.13)$$

Eq. (9.13) is similar to Eq. (7.32) for a plane wave [b] and has a simple physical meaning: Field inhomogeneities characterized by the wave number κ (i.e. by the dimensions $\ell = \frac{2\pi}{\kappa}$) owe their origin to inhomogeneities of the medium with characteristic wave number $\kappa \frac{L}{x}$, or with dimensions $\ell' = \ell \frac{x}{L}$. These inhomogeneities are at the distance x from the wave source. The factor x/L takes into account the magnification of the dimensions of the image due to illumination by a divergent ray bundle. The quantity $L(L - x)\kappa^2/2kx$ in the argument of the exponential is equal to $\pi \Lambda^2/\ell'^2$, where $\Lambda^2 = \frac{\lambda x(L - x)}{L}$ is the square of the radius of the first Fresnel zone for a spherical wave, and ℓ' is the size of the inhomogeneities in the x-plane which produce field inhomogeneities of size ℓ. Using relations similar to (7.35) and (7.36), we can find the spectral amplitudes of the quantities $\chi = \log(A/A_0)$ and $S_1 = S - S_0$. Denoting them, as before, by da and $d\sigma$, we obtain

$$da(\kappa_2,\kappa_3,L) = -k \int_0^L dx \sin\left[\frac{L(L-x)(\kappa_2^2+\kappa_3^2)}{2kx}\right] d\nu\left(\kappa_2 \frac{L}{x}, \kappa_3 \frac{L}{x}, x\right), \tag{9.14}$$

$$d\sigma(\kappa_2,\kappa_3,L) = -k \int_0^L dx \cos\left[\frac{L(L-x)(\kappa_2^2+\kappa_3^2)}{2kx}\right] d\nu\left(\kappa_2 \frac{L}{x}, \kappa_3 \frac{L}{x}, x\right). \tag{9.15}$$

We now turn to the spectral expansions of the correlation (structure) functions of the quantities χ and S. To do this, we form the expression

$$\overline{da(\kappa_2,\kappa_3,L)da^*(\kappa_2',\kappa_3',L)} = k^2 \int_0^L\int_0^L dx_1 dx_2 \times$$

$$\times \sin\left[\frac{L(L-x_1)(\kappa_2^2+\kappa_3^2)}{2kx_1}\right] \sin\left[\frac{L(L-x_2)(\kappa_2'^2+\kappa_3'^2)}{2kx_2}\right] \times$$

$$\times \overline{d\nu\left(\kappa_2 \frac{L}{x_1}, \kappa_3 \frac{L}{x_1}, x_1\right) d\nu^*\left(\kappa_2' \frac{L}{x_2}, \kappa_3' \frac{L}{x_2}, x_2\right)} \tag{9.16}$$

and the analogous expression for $\overline{d\sigma d\sigma^*}$, which contains cosines instead of sines. Using the relation (9.7), and writing $\kappa^2 = \kappa_2^2 + \kappa_3^2$, $\kappa'^2 = \kappa_2'^2 + \kappa_3'^2$, we obtain

$$\overline{da(\kappa_2,\kappa_3,L)da^*(\kappa_2',\kappa_3',L)} = k^2L^4 \int_0^L\int_0^L dx_1dx_2 \frac{F_n\left(\frac{\kappa_2 L}{x_1}, \frac{\kappa_3 L}{x_1}, |x_1 - x_2|\right)}{x_1^2x_2^2} \times$$

$$\times \sin\left[\frac{L(L - x_1)\kappa^2}{2kx_1}\right] \sin\left[\frac{L(L - x_2)\kappa'^2}{2kx_2}\right] \delta\left(\frac{\kappa_2 L}{x_1} - \frac{\kappa_2' L}{x_2}\right) \times$$

$$\times \delta\left(\frac{\kappa_3 L}{x_1} - \frac{\kappa_3' L}{x_2}\right) d\kappa_2 d\kappa_3 d\kappa_2' d\kappa_3' . \qquad (9.17)$$

It follows from the relation (9.17) that the fields of χ and S are not statistically homogeneous in the plane $x = L$ (for these fields to be statistically homogeneous, the factors $\delta(\kappa_2 - \kappa_2')$, $\delta(\kappa_3 - \kappa_3')$ would have to appear in the right hand side of (9.17). It is clear that these fields must be homogeneous on the sphere $r = L$. The departure from statistical homogeneity is related in the first place to the fact that we are examining the field in the $x = L$ plane and not on the sphere $r = L$, and in the second place to the fact that the unperturbed wave appears in our case in the form

$$u_o = \frac{Q}{x} \exp\left[ik\left(x + \frac{y^2 + z^2}{2x}\right)\right] ,$$

so that the direction $y = 0$, $z = 0$ is singled out.

We now calculate the mean square fluctuation $\overline{\chi^2}$ of the logarithmic amplitude. Since

$$\chi(L,y,z) = \iint_{-\infty}^{\infty} e^{i(\kappa_2 y + \kappa_3 z)} da(\kappa_2,\kappa_3,L) ,$$

then, setting $y = z = 0$, we obtain the formula

$$X(L,0,0) = \iint\limits_{-\infty}^{\infty} da(\kappa_2,\kappa_3,L) .$$

Consequently, we have

$$\overline{X^2}(L,0,0) = \overline{X(L,0,0)X^*(L,0,0)} =$$

$$= \iiiint\limits_{-\infty}^{\infty} \overline{da(\kappa_2,\kappa_3,L)da^*(\kappa_2',\kappa_3',L)} . \tag{9.18}$$

Using the expression (9.17), we find

$$\overline{X^2} = k^2L^4 \int_0^L\int_0^L \frac{dx_1dx_2}{x_1^2\,x_2^2} \iiiint\limits_{-\infty}^{\infty} F_n\left(\frac{\kappa_2L}{x_1}, \frac{\kappa_3L}{x_1}, |x_1 - x_2|\right) \sin \frac{L(L - x_1)\kappa^2}{2kx_1} \times$$

$$\times \sin \frac{L(L - x_2)\kappa'^2}{2kx_2}\, \delta\left(\frac{\kappa_2L}{x_1} - \frac{\kappa_2'L}{x_2}\right) \delta\left(\frac{\kappa_3L}{x_1} - \frac{\kappa_3'L}{x_2}\right) d\kappa_2 d\kappa_3 d\kappa_2' d\kappa_3' . \tag{9.19}$$

Taking into account that

$$\delta\left(\frac{\kappa_2L}{x_1} - \frac{\kappa_2'L}{x_2}\right) = \frac{x_2}{L}\,\delta\left(\kappa_2' - \kappa_2\frac{x_2}{x_1}\right) \text{ and } \delta\left(\frac{\kappa_3L}{x_1} - \frac{\kappa_3'L}{x_2}\right) = \frac{x_2}{L}\,\delta\left(\kappa_3' - \kappa_3\frac{x_2}{x_1}\right) ,$$

we carry out the integration with respect to κ_2' and κ_3', obtaining

$$\overline{\chi^2} = k^2L^2 \int_0^L\int_0^L \frac{dx_1 dx_2}{x_1^2} \iint_{-\infty}^{\infty} F_n\left(\frac{\kappa_2 L}{x_1}, \frac{\kappa_3 L}{x_1}, |x_1 - x_2|\right) \sin \frac{L(L - x_1)\kappa^2}{2kx_1} \times$$

$$\times \sin \frac{Lx_2(L - x_2)\kappa^2}{2kx_1^2} \, d\kappa_2 d\kappa_3 \,. \qquad (9.20)$$

Since

$$F_n(\kappa_2, \kappa_3, |\xi|) = F_n\left(\sqrt{\kappa_2^2 + \kappa_3^2}\,, |\xi|\right) = F_n(\kappa, |\xi|)$$

in the case of isotropic turbulence, then in Eq. (9.20) we can go over to polar coordinates in the (κ_2, κ_3) plane and carry out the integration over the angular variable, on which the integrand does not depend. As a result, we obtain the formula

$$\overline{\chi^2} = 2\pi k^2L^2 \int_0^\infty \kappa d\kappa \int_0^L\int_0^L F_n\left(\frac{\kappa L}{x_1}, |x_1 - x_2|\right) \sin \frac{L(L - x_1)\kappa^2}{2kx_1} \times$$

$$\times \sin \frac{Lx_2(L - x_2)\kappa^2}{2kx_1^2} \frac{dx_1 dx_2}{x_1^2} \,. \qquad (9.21)$$

We designate the inner integral in (9.21) by $P(\kappa)$, i.e.

$$P(\kappa) = k^2L^2 \int_0^L\int_0^L F_n\left(\frac{\kappa L}{x_1}, |x_1 - x_2|\right) \sin \frac{L(L - x_1)\kappa^2}{2kx_1} \times$$

$$\times \sin \frac{Lx_2(L - x_2)\kappa^2}{2kx_1^2} \frac{dx_1 dx_2}{x_1^2} \,. \qquad (9.22)$$

We make the change of variables $x_1 - x_2 = \xi$, $x_1 = \eta$ in this integral. Then we have

$$P(\kappa) = k^2L^2 \int_0^L \frac{d\eta}{\eta^2} \sin \frac{L(L-\eta)\kappa^2}{2k\eta} \int_{\eta - L}^{\eta} F_n\left(\frac{\kappa L}{\eta}, |\xi|\right) \times$$

$$\times \sin \frac{L(\eta - \xi)(L - \eta + \xi)\kappa^2}{2k\eta^2} d\xi . \quad (9.23)$$

Consider now the inner integral

$$Q = \int_{\eta - L}^{\eta} F_n\left(\frac{\kappa L}{\eta}, |\xi|\right) \sin \frac{L(\eta - \xi)(L - \eta + \xi)\kappa^2}{2k\eta^2} d\xi . \quad (9.24)$$

Since the function $F_n(\kappa, |\xi|)$ is appreciably different from zero only for $\kappa\xi \lesssim 1$, then only the part of the region of integration where $|\xi|\kappa L/\eta \lesssim 1$ or $|\xi| \lesssim \eta/\kappa L$ contributes appreciably to the integral (9.24). Since $\kappa L \gg 1$ (the chief influence on the values of the fluctuation field at the observation point is due to inhomogeneities with dimensions of the order $\sqrt{\lambda L}$, i.e. $\kappa L \sim \sqrt{L/\lambda} \gg 1$ (see page 140), then $|\xi| \ll \eta$ in the important region of integration. Therefore, we have $\eta - \xi \sim \eta$ and $L - \eta + \xi \sim L - \eta$. It can be shown that the discarded terms in the argument of the sine are of order no larger than $\sqrt{\lambda/L} \ll 1$. Therefore Eq. (9.24) takes the form

$$Q = \sin \frac{L(L - \eta)\kappa^2}{2k\eta} \int_{\eta - L}^{\eta} F_n\left(\frac{\kappa L}{\eta}, |\xi|\right) d\xi . \quad (9.25)$$

Since the function $F_n\left(\frac{\kappa L}{\eta}, |\xi|\right)$ falls off quickly to zero even for $|\xi| \ll \eta$, the integration (9.25) can be extended between the limits $-\infty$ and ∞. Taking into account that (see page 24)

$$\int_{-\infty}^{\infty} F_n\left(\frac{\kappa L}{\eta}, |\xi|\right) d\xi = 2\pi \, \Phi_n\left(\frac{\kappa L}{\eta}\right) ,$$

we obtain for Q the expression [c]

$$Q = 2\pi \sin \frac{L(L - \eta)\kappa^2}{2k\eta} \; \Phi_n \left(\frac{\kappa L}{\eta}\right) . \tag{9.26}$$

Thus we have

$$P(\kappa) = 2\pi k^2 L^2 \int_0^L \sin^2\left[\frac{L(L - \eta)\kappa^2}{2\kappa\eta}\right] \Phi_n \left(\frac{\kappa L}{\eta}\right) \frac{d\eta}{\eta^2} . \tag{9.27}$$

Making the change of variables $\kappa L/\eta = \kappa'$ in (9.27), we obtain

$$P(\kappa) = \frac{2\pi k^2 L}{\kappa} \int_\kappa^\infty \sin^2\left[\frac{\kappa L}{2k} (\kappa' - \kappa)\right] \Phi_n(\kappa')d\kappa' . \tag{9.28}$$

Substituting this expression in Eq. (9.21), we have

$$\overline{\chi^2} = 4\pi^2 k^2 L \int_0^\infty d\kappa \int_\kappa^\infty \sin^2\left[\frac{\kappa L}{2k} (\kappa' - \kappa)\right] \Phi_n(\kappa')d\kappa' . \tag{9.29}$$

Changing the order of integration with respect to κ and κ' in (9.29) and simultaneously relabeling the variables of integration κ and κ', we obtain

$$\overline{\chi^2} = 4\pi^2 k^2 L \int_0^\infty \Phi_n(\kappa)d\kappa \int_0^\kappa \sin^2\left[\frac{L\kappa'(\kappa - \kappa')}{2k}\right]d\kappa' . \tag{9.30}$$

The inner integral in (9.30) reduces to the Fresnel integrals

$$C(x) = \int_0^x \cos \frac{\pi t^2}{2}\, dt , \qquad S(x) = \int_0^x \sin \frac{\pi t^2}{2}\, dt ,$$

and equals

$$\frac{\kappa}{2} - \frac{1}{2}\sqrt{\frac{2\pi k}{L}}\left[\cos\frac{\kappa^2 L}{4k}\, C\left(\sqrt{\frac{\kappa^2 L}{2\pi k}}\right) + \sin\frac{\kappa^2 L}{4k}\, S\left(\sqrt{\frac{\kappa^2 L}{2\pi k}}\right)\right],$$

so that

$$\overline{\chi^2} = 2\pi^2 k^2 L \int_0^\infty \left\{1 - \sqrt{\frac{2\pi k}{\kappa^2 L}}\left[\cos\frac{\kappa^2 L}{4k}\, C\left(\sqrt{\frac{\kappa^2 L}{2\pi k}}\right) + \sin\frac{\kappa^2 L}{4k}\, S\left(\sqrt{\frac{\kappa^2 L}{2\pi k}}\right)\right]\right\} \Phi_n(\kappa)\kappa d\kappa \;. \tag{9.31}$$

Eq. (9.31) expresses the mean square fluctuation of the logarithmic amplitude of a spherical wave in the case $\lambda \ll \ell_0$ in terms of the spectral density $\Phi_n(\kappa)$ of the refractive index fluctuations [d]. A similar formula exists for the mean square phase fluctuation of the wave, namely

$$\overline{S_1^2} = 2\pi^2 k^2 L \int_0^\infty \left\{1 + \sqrt{\frac{2\pi k}{\kappa^2 L}}\left[\cos\frac{\kappa^2 L}{4k}\, C\left(\sqrt{\frac{\kappa^2 L}{2\pi k}}\right) + \sin\frac{\kappa^2 L}{4k}\, S\left(\sqrt{\frac{\kappa^2 L}{2\pi k}}\right)\right]\right\} \Phi_n(\kappa)\kappa d\kappa \;. \tag{9.32}$$

However, we note that while Eq. (9.31) can be extended to the case of locally isotropic turbulence (since the term in curly brackets in (9.31) goes to zero like κ^4 as $\kappa \to 0$), Eq. (9.32) is valid only in the case of homogeneous and isotropic turbulence.

Consider the case where the relation $\sqrt{\lambda L} \ll \ell_0$ holds. In this case, the relation $\frac{\kappa^2 L}{2\pi k} \ll$ holds for all values of κ for which $\Phi_n(\kappa)$ is different from zero. Making a series expansion of the integrand of (9.31) in powers of $\sqrt{\kappa^2 L/2\pi k}$, we obtain the formula

$$\overline{\chi^2} = \frac{1}{30}\pi^2 L^3 \int_0^\infty \Phi_n(\kappa)\kappa^5 d\kappa \, . \tag{9.33}$$

For comparison, we give here the formula which determines $\overline{\chi^2}$ for a plane wave when $\sqrt{\lambda L} \ll \ell_o$. In Chapter 6, we obtained the formula

$$F_A(\kappa,0) = \frac{1}{6}\pi L^3 \kappa^4 \Phi_n(\kappa) \, ,$$

from which it follows that

$$\overline{\chi^2} = 2\pi \int_0^\infty F_n(\kappa,0)\kappa d\kappa = \frac{1}{3}\pi^2 L^3 \int_0^\infty \Phi_n(\kappa)\kappa^5 d\kappa \, . \tag{9.34}$$

Comparing Eqs. (9.33) and (9.34), we convince ourselves that when $\sqrt{\lambda L} \ll \ell_o$, the mean square fluctuation of the logarithmic amplitude of a spherical wave is ten times smaller than the corresponding quantity for a plane wave, and that this ratio does not depend on the form of the spectral density of the refractive index fluctuations (or on the form of its correlation or structure function) [e].

We now consider the case where the correlation function of the refractive index fluctuations exists and has the finite integral scale L_n (see page 144):

$$L_n = \frac{1}{B_n(0)} \int_0^\infty B_n(r)dr = \frac{2\pi^2}{B_n(0)} \int_0^\infty \Phi_n(\kappa)\kappa d\kappa \, .$$

For $\sqrt{\lambda L} \gg \ell_o$, we can neglect the rapidly oscillating function in the integrals (9.31) and (9.32) (see the similar example for a plane wave on pages 143-144), obtaining the formula

$$\overline{\chi^2} = \overline{S_1^2} = 2\pi^2 k^2 L \int_0^\infty \Phi_n(\kappa)\kappa d\kappa = \overline{n_1^2}\, k^2 \, L \, L_n \, , \tag{9.35}$$

which coincides with Eq. (7.68) for a plane wave. Thus, for $\sqrt{\lambda L} \gg \ell_0$, the mean square amplitude fluctuations of a plane wave and of a spherical wave are equal to each other.

We now consider two concrete examples.

1. Let the field of refractive index fluctuations be homogeneous and isotropic and let it be described by the correlation function

$$B_n(r) = \overline{n_1^2}\, e^{-r^2/a^2} . \tag{9.36}$$

The mean square fluctuation of the logarithmic amplitude of the wave for $\sqrt{\lambda L} \ll a$ can be found by using Eq. (7.78) for a plane wave. Bearing in mind that for a spherical wave the quantity $\overline{\chi^2}$ is 10 times smaller than (7.78), we obtain

$$\overline{\chi^2} = \frac{4\sqrt{\pi}}{15}\, \overline{n_1^2}\, \frac{L^3}{a^3} . \tag{9.37}$$

This expression agrees with the quantity found in Bergmann's paper [45] by using the equations of geometrical optics. If $\sqrt{\lambda L} \gg a$, the mean square fluctuation of the logarithmic amplitude of the spherical wave agrees with the corresponding expression for a plane wave. Using Eq. (7.80), we obtain

$$\overline{\chi^2} = \frac{\sqrt{\pi}}{2}\, \overline{n_1^2}\, k^2 a L . \tag{9.38}$$

A more detailed investigation of the expressions for $\overline{\chi^2}$ and $\overline{S_1^2}$ is carried out in the papers [58,61] for the special case where the correlation function of the refractive index fluctuations has the form of the Gaussian curve (9.36). However, we shall not give the expressions appearing in these papers, which express $\overline{\chi^2}$ and $\overline{S_1^2}$ for an arbitrary value of the ratio $\sqrt{\lambda L}/a$, because of their excessive complexity. (In the limiting cases of small and large values of the parameter $\sqrt{\lambda L}/a$, these formulas agree with the relations (9.37) and (9.38).) Moreover, the applicability of Eqs. (9.37) and (9.38) in practice is quite doubtful, since the correlation function of the refractive index fluctuations does not have the form of a Gaussian curve under actual atmospheric conditions.

2. We now consider a much more realistic example, when the field of refractive index fluctuations is locally isotropic and is described by the "two-thirds law". As we have already seen, the spectral density $\Phi_n(\kappa)$ corresponding to this law can be taken to be

$$\Phi_n(\kappa) = \begin{cases} 0.033\, C_n^2\, \kappa^{-11/3} & \text{for } \kappa < \kappa_m , \\ 0 & \text{for } \kappa > \kappa_m . \end{cases} \tag{9.39}$$

We calculate the size of the amplitude fluctuations separately for $\sqrt{\lambda L} \ll \ell_o$ and $\sqrt{\lambda L} \gg \ell_o$. In the first case we can use the expression $\overline{\chi^2} = 2.46\, C_n^2\, L^3\, \ell_o^{-7/3}$ which is valid for a plane wave. Dividing this expression by 10, we obtain

$$\overline{\chi^2} = 0.25\, C_n^2\, L^3\, \ell_o^{-7/3} . \tag{9.40}$$

For $\sqrt{\lambda L} \gg \ell_o$ (and at the same time $\sqrt{\lambda L} \ll L_o$) we have to use the general formula (9.31):

$$\overline{\chi^2} = 2\pi^2(0.033)C_n^2\, k^2 L \int_0^{\kappa_m} \kappa^{-11/3} \left\{ 1 - \sqrt{\frac{2\pi k}{\kappa^2 L}} \left[\cos \frac{\kappa^2 L}{4k}\, C\left(\sqrt{\frac{\kappa^2 L}{2\pi k}}\right) + \sin \frac{\kappa^2 L}{4k}\, S\left(\sqrt{\frac{\kappa^2 L}{2\pi k}}\right) \right] \right\} \kappa d\kappa . \tag{9.41}$$

For $\sqrt{\lambda L} \gg \ell_o$, the upper limit of integration in (9.41) can be replaced by infinity. Making in addition the change of variables $\sqrt{\kappa^2 L/2\pi k} = x$, we obtain the expression

$$\overline{\chi^2} = 0.14\, C_n^2\, k^{7/6}\, L^{11/6} \int_0^{\infty} x^{-8/3} \left(1 - \frac{1}{x}\left[\cos \frac{\pi x^2}{2}\, C(x) + \sin \frac{\pi x^2}{2}\, S(x) \right] \right) dx . \tag{9.42}$$

By numerical integration, we find the integral in (9.42) to be equal to 0.90. Thus, for $\sqrt{\lambda L} \gg \ell_o$, we have

$$\overline{\chi^2} = 0.13\, C_n^2\, k^{7/6}\, L^{11/6} \,. \tag{9.43}$$

The expression (9.43) differs from the corresponding expression (7.94) for a plane wave only by the numerical coefficient. The mean square fluctuation of the logarithmic amplitude of a spherical wave in the case $\sqrt{\lambda L} \gg \ell_o$ is approximately 2.4 times smaller than the corresponding quantity for a plane wave.

Part IV

EXPERIMENTAL DATA ON PARAMETER FLUCTUATIONS OF LIGHT AND SOUND WAVES PROPAGATING IN THE ATMOSPHERE

Chapter 10

EMPIRICAL DATA ON FLUCTUATIONS OF TEMPERATURE AND WIND VELOCITY IN THE LAYER OF THE ATMOSPHERE NEAR THE EARTH AND IN THE LOWER TROPOSHERE

Experimental investigations of the fluctuations of meteorological fields have been initiated comparatively recently, so that there is a lack of detailed data, with the exception of some investigations devoted to the study of fluctuations of wind velocity and temperature in the layer of the atmosphere near the earth [17, 36, 37, 62, 63]. It is characteristic of turbulence in the layer of the atmosphere near the earth that the turbulent regime is strongly influenced by the earth's surface; therefore such turbulence has its own special peculiarities. The layer of air several tens of meters thick lying near the earth's surface is a turbulent boundary layer [14, 64, 65]. In the simplest case, where the air moves over a plane surface, its mean velocity $\overline{u}$ is a function of the height. In the case where we can neglect the effect of the buoyancy forces on the motion (the buoyancy forces appear when the mean air temperature depends on the height), the wind velocity varies with the height according to the logarithmic law [14, 64, 65]

$$\overline{u}(z) = \frac{v_*}{\kappa} \log \frac{z}{z_0} , \qquad (10.1)$$

which is valid for $z \gg z_0$. Here v_* is a constant with the dimensions of velocity, κ is a constant approximately equal to 0.4, and z_0 is a height determined by the roughness of the underlying surface.

Eq. (10.1) is valid up to heights of the order of several tens of meters (30-50 m); for large values of z, the growth of $\overline{u}(z)$ slows down. Within the logarithmic boundary layer of the atmosphere, characteristics of the turbulence like the rate of energy dissipation ϵ, the coefficient of turbulent diffusion K, etc., also depend on the height. To a first approximation, the quantities K and ϵ (see pages 29, 41) are given by the formulas [64, 65]

$$\epsilon = \frac{v_*^3}{\kappa z}, \tag{10.2}$$

$$K = \kappa v_* z . \tag{10.3}$$

In Part I, we obtained the expression $D_{rr}(r) = C_v^2 r^{2/3}$, where $C_v^2 = C\epsilon^{2/3}$, for the structure function of the wind velocity. Substituting Eq. (10.2) into this last formula, we obtain

$$C_v^2 = \frac{C}{\kappa^{2/3}} \frac{v_*^2}{z^{2/3}} . \tag{10.4}$$

Thus, in the logarithmic boundary layer of the atmosphere, the structure constant C_v falls off with height like $z^{-1/3}$ [a].

We can also write a similar expression for the concentration fluctuations of a conservative passive additive ϑ. In Part I we obtained the following formula for the structure function of ϑ:

$$D_\vartheta(r) = C_\vartheta^2 r^{2/3}, \text{ where } C_\vartheta^2 = a^2 \left(\frac{K}{d\bar{u}/dz}\right) \left(\frac{d\bar{\vartheta}}{dz}\right)^2 = a^2 L_o^{4/3} \left(\frac{d\bar{\vartheta}}{dz}\right)^2$$

$$\text{and } L_o = \sqrt{\frac{K}{d\bar{u}/dz}} .$$

Substituting the expressions (10.3) and (10.1), we obtain the formula

$$C_\vartheta^2 = a^2 (\kappa z)^{4/3} \left(\frac{d\bar{\vartheta}}{dz}\right)^2 . \tag{10.5}$$

In the case of a logarithmic wind velocity profile, the mean concentration $\bar{\vartheta}$ of a passive conservative additive is also distributed according to a logarithmic law [64, 65]:

$$\bar{\vartheta}(z) = \text{const} + \vartheta_* \log \frac{z}{z_0} , \qquad (10.6)$$

where ϑ_* is a constant with the same dimensions as ϑ. Substituting (10.6) into Eq. (10.5), we obtain the expression

$$C_\vartheta^2 = a^2 \kappa^{4/3} \frac{\vartheta_*^2}{z^{2/3}} , \qquad (10.7)$$

similar to Eq. (10.4) for C_V^2.

Eqs. (10.6) and (10.7) can be applied to describe the form of the mean temperature profile and the character of the temperature fluctuations in the layer of the atmosphere near the earth. However, we should remark at once that in the case where the mean temperature of the air varies with height, in particular when

$$\bar{T}(z) = \text{const} + T_* \log \frac{z}{z_0} , \qquad (10.8)$$

Eq. (10.1), which describes the wind profile, becomes inapplicable. However, when the vertical gradients of the mean temperature have small values, the correction to Eq. (10.1) is also small, and to a first approximation we can disregard it. In this case, we have approximately $D_T(r) = C_T^2 r^{2/3}$, where

$$C_T^2 = a^2 \kappa^{4/3} \frac{T_*^2}{z^{2/3}} . \qquad (10.9)$$

The quantities C_V^2 and C_ϑ^2 defined by Eqs. (10.4) and (10.7) depend on z and change appreciably when z is changed by an amount of the same order of magnitude as the value of z itself. Therefore, in the boundary layer, the "two-thirds law" holds for distances r which are restricted by the condition

$$r \ll z \qquad (10.10)$$

(see page 50). For large values of r, the structure functions $D_V(r)$ and $D_T(r)$ grow more slowly than $r^{2/3}$ [66, 67].

In experimental investigations of the microstructure of the fields of wind velocity, temperature, humidity, etc., in the atmosphere, one must use very sensitive, low inertia instruments. Ordinarily, hot wire anemometers are used to measure wind velocity fluctuations [17, 68], and resistance thermometers are used to measure temperature fluctuations [68,36,37]. There still do not exist sufficiently low inertia humidity detectors, which satisfy the necessary requirements (high sensitivity, small working volume) for measuring turbulent fluctuations. A hot wire anemometer is a thin wire (usually of platinum), which is heated by an electrical current to temperatures of several hundred degrees centigrade. The heat exchange of the wire, and consequently its temperature, depends on the velocity of the wind flowing past it; this allows one to relate the electrical resistance of the wire to the velocity of the flow incident on it [b]. The inertia of the hot wire anemometer is very small (for a wire of diameter 20 μ, it does not exceed 0.1 sec [68]), and its dimensions are of the order of one or two centimeters. To measure the structure function of the wind velocity, two hot wire anemometers are put in opposite arms of a Wheatstone bridge, so that the current through the galvanometer is a function of the difference of the wind velocities at the points where the anemometers are located. For a detailed description of the apparatus, see the papers [17, 68].

Measurements of wind velocity fluctuations in the atmosphere made by both Soviet [17] and foreign workers [69] have confirmed the "two-thirds law" to a sufficient degree of accuracy. In Fig. 14, we show the empirical structure functions obtained by Obukhov at various heights above the earth's surface [17]; the curves correspond to the "two-thirds law". The dependence of the structure constant C_v on height, expressed by Eq. (10.4), agrees satisfactorily with the experimental data, where, according to Obukhov's data, the constant C equals 1.2. Measurements performed by Townsend [70], lead to the value $\sqrt{C} = 1.4$ [c]. Thus, the formulas $D_{rr}(r) = C_v^2\, r^{2/3}$ and $C_v^2 = Cv_*^2(\kappa^2 z^2)^{-1/3}$ have been confirmed experimentally. This allows us to make quantitative estimates of the fluctuations of wind velocity using simple measurements of the profile of the mean wind speed in the layer of the atmosphere near the earth. Measuring the mean values $\bar{u}_1$ and $\bar{u}_2$ of the wind speed at two heights z_1 and z_2 within the layer of the atmosphere near the earth and applying Eq. (10.1), we can determine the quantity v_*:

$$v_* = \frac{\kappa(\bar{u}_1 - \bar{u}_2)}{\log z_1 - \log z_2}\,. \qquad (10.11)$$

Then the quantity C_v can be determined from the formula

$$C_v = \frac{\sqrt{C}\,\kappa^{2/3}(\bar{u}_1 - \bar{u}_2)}{z^{1/3}\log(z_1/z_2)}, \qquad (10.12)$$

where $\kappa \sim 0.4$ and $\sqrt{C} \sim 1.4$ [d]. In the layer of the atmosphere near the earth, C_v is equal to a few cgs units in order of magnitude.

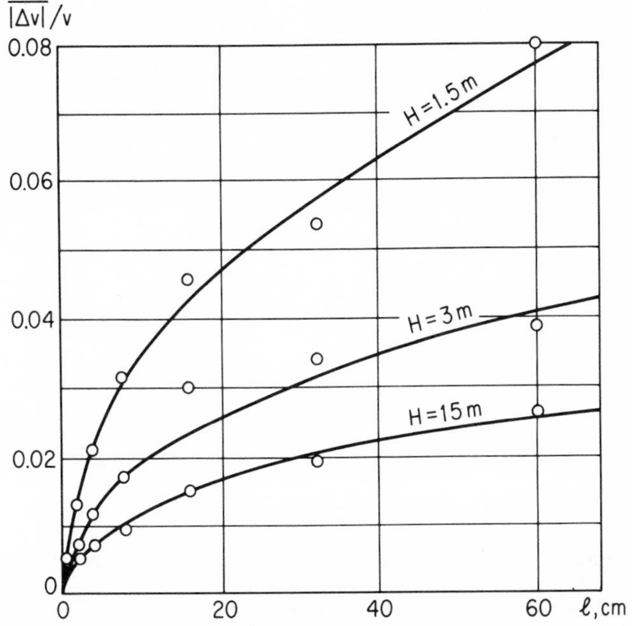

Fig. 14 Empirical structure functions of the wind field in the layer of the atmosphere near the earth [17].

We now consider measurements of temperature fluctuations in the layer of the atmosphere near the earth. The difference between the temperatures at two points can be measured by using a pair of low-inertia resistance thermometers (platinum wires a few tens of microns in diameter), included in the circuit of an unbalanced Wheatstone bridge. The voltage across the galvanometer arm, which is proportional to the temperature difference of the detectors, is amplified and then subjected to statistical analysis. (For a discussion of the apparatus, see the papers [36, 37, 68].) Fig. 15 shows the empirical structure function of the temperature field obtained by Krechmer; the curve corresponds to the "two-thirds law".

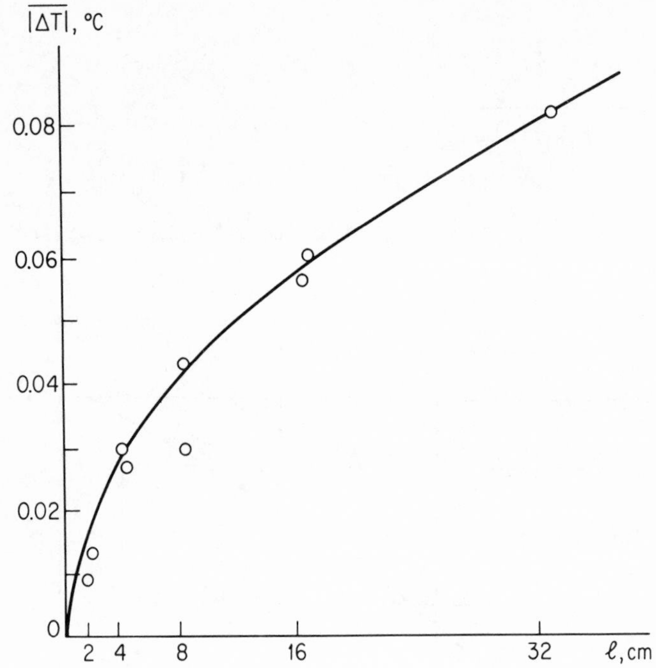

Fig. 15 Empirical structure functions of the temperature field in the layer of the atmosphere near the earth.

Numerous measurements of the structure functions of the temperature field in the layer of the atmosphere near the earth's surface have been made by the author of this book [37]. The measurements confirmed the "two-thirds law" for the temperature field and allowed the intensity of the temperature fluctuations to be related to the mean temperature profile. Fig. 16 shows the experimentally obtained dependence of the quantity C_T on $\kappa^{2/3}z^{-1/3}T_*$ (see Eq. (10.9)); each point of the graph was obtained as a result of measuring the structure function $D_T(r)$ for four values of r, beginning with r = 3 cm and ending with r = 1 m. The right hand half of the graph corresponds to unstable stratification of the atmosphere, i.e. to a decrease of the mean temperature with height, while the left hand side corresponds to stable stratification (temperature inversion), i.e. to an increase of the mean temperature with height. As is evident from the graph, for unstable stratification the empirical dependence of C_T on $\kappa^{2/3}z^{-1/3}T_*$ corresponds to Eq. (10.9), and the coefficient a turns out to be equal to 2.40. For stable stratification (temperature inversion), the growth of C_T lags behind the growth of $\kappa^{2/3}z^{-1/3}T_*$, which is a consequence of the influence of the temperature stratification on the urbulent regime (violation of the condition that the additive be passive). However, even n this case we can determine the empirical dependence of C_T on $\kappa^{2/3}z^{-1/3}T_*$ (see Fig. 16, where the curve indicates the empirical law obtained by analyzing the experimental data by the method of least squares [e]).

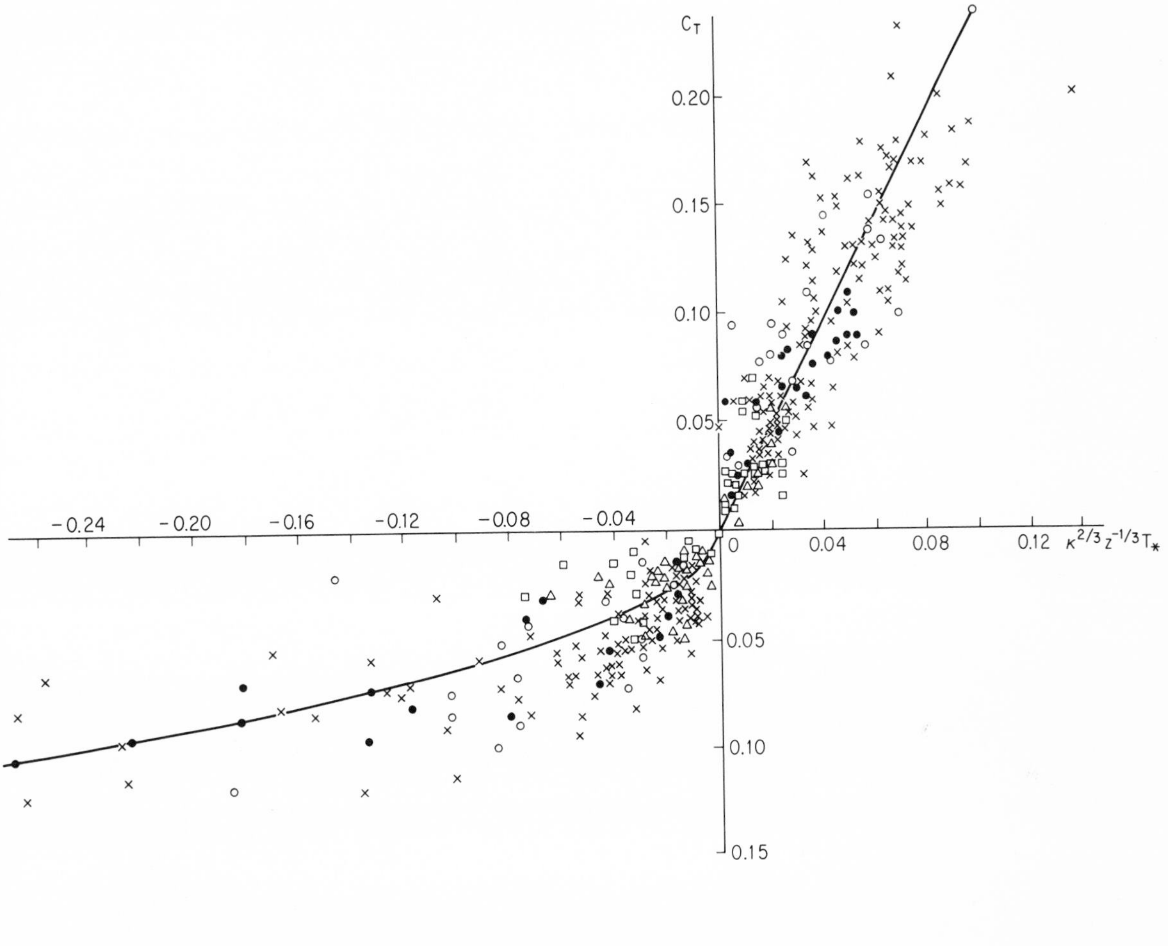

Fig. 16 Dependence of C_T, the characteristic of the temperature microfluctuations, on meteorological conditions.
●, August 1954; △, March-April 1955; O, June-July 1955 (1.5 m); □, June-July 1955 (22 m); ×, July-September, (1955) (The values of C_T plotted in the lower left hand quadrant are positive.)

The graph in Fig. 16, or Eq. (10.9) in the case of unstable stratification, allows us to make quantitative estimates of the size of the temperature fluctuations by using comparatively simple measurements of the mean temperature profile in the layer of the atmosphere nea the earth. By measuring the values $\overline{T}_1$ and $\overline{T}_2$ at two heights z_1 and z_2 and applying Eq. (10.8 we can determine T_*:

$$T_* = \frac{\overline{T}_1 - \overline{T}_2}{\log(z_1/z_2)} . \tag{10.13}$$

Then the quantity C_T can be determined in the case of unstable stratification by using the formula

$$C_T = 2.40\, \kappa^{2/3} \frac{\overline{T}_1 - \overline{T}_2}{z^{1/3} \log \frac{z_1}{z_2}} = 1.4 \frac{\overline{T}_1 - \overline{T}_2}{z^{1/3} \log \frac{z_1}{z_2}} \tag{10.14}$$

or by using the graph (Fig. 16) in the case of stable stratification. It is clear from the figure that the size of C_T in the layer of the atmosphere near the earth varies from zero (for isothermal stratification of the atmosphere) to values of the order of 0.2 deg $cm^{-1/3}$. Fig. 17 shows the monthly-averaged diurnal trend of the quantity C_T (for August 1955); this curve can also be used to estimate the size of C_T.

In addition to measurements of the temperature structure function in the layer of the atmosphere near the earth, measurements have also been made of the temperature fluctuations in the lower troposphere up to heights of the order of 500-700 m (on tethered balloons) [60]. These measurements have also confirmed the "two-thirds law". The values of C_T so obtained lie in the range 0 - 0.03 deg $cm^{-1/3}$. At nighttime, appreciable temperature fluctuations ($C_T \sim 0.01 - 0.03$ deg $cm^{-1/3}$) are observed only in the inversion layer near the earth, which usually extends from the level of the earth up to heights of the order of hundreds of meters. During the day when the stratification is unstable, temperature fluctuations in the lower troposphere are usually observed up to greater heights [f].

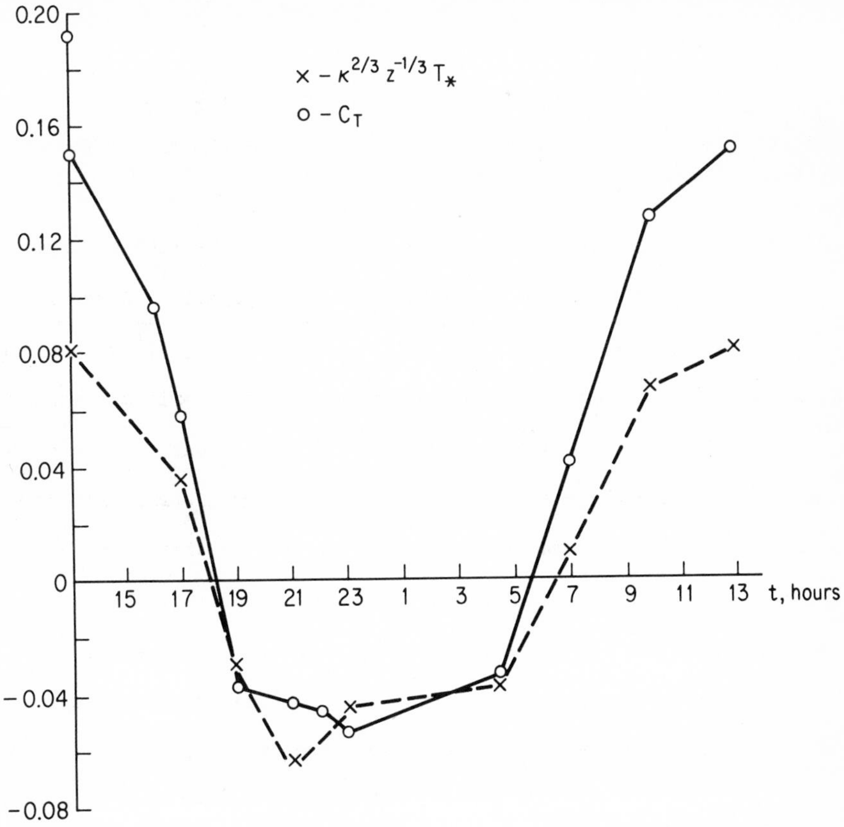

Fig. 17 Diurnal trend of C_T in the layer of atmosphere near the earth (August 1955).

Chapter 11

EXPERIMENTAL DATA ON THE AMPLITUDE AND PHASE FLUCTUATIONS OF SOUND WAVES PROPAGATING IN THE LAYER OF THE ATMOSPHERE NEAR THE EARTH

Beginning in 1941, Krasilnikov and his coworkers performed a series of experiments to study the amplitude and phase fluctuations of a sound wave propagating in the layer of the atmosphere near the earth. The time structure function $\overline{[S(t+\tau) - S(t)]^2}$ of the phase fluctuations and the mean value $\overline{[\log(A/A_0)]^2}$ of the fluctuations of logarithmic amplitude of the sound wave were measured in Krasilnikov's experiments. First we consider the phase fluctuations of the wave. In the case where the inhomogeneities in the distribution of wind velocity and temperature do not have time to change appreciably in the time τ, we can assume that they are merely convected (without "evolution") by the mean wind [a]. If the direction of the wind is perpendicular to the direction of propagation of the sound and if its velocity is $\bar{v}$, then the value $S(t+\tau)$ of the phase at the point M coincides with the value at the time t of the phase at the point which is a distance $\bar{v}\tau$ away from M. Thus we have

$$\overline{[S(t + \tau) - S(t)]^2} = D_S(\tau\bar{v}) \ . \tag{11.1}$$

According to Eq. (7.101)

$$D_S(\rho) = 2.91\ k^2 L C_n^2 \rho^{5/3}$$

for $\ell_0 \ll \rho$. Thus, the relation

$$\sigma_S = \sqrt{\overline{[S(t + \tau) - S(t)]^2}} = 1.7\ C_n k L^{1/2} (\bar{v}\tau)^{5/6} , \tag{11.2}$$

must be satisfied, i.e., the phase variability is proportional to the structure constant C_n, to the sound frequency, to the square root of the distance traversed by the sound wave, and to the time interval raised to the power 5/6. Fig. 18 shows the dependence of σ_S on L, obtained by Krasilnikov and Ivanov-Shyts [71], while Fig. 19 shows the dependence of σ_S on $\bar{v}\tau$; the sound frequency is 3000 Kcps, the distance L = 22, 45 and 67 m, $\bar{v}$ = 5 m/sec, τ = 0.04, 0.08 and 0.2 sec.

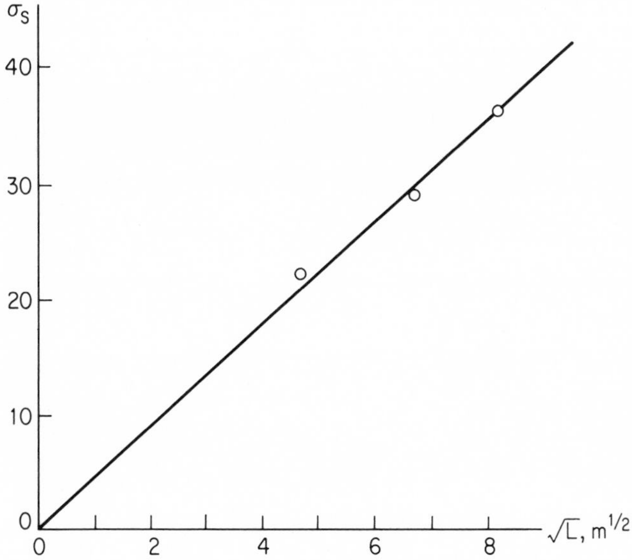

Fig. 18 Dependence of the phase fluctuations of of a sound wave on distance. (The quantity $\sqrt{L}$ is plotted as abcissa, and the average value of σ_S for various Δt is plotted as ordinate.

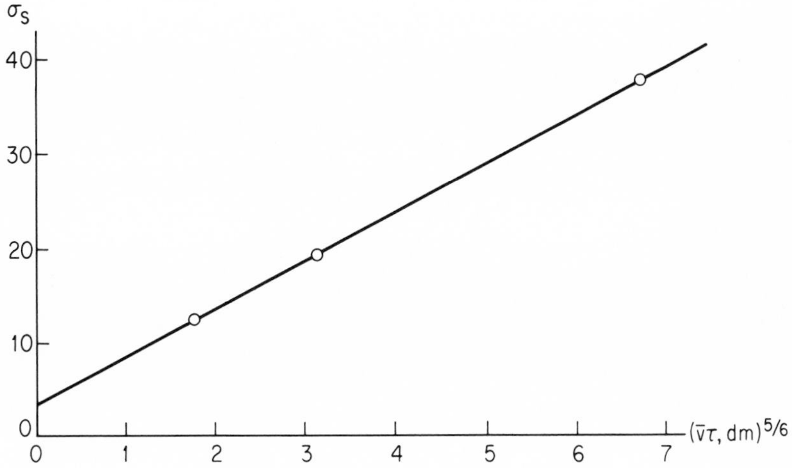

Fig. 19 Dependence of the fluctuations of the phase difference $\sigma_S = \sqrt{\overline{[S(t+\tau) - S(t)]^2}}$ on τ. (The quantity $(\bar{v}\tau)^{5/6}$ is plotted as abcissa, and the average of σ_S for various values of L is plotted as ordinate).

As can be seen from the figures, the dependence of σ_S on L and $\bar{v}\tau$ agrees satisfactorily with Eq. (11.2). Ultrasonic experiments performed at frequencies up to 50 Kcps also lead to satisfactory agreement between the experimental and theoretical results [72]. Thus, the dependence (11.2) has been confirmed experimentally over a frequency range from 1 to 50 Kcps.

Fig. 20 shows the dependence of the quantity $\sigma_A = \sqrt{\overline{[\log(A/A_o)]^2}}$ on the distance (all the data are referred to the distance 22 m). The dependence of σ_A on L is satisfactorily approximated by the formula $\sigma_A = AL^\alpha$, where $\alpha \sim 0.8$. Note that we ought to have $\alpha \sim 0.92$, according to Eq. (7.94). (In the experiments under consideration $\sqrt{\lambda L} \gg \ell_o$.) Thus, the experiments of Krasilnikov and Ivanov-Shyts agree satisfactorily with the theoretical formula (7.94).

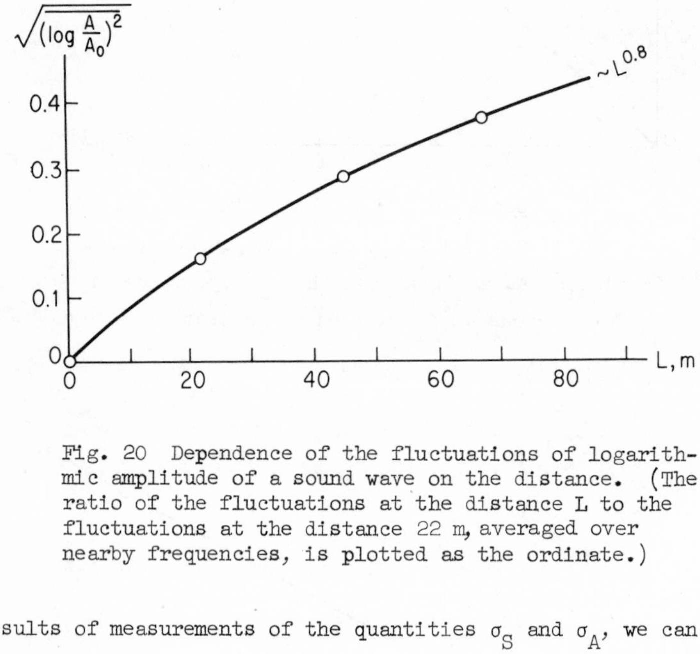

Fig. 20 Dependence of the fluctuations of logarithmic amplitude of a sound wave on the distance. (The ratio of the fluctuations at the distance L to the fluctuations at the distance 22 m, averaged over nearby frequencies, is plotted as the ordinate.)

Using the results of measurements of the quantities σ_S and σ_A, we can estimate the quantity C_n appearing in Eqs. (11.2) and (7.94), which characterizes the intensity of the fluctuations of the sound velocity. If we use the formula

$$C_n = \frac{\sigma_S}{1.7\ k\ L^{1/2}(\bar{v}\tau)^{5/6}}$$

to find C_n, with the values $\sigma_S = 46^\circ = 0.8$ rad, $k = 58\ m^{-1}$ (f = 3 Kcps), L = 67 m, $\bar{v} = 5$ m/se $\tau = 0.2$ sec, then C_n turns out to be equal to $0.0010\ m^{-1/3}$. This same quantity, determined from the relation [b]

$$C_n = \frac{\sigma_A}{0.56\, k^{7/12}\, L^{11/12}}$$

with the value $\sigma_A = 0.44$ and the same values of k and L, turns out to be equal to $0.0016\ m^{-1/3}$ (σ_A and σ_S are taken from the paper [71]). If we bear in mind that the values of σ_S and σ_A were obtained as a result of analyzing phase and amplitude fluctuation records of different lengths, then the agreement we obtain between the values of C_n must be regarded as satisfactory. In Part III we obtained Eq. (6.91), which relates the quantity C_n for acoustic waves to the quantities C_T^2 and C_v^2 determining the fluctuations of temperature and wind speed, i.e.

$$C_n^2 = \frac{C_T^2}{4\overline{T}^2} + \frac{C_v^2}{c_o^2}, \tag{11.3}$$

where c_o is the mean sound velocity [c]. Using Eqs. (10.12) and (10.14), which express C_T and C_v in terms of the mean values of the temperature and wind speed at two heights z_1 and z_2 in the layer of the atmosphere near the earth, we obtain the formula

$$C_n^2 = \frac{5.8 \times 10^{-6}}{z^{2/3}\left(\log \frac{z_2}{z_1}\right)^2}\left[(\Delta\overline{T})^2 + 0.9(\Delta\overline{v})^2\right], \tag{11.4}$$

where we have used the values $\overline{T} = 290^{\circ}C$ and $c_o = 340$ m/sec. Here $\Delta T = \overline{T}(z_2) - \overline{T}(z_1)$ and $\Delta\overline{v} = \overline{v}(z_2) - \overline{v}(z_1)$ are expressed in $^{\circ}C$ and m/sec, respectively. The value $C_n = 0.0010\ m^{-1/3}$ obtained above corresponds to a velocity difference $\Delta\overline{v}$ for the heights $z_2 = 8$ m and $z_1 = 4$ m equal to 1 m/sec [d], which represents a typical value. Thus, Eqs. (11.2) and (7.94) give the correct results for the order of magnitude both of the amplitude fluctuations and of the phase fluctuations of the wave.

Quite similar measurements of the amplitude fluctuations of a sound wave were made by Suchkov [73] in 1954. The measurements of the fluctuations of acoustic amplitude were accompanied by simultaneous measurements of the profiles of mean temperature and mean velocity, which permitted the calculation of C_n by using Eq. (11.4). Fig. 21 shows the dependence of $\sigma_A = \sqrt{\overline{[\log(A/A_o)]^2}}$ on L obtained by Suchkov (for a frequency of 76 Kcps). It is clear from the figure that the experimental results are well described by the theoretical formula (7.94), i.e.

$$\sigma_A^2 = 0.31\, C_n^2\, k^{7/6}\, L^{11/6} \, . \qquad (11.5)$$

(In all the experiments, the condition $\sqrt{\lambda L} \gg \ell_0$ was satisfied.)

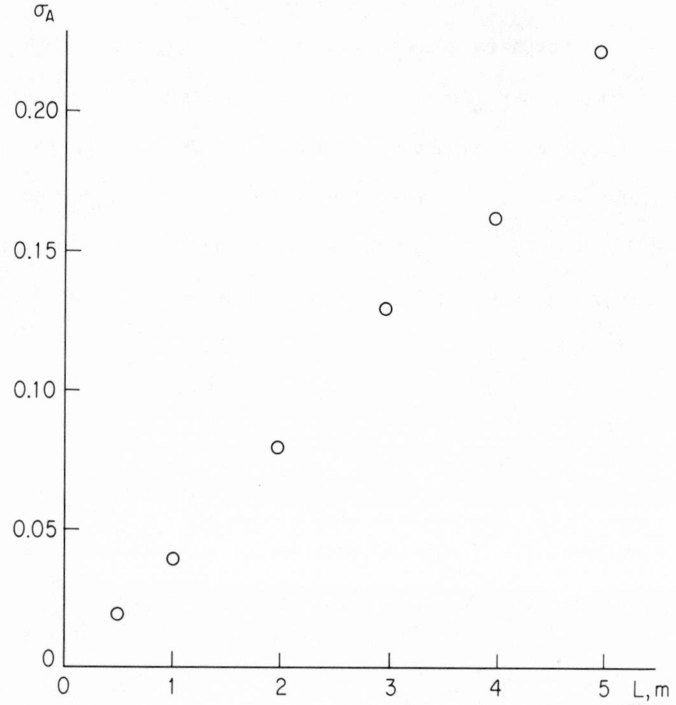

Fig. 21 Dependence of the fluctuations of logarithmic amplitude of an ultrasonic wave on the distance (f = 76 Kcps).

Suchkov carried out 28 series of measurements of the dependence of the quantity $\sigma_A^2 = f(L)$ on frequencies from 3 to 76 Kcps. The experimental data were approximated by the formula $\sigma_A = AL^{\alpha}$. The mean value of α for acoustic waves (18 series) was equal to 1.1, while the mean value of α for ultrasonic waves (30-76 Kcps) was 0.95. The values of α obtained are close to the theoretical value of $\alpha = 11/12 = 0.92$. Suchkov calculated the value of the quantity σ_A using Eqs. (11.4) and (11.5) and measurements of the profiles of temperature and wind velocity. Fig. 22 shows a comparison of the values of σ_A (denoted by σ_{ac}) obtained as a result of direct measurement and the values of σ_A (denoted by σ_{met}) calculated from Eqs. (11.4) and (11.5) by using simultaneous measurements of the profiles of mean temperature and mean wind velocity.

The correlation coefficient between the quantities log σ_{ac} and log σ_{met} equals 0.90 (97 points are plotted in the figure). In calculating C_V, the constant $\sqrt{C}$ (see p. 190) was taken to equal 1.4. If we take C = 1.2 (see p. 192), then the whole group of points is translated upward, and the regression line does not go through the origin of coordinates. Thus, measurements of the quantity σ_A lead to the same value $\sqrt{C} = 1.4$ as obtained by Townsend using a wind tunnel.

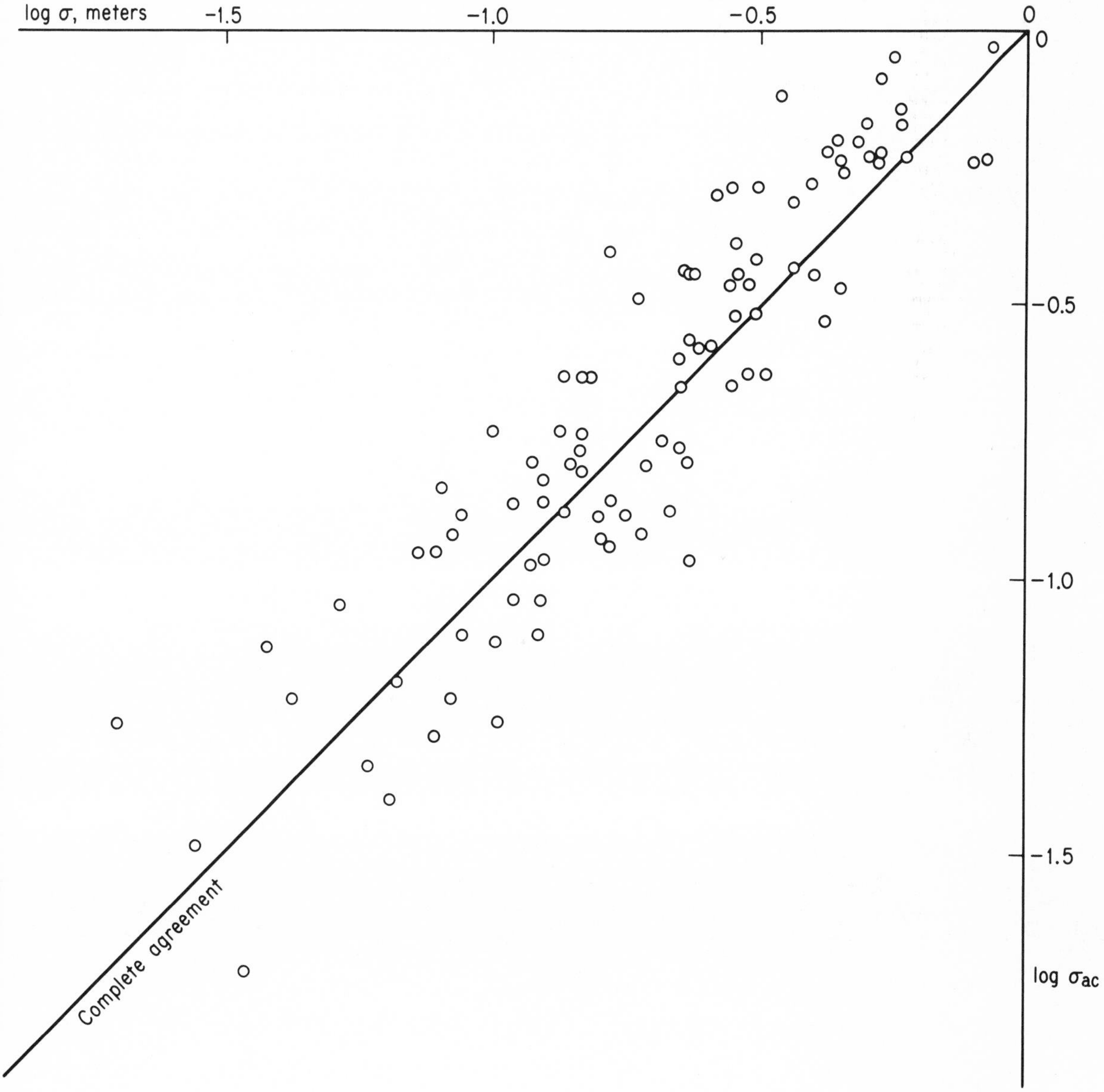

Fig. 22 Comparison of measured values of the amplitude fluctuations of sound waves (3 Kcps < f < 76 Kcps) with values calculated by using measurements of the profiles of wind velocity and temperature.

Suchkov also made measurements of the time autocorrelation function of the amplitude fluctuations of a sound wave. In the case where the direction of the wind is perpendicular to the direction of propagation of the sound and the correlation time is considerably less than $\kappa z/v_*$ [a], the relation

$$\overline{\log \frac{A(t+\tau)}{A_0} \log \frac{A(t)}{A_0}} = B_A(\overline{v}\tau) \tag{11.6}$$

is approximately valid. The function $B_A(\rho)$ for $\sqrt{\lambda L} \gg \ell_0$ was calculated above (see Fig. 13). The correlation distance of the amplitude fluctuations is equal to $\sqrt{\lambda L}$ in order of magnitude. It follows from (11.6) that the correlation time of the amplitude fluctuations is of order $\sqrt{\lambda L} / \overline{v}$. Fig. 23 shows correlation functions obtained by Suchkov for the amplitude fluctuations, where the $\overline{v}\tau / \sqrt{\lambda L}$ is plotted as abcissa

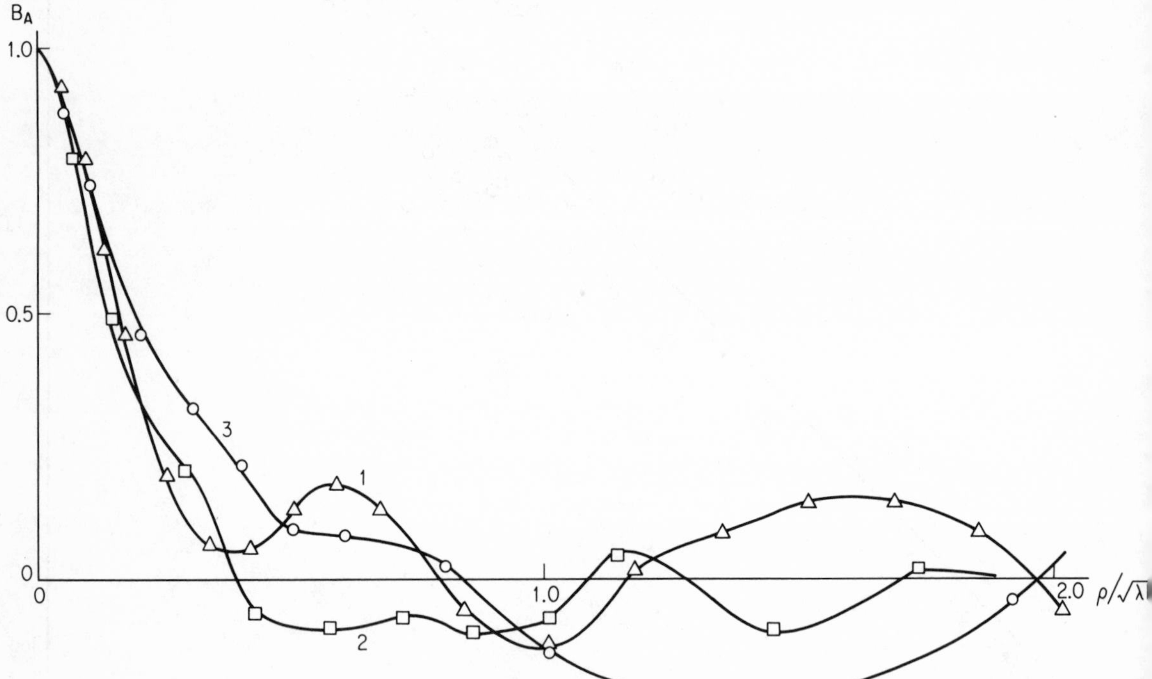

Fig. 23 Empirical autocorrelation functions of the fluctuations of logarithmic amplitude. (1, L = 4 m; 2, L = 8 m; 3, L = 16 m)

The different curves correspond to different distances between the transmitter and the receiver (4, 8 and 16 m). If we plot the quantities $\overline{\log(A/A_o)\log(A'/A_o)} = f(\tau)$ in natural units, i.e. as functions of τ, then the curves obtained for different L have a different appearance. If we plot the curves in units of $\tau_o = \sqrt{\lambda L} / \overline{v}$, all three curves come closer together, especially for small values of $\overline{v}\tau / \sqrt{\lambda L}$.

Suchkov's experiments are in good agreement with the fluctuation theory presented in Part III. The comparison of measured and calculated values of the quantity σ_A illustrates the possibility of making quantitative estimates of the size of the amplitude fluctuations of sound waves by using simple measurements of the wind velocity and temperature profiles in the atmosphere.

Chapter 12

EXPERIMENTAL INVESTIGATION OF THE SCINTILLATION OF TERRESTRIAL LIGHT SOURCES

Introductory remarks

An investigation of the scintillation of a terrestrial light source was carried out during 1956 and 1957 at the Institute of Atmospheric Physics of the Academy of Sciences of the USSR [74,75]. Experiments in the layer of the atmosphere near the earth are very attractive, since in such experiments, in addition to measurements of the amount of scintillation of the light source, one can simultaneously make measurements of the refractive index fluctuations (i.e. determine the size of C_n^2); moreover, one can make measurements for different and accurately known values of L. Thus, terrestrial experiments can give much more complete data than stellar scintillation experiments, data which can easily be compared with the theory of the phenomenon.

A portion of steppe with a regular profile was selected for making the experiment; this guaranteed homogeneity of the turbulent regime along the entire propagation path of the ray. (The light was propagated in the horizontal direction at an approximately uniform height above the underlying surface.) The light source could be moved to different points, located at distances of 250, 500, 1000 and 2000 meters from a fixed point. At distances closer than 250 m, the effect of scintillation was lower than the noise characterizing the apparatus which was used, and therefore measurements were not made at such distances. It was difficult to use distances greater than 2000 m, because of irregularities of the profile of the terrain. The average height of the ray above the underlying surface was 1.5 m for operation of distances of 250 and 500 m, 2 m for operation at a distance of 1000 m, and 5 m at a distance of 2000 m.

A 30 watt incandescent lamp was used as a primary light source. The light from it was focused on a diaphragm 0.5 mm in diameter by using a light-concentrating objective. Behind the diaphragm was placed a light chopper rotating at 100 revolutions per second, whose disc contained 150 slits. The diaphragm was located at the focus of the exit objective (with a focal distance of 250 mm and diameter of 100 mm) of the light source, out of which emanated a weakly divergent bundle of light, modulated with a frequency of 15,000 cps. The modulation of the light, with subsequent resonant amplification of the signal at the "carrier" frequency, made it possible to avoid the influence of extraneous, unmodulated light sources, and also simplified the receiving apparatus (the need for using a dc amplifier disappeared).

The light receiver (Fig. 24) consisted of two type FEU-19 photomultipliers; the light incident on these tubes had first passed through two diaphragms located in the plane perpendicular to the ray and then through a system of prisms. The distance ρ between the diaphragms could be varied over a range from 0.5 to 50 cm. The diameter of the receiving diaphragms was equal to 2 mm, which completely eliminated the effect of "objective-averaging" (see below). The ac components of the output voltages of the photomultipliers, the amplitudes of which were proportional to $I(M_1)$ and $I(M_2)$, where $I(M)$ is the instantaneous value of the light current through the diaphragm located at the point M, were amplified by tuned amplifiers with pass bands of about 2000 cps, and then detected. Voltages V_1 and V_2, proportional to $I(M_1)$ and $I(M_2)$, were formed at the detector outputs. In the amplifiers there was a special tracking system which assured that the relation $\overline{V}_1 = \overline{V}_2$ was satisfied (with a constant averaging time of 100 sec). After subtracting out the dc components, voltages $V_1' = V_1 - \overline{V}_1$ and $V_2' = V_2 - \overline{V}_2$ were formed, proportional to the light current fluctuations $I'(M_1) = I(M_1) - \overline{I(M_1)}$ and $I'(M_2) = I(M_2) - \overline{I(M_2)}$, respectively. The voltages V_1' and V_2' were subjected to automatic statistical analysis by using a special equipment setup (see [76]).

The following were measured (in identical units): the probability distribution of the fluctuations $I'(M_1)$, the mean square fluctuation $\overline{[I'(M_1)]^2}$, the mean value $\overline{I(M_1)}$, the correlation function $\overline{I'(M_1)I'(M_2)} = B(M_1,M_2)$, and the frequency spectrum of the fluctuations $I'(M_1)$ in the frequency range from 0.05 to 1000 cps. At the same time that the measurements of the scintillation of the terrestrial light source were made, meteorological measurements were made along the propagation path, which allowed the quantity C_n^2 to be calculated. Temperature profiles were measured in the layer from 0.5 to 12 m, as well as profiles of the wind velocity and wind direction in the same range. By using these measurements, it was possible to determine the turbulence parameters ϵ, K and T_*. Since the experiment was carried out over a very level portion of steppe and since the turbulent regime was identical over different parts of the propagation path, meteorological measurements were set up only at one point.

We now give the basic results of the measurements.

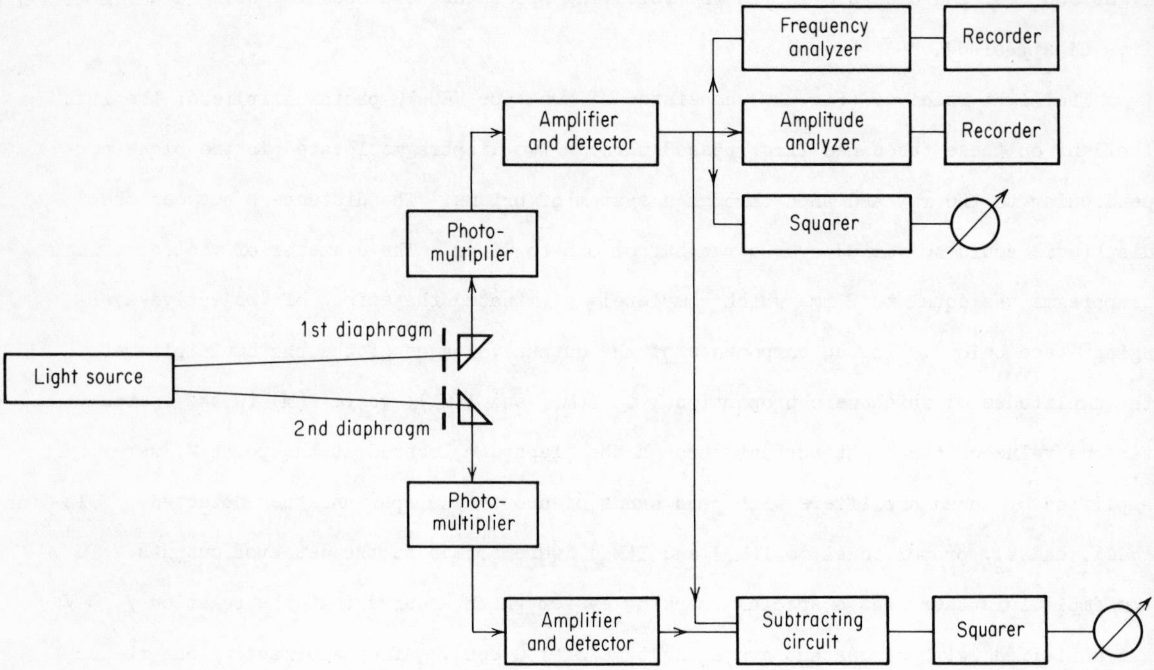

Fig. 24 Block diagram of apparatus for measuring the scintillation of a terrestrial light source.

12.1 The probability distribution function of the fluctuations of light intensity

It follows from the theory of the phenomenon that the logarithm of the amplitude of the light wave is expressed in terms of the refractive index fluctuations along the propagation path by using an integral of the type

$$\log(A/A_0) = \iiint_D F(\vec{r}\,')n'(\vec{r}\,')dV'.$$

In this integral we can subdivide the whole region of integration D into a large number of regions D_i with linear dimensions of the order of the outer scale of turbulence L_o, which under the conditions of the experiment are of the order of the height of the ray above the ground. There is no correlation between the fluctuations of $n(\vec{r}\,')$ in these regions. Therefore, we obtain the formula

$$\log(A/A_o) = \sum_i \iiint_{D_i} F(\vec{r}\,')n'(\vec{r}\,')dV' ,$$

which expresses $\log(A/A_o)$ as the sum of a large number of uncorrelated terms. Because of the central limit theorem, the quantity $\log(A/A_o)$ must be distributed according to a normal law [a]. Since $\log(I/I_o) = 2 \log(A/A_o)$, the quantity $\log(I/I_o)$ must also be distributed normally, and the quantity I must have a log normal distribution.

The experiment gives good confirmation of this fact. In Fig. 25 the quantity $\Phi^{-1}[F(I)]$ is plotted as abcissa, where $\Phi^{-1}(x)$ is the function which is the inverse of

$$\Phi(x) = \frac{1}{\sqrt{2\pi}} \int_{-\infty}^{x} \exp(-t^2/2)dt$$

and $F(I)$ is the empirical distribution function of I, while the quantity $\log(I/I_o)$ is plotted as ordinate. In these coordinates the log normal law is indicated by a straight line [b]. In all, about 100 empirical distribution functions $F(I)$ were analyzed. All of them are in good agreement with the hypothesis of a normal distribution of the quantity log I.

Using the hypothesis that the quantity log I has a normal distribution, we can relate the experimentally measured quantities $\sigma_1^2 = \overline{(I - \bar{I})^2}$ and $\bar{I}$ to the quantity

$$\overline{\left(\log \frac{I}{I_o}\right)^2} = 4 \overline{\left(\log \frac{A}{A_o}\right)^2} ,$$

which figures in the theory. We can easily convince ourselves that they are connected by the relation

$$\sigma^2 \equiv \overline{\left(\log \frac{I}{I_o}\right)^2} = \overline{4\chi^2} = \log \left(1 + \frac{\sigma_1^2}{(\bar{I})^2}\right) . \qquad (12.1)$$

This formula was used to further analyze the experimental data.

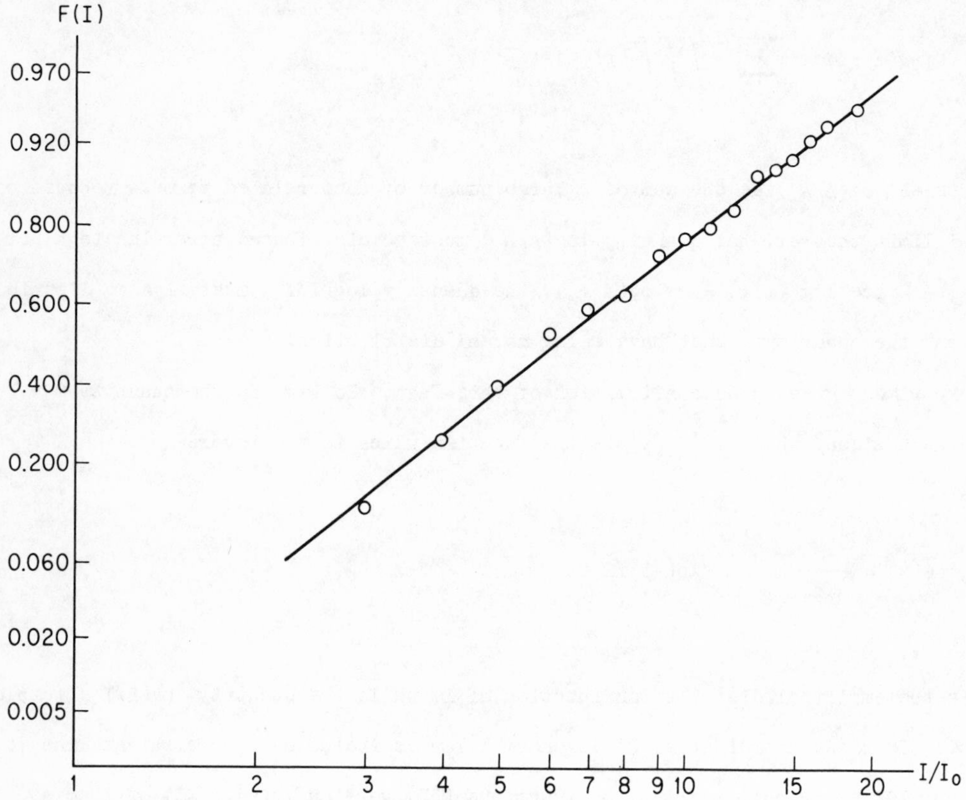

Fig. 25 Probability distribution of the intensity fluctuations of light on a log normal scale.

12.2 Dependence of the amount of scintillation on the distance and on the meteorological conditions

As already noted above, in the atmosphere the quantity ℓ_o is a few millimeters in order of magnitude. Therefore, the parameter $L_{cr} = \ell_o^2/\lambda$, which determines the limit of applicability of geometrical optics, is 100 meters in order of magnitude. Consequently, in our experiments the condition $L > L_{cr}$ was satisfied, and geometrical optics was not applied in making the calculations. As follows from (11.5), in the case under consideration, σ^2 is expressed by the formula

$$\sigma^2 = 1.23\, C_n^2\, k^{7/6}\, L^{11/6} .$$

In the experiments described, simultaneous measurements of σ^2 at different distances between the light source and the receiver were not made. During the time necessary for transporting the light source from one point to another and for aiming the light source at the receiver, the meteorological conditions had time to change substantially. Therefore, in order to compare values of σ^2 obtained at different distances, it is first necessary to reduce them to identical meteorological conditions. The simplest way of making such a reduction is to average the values of σ^2 pertaining to one distance over all the measurements; this gives a value $\sigma^2(L)$ which pertains to the average meteorological conditions. The averaged values of σ^2 are given in Table 1.

TABLE 1

L, meters	σ^2_{av}	$\sqrt{\sigma^2_{av}}$	Number of Measurements
2000	0.420	0.65	75
1000	0.128	0.36	171
500	0.027	0.16	78
250	0.0078	0.088	50

A more accurate reduction of the values of σ^2 to identical meteorological conditions was also made. For every distance L, the measured values of σ were compared with simultaneously measured values of the vertical temperature gradient $d\overline{T}/dz$, or more precisely, of the quantity $C_T = a(\kappa z)^{2/3}(d\overline{T}/dz)$, defining the intensity of the temperature fluctuations in the layer of the atmosphere near the earth (see Chapter 10). For each distance the dependence between σ and $C_T = a(\kappa z)^{2/3}(d\overline{T}/dz)$ was approximated by the formula $\sigma = AC_T^{\alpha}$, where A and α were found for each distance by the method of least squares (in logarithmic units). The values of α found for different distances L turned out to be quite close together. The average for the four distances was $\alpha = 0.2$. Thus, for all the distances, the dependence of σ on C_T can be approximated by the same formula

$$\sigma = K(L)C_T^{0.2} .$$

The values of $K(L)$ (see Table 2) can now be determined for each distance as the regression coefficient of the values of σ on $C_T^{0.2}$ (the quantity C_T is expressed in degrees per $cm^{1/3}$). The results given in Tables 1 and 2 are in good agreement with the theoretical dependence $\sigma \propto L^{11/12}$.

TABLE 2

L, meters	2000	1000	500	250
K (L)	1.3	0.86	0.32	0.14

If we approximate the data of Table 1 (Fig. 26) by the formula σ^2 = const L^n and find the values of n and the constant by the method of least squares, then for n we obtain the value 1.96, which is very close to the theoretical value of 11/6 = 1.83. A similar value of n, determined from the data of Table 2, turns out to be equal to 2.1. This value of n is also close to the theoretical value of 11/6. Thus, we can regard the dependence of the amount of scintillation of light on the distance as agreeing satisfactorily with the theoretical formula $\sigma^2 \propto L^{11/6}$.

12.3 The correlation function of the fluctuations of light intensity in the plane perpendicular to the ray

As already noted [c], for $\sqrt{\lambda L} \gg \ell_o$ (for light this is practically always the case), the correlation distance of the fluctuations of light intensity is of order $\sqrt{\lambda L}$, and the correlation function of the intensity fluctuations depends on the argument $\rho/\sqrt{\lambda L}$. In the experiments which were carried out, this similarity hypothesis was immediately verified. Measurements of the correlation coefficient R were made for different values of $\sqrt{\lambda L}$, corre-

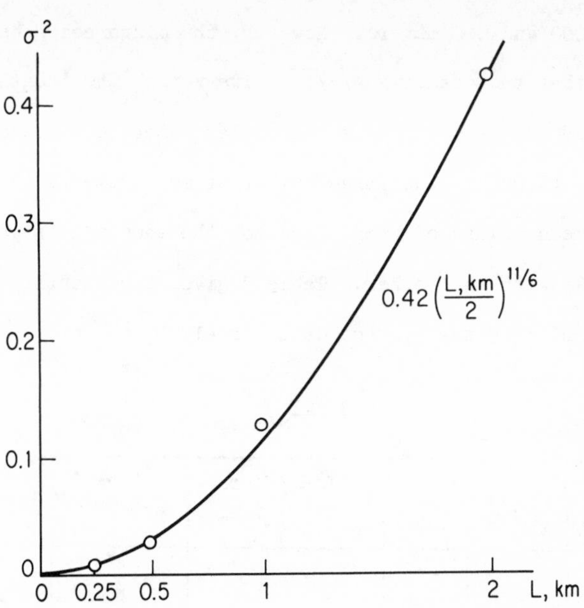

Fig. 26 Distance dependence of the logarithmic intensity fluctuations of light.

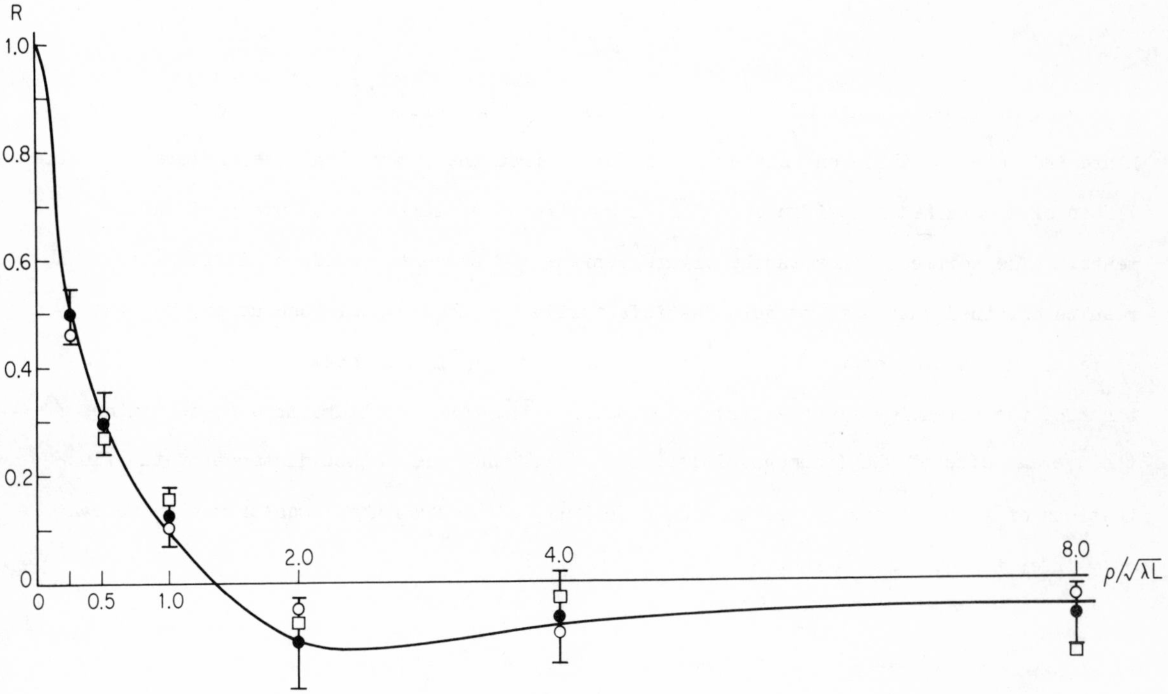

Fig. 27 Empirical correlation function of the flucuations of light intensity.

sponding to L = 2000, 1000 and 500 meters. However, the distances ρ between the diaphragms were set in such a way that the quantity $\rho/\sqrt{\lambda L}$ always took the identical values 0.25, 0.5, 1, 2, 4 and 8. The measurements of R had a rather large scatter, caused by insufficient accuracy of measurement. However, the large number of measurements of R greatly decreased the error, so that the mean values of R obtained for the same $\rho/\sqrt{\lambda L}$ but different $\sqrt{\lambda L}$ agree very satisfactorily with each other. Table 3 gives the quantities R obtained for different values of L, and also the average data for all L.

TABLE 3

$\rho/\sqrt{\lambda L}$	L = 2000 m $\sqrt{\lambda L}$ = 3.2 cm		L = 1000 m $\sqrt{\lambda L}$ = 2.2 cm		L = 500 m $\sqrt{\lambda L}$ = 1.6 cm		Averages for all L		
	R	n	R	n	R	n	R	n	5% confidence intervals
0.25	0.58	8	0.46	15	—	—	0.50	23	0.05
0.5	0.27	9	0.31	19	0.27	12	0.29	40	0.05
1.0	0.09	11	0.10	18	0.16	15	0.12	43	0.06
2	-0.05	7	-0.05	15	-0.07	14	-0.055	36	0.08
4	-0.08	6	-0.09	13	-0.03	14	-0.062	33	0.08
8	-0.08	7	-0.03	14	-0.13	9	-0.072	30	0.06

Fig. 27 gives a graph of the data of Table 3. The values of R obtained for different L are indicated by different signs. It is clear from the figure that the difference in the values of R obtained for different $\sqrt{\lambda L}$ lies within the limits of accuracy of the measurements. (The vertical lines in the figure represent 5 percent confidence limits [d].) The results obtained substantiate quite satisfactorily the theoretical conclusion that the correlation function of the fluctuations depends on $\rho/\sqrt{\lambda L}$ and that the correlation distance of the intensity fluctuations is of order $\sqrt{\lambda L}$. Thus, all attempts to determine "the average size of the inhomogeneities" in terms of the correlation distance of the fluctuations of light intensity are doomed to failure, since from these measurements one can only infer the quantity $\sqrt{\lambda L}$.

12.4 Frequency spectra of the fluctuations of the logarithm of the light intensity (theory)

Before presenting the results of measurements of the frequency spectrum of the intensity fluctuations, we consider the problem theoretically. Let $I(y,z)$ be the distribution of the intensity of light in the observation plane $x = L$. Let the mean velocity of motion of the refractive index inhomogeneities be constant and equal to $\vec{v}$ along the entire wave propagation path. We assume from the beginning that the refractive index inhomogeneities are "frozen-in", i.e., do not change during the process of convection. Below, we shall find the conditions which must be satisfied if such an approach to the problem is not to lead to appreciable errors.

We resolve the velocity of motion $\vec{v}$ of the inhomogeneities into two components, i.e. $\vec{v} = \vec{v}_n + \vec{v}_t$, where $\vec{v}_n$ is perpendicular to the direction of wave propagation and $\vec{v}_t$ is parallel to it. It is easy to convince oneself that convection of the inhomogeneities along the propagation direction does not lead to appreciable changes of the field $I(y,z)$, provided only that the angle α between the wind velocity $\vec{v}$ and the direction of wave propagation satisfies the inequality $\alpha \gg \sqrt{\lambda/L}$ [e]. Therefore, we can assume that the field at the point (y_o, z_o) at the time $t_o + \tau$ coincides with the field at the point $(y_o - v_y\tau, z_o - v_z\tau)$ at the time t_o. Using this relation, we can express the time autocorrelation function $R_A(\tau)$ of the fluctuations of logarithmic amplitude at the point (y_o, z_o) in terms of the space correlation function $B_A(\rho)$:

$$R_A(\tau) = B_A(v_n\tau). \tag{12.2}$$

As shown above, the transverse correlation distance of the amplitude fluctuations of the wave is of order $\sqrt{\lambda L}$. It follows from (12.2) that the correlation time of the field is of order $\tau_o = \sqrt{\lambda L}/v_n$.

We now formulate the condition which when satisfied allows us to regard the refractive index inhomogeneities as "frozen-in". It is clear that for this to be the case, it is sufficient that the inhomogeneities of size $\sqrt{\lambda L}$, which are chiefly responsible for producing the amplitude fluctuations of the wave, should not have time to change appreciably during the time τ_o. As shown above (see Chapter 2), the "lifetime" of an inhomogeneity of size ℓ is equal to $\tau_\ell \sim \ell/v_\ell \sim \ell/(\epsilon\ell)^{1/3}$. For $\ell \sim \sqrt{\lambda L}$ we obtain $\tau_{\sqrt{\lambda L}} \sim \sqrt{\lambda L}\,(\epsilon\sqrt{\lambda L})^{-1/3}$. This quantity must be large compared to τ_o, whence $v_n \gg (\epsilon\sqrt{\lambda L})^{1/3}$. But v_n is in order of magnitude equal to the velocity of the flow as a whole and can be expressed in terms of the outer scale of turbulence L_o, i.e. $v_n \sim (\epsilon L_o)^{1/3}$. Therefore, the "frozen-in" condition can be used in the case where $\sqrt{\lambda L} \ll L_o$. (This condition is practically always satisfied for light propagating in the atmosphere.)

We now calculate the frequency (time) spectrum of the amplitude fluctuations of the wave. Denoting the spectral density of the fluctuations by W(f), we have by definition [f]

v_n is in order of magnitude equal to the velocity of the flow as a whole and can be expressed in terms of the outer scale of turbulence L_o, i.e. $v_n \sim (\epsilon L_o)^{1/3}$. Therefore, the "frozen-in" condition can be used in the case where $\sqrt{\lambda L} \ll L_o$. (This condition is practically always satisfied for light propagating in the atmosphere.)

We now calculate the frequency (time) spectrum of the amplitude fluctuations of the wave. Denoting the spectral density of the fluctuations by W(f), we have by definition [f]

$$W(f) = 4\int_0^\infty \cos(2\pi f\tau) R_A(\tau)\,d\tau$$

or

$$W(f) = 4\int_0^\infty \cos(2\pi f\tau) B_A(v_n\tau)\,d\tau. \tag{12.3}$$

Using the expression [g]

$$B_A(\rho) = 2\pi\int_0^\infty F_A(\kappa,0) J_o(\kappa\rho)\kappa\,d\kappa$$

and changing the order of integration, we obtain the formula

$$W(f) = 8\pi\int_0^\infty F_A(\kappa,0)\kappa\,d\kappa\int_0^\infty J_o(\kappa v_n\tau)\cos(2\pi f\tau)\,d\tau.$$

The inner integral is the well known discontinuous Weber integral [53]:

$$\int_0^{\infty} J_o(\kappa v_n \tau)\cos(2\pi f\tau)d\tau = \begin{cases} \dfrac{1}{\sqrt{\kappa^2 v_n^2 - 4\pi^2 f^2}} & \text{for } \kappa^2 v_n^2 > 4\pi^2 f^2 \\ 0 & \text{for } \kappa^2 v_n^2 < 4\pi^2 f^2. \end{cases}$$

Consequently we have

$$W(f) = 8\pi \int_{\frac{2\pi f}{v_n}}^{\infty} F_A(\kappa,0) \frac{\kappa d\kappa}{\sqrt{\kappa^2 v_n^2 - 4\pi^2 f^2}} .$$

By the change of variables $\sqrt{\kappa^2 v_n^2 - 4\pi^2 f^2} = \kappa' v_n$, this expression finally reduces to

$$W(f) = \frac{8\pi}{v_n} \int_0^{\infty} F_A\left(\sqrt{\kappa^2 + \frac{4\pi^2 f^2}{v_n^2}}\, , 0\right) d\kappa. \qquad (12.4)$$

Eq. (12.4) relates the frequency (time) spectrum of the amplitude fluctuations of the wave to the two-dimensional spectral density $F_A(\kappa,0)$ of the amplitude fluctuations. For comparing the theory with experimental data it is convenient to consider the dimensionless quantity

$$U(f) = \frac{fW(f)}{\int_0^{\infty} W(f)df}$$

which satisfies the condition of being normalized in logarithmic units, i.e.

$$\int_0^\infty U(f)\, d\log f = 1.$$

We use Eq. (7.87) for $F_A(\kappa,0)$ and Eq. (7.94) for $\overline{\chi^2} = \int_0^\infty W(f)df$, expressions which are valid for the case C_n^2 = const. Then for U(f) we obtain the expression [h]

$$U(f) = \frac{fW(f)}{\overline{\chi^2}} = 1.35\Omega \int_0^\infty \left[1 - \frac{\sin(t^2 + \Omega^2)}{t^2 + \Omega^2}\right](t^2 + \Omega^2)^{-11/6} dt\,, \tag{12.5}$$

where

$$\Omega = f/f_o \quad \text{and} \quad f_o = \frac{v_n}{2\pi}\sqrt{\frac{k}{L}} = \frac{v_n}{\sqrt{2\pi\lambda L}}\,. \tag{12.6}$$

As follows from Eq. (12.5), the quantity $fW(f)/\overline{\chi^2}$ is a function of $\Omega = f/f_o$, which does not change its appearance when v_n and L are changed. (In logarithmic units, change of v_n or L corresponds to translation of the curve U(f) along the horizontal axis.) The function $f_oW(f) / \int_0^\infty W(f)df$ is shown in Fig. 28, and the normalized function U(f) obtained by numerical integration of (12.5) is shown in Fig. 31 [i].

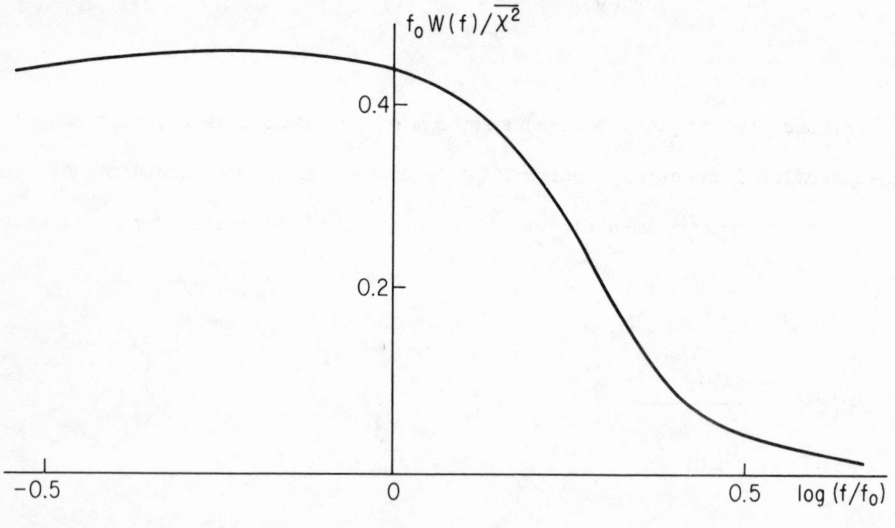

Fig. 28 Theoretical shape of the frequency spectrum of the fluctuations of logarithmic amplitude for constant wind velocity.

12.5 Frequency spectrum of fluctuations of light intensity (experimental results)

The frequency spectrum of the fluctuations of light flux was measured by using a frequency analyzer consisting of 30 filters, each with a bandwidth of one half octave ($f_{upper}/f_{lower} = \sqrt{2}$), arranged in a bank one half octave apart, from 0.05 to 1160 cps. 80 scintillation spectra were analyzed, obtained at distances L of 1000 and 2000 meters. The quantity v_n, the component of the mean wind velocity perpendicular to the ray, was calculated by using synchronous meteorological measurements. The measurements at each distance were divided into 3 groups depending on the size of v_n, namely

$$1 < v_n < 2 \text{ m/sec}, \quad 2 < v_n < 3 \text{ m/sec}, \quad \text{and} \quad 3 < v_n < 4 \text{ m/sec}.$$

Average spectral densities W(f) of the fluctuations were obtained for each group (the averaging was carried out in logarithmic units). Then the "normalized" spectral densities $W(f) / \int_0^\infty W(f)df$ were calculated. Fig. 29 gives the quantities $U(f) = fW(f) / \int_0^\infty W(f)df$ corresponding to the different wind velocities v_n, which are the averages for the given group of measurements; the abcissas are measured in logarithmic units.

It is clear from the figure that when the mean wind velocity is increased, the curves of U(f) are shifted in the high-frequency direction. We can find the frequencies f_m corresponding to the maximum of the curve U(f); f_m is defined as one half the sum of the frequency values for which $U(f) = \frac{1}{2}[U(f)]_{max}$. Table 4 gives the values of the mean wind velocity v_n for groups of the quantities f_m and $f_m\sqrt{\lambda L} / v_n$.

TABLE 4

	L = 1000 m			L = 2000 m		
v_n, m/sec^{-1}	1.46	2.18	3.46	1.61	2.59	3.51
f_m, cps	20	25.6	45.7	18.1	25.6	39.8
$f_m\sqrt{\lambda L}/v_n$	0.31	0.26	0.30	0.35	0.31	0.36

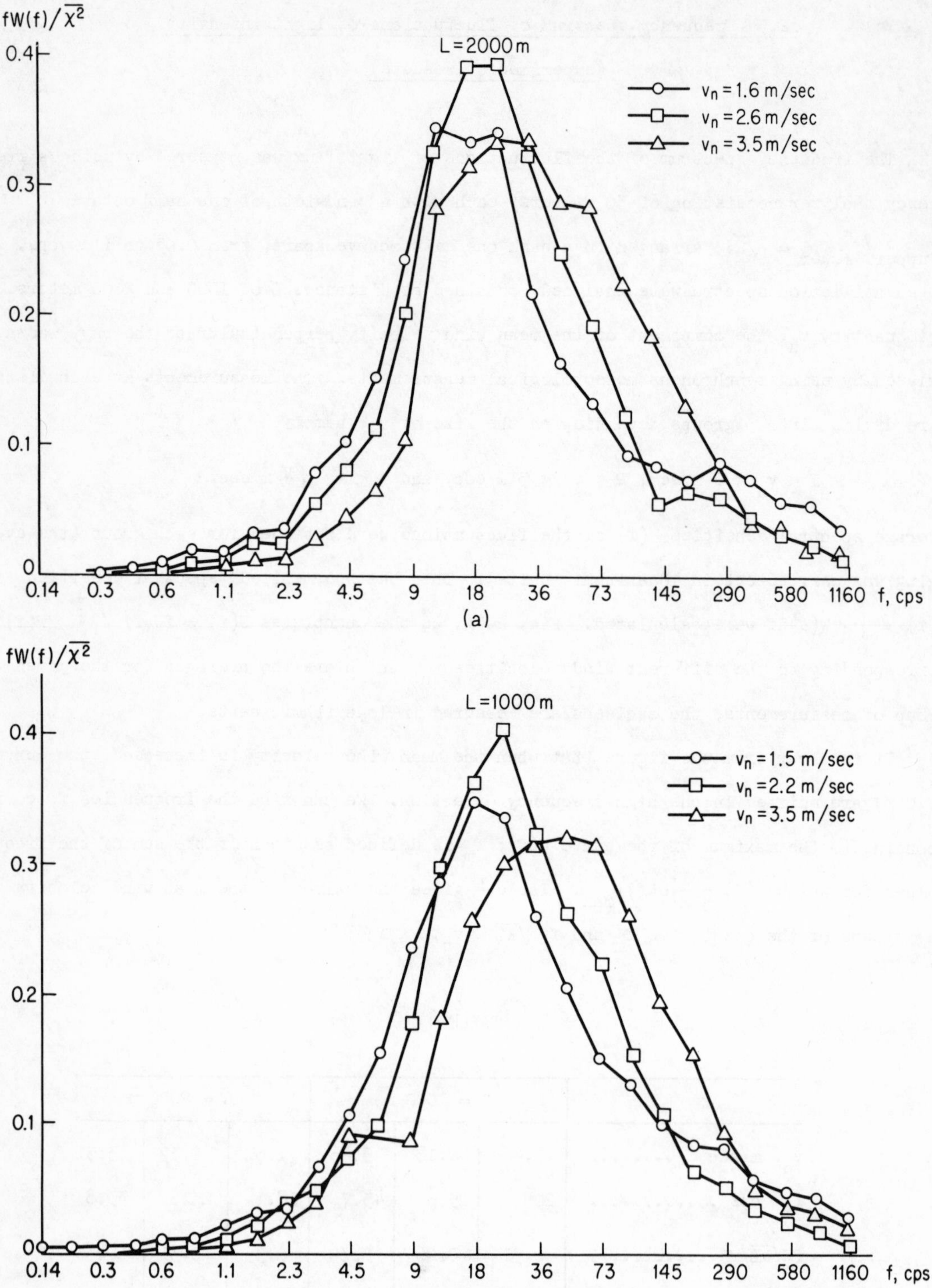

Fig. 29 Empirical frequency spectrum of fluctuations of light intensity for different wind velocities (a, L = 2000 m; b, L = 1000 m).

The quantity $f_m \sqrt{\lambda L} / v_n$ is approximately constant, with mean value equal to 0.32. Thus, the frequencies f_m are connected with v_n and $\sqrt{\lambda L}$ by the relation

$$f_m = 0.32 \frac{v_n}{\sqrt{\lambda L}} . \qquad (12.7)$$

We note that a calculation based on the hypothesis of "frozen-in" turbulence, leads to the relation $f_m = 0.55\ v_n / \sqrt{\lambda L}$, which differs from (12.7) by a numerical coefficient. However, the theoretical relation between the spatial correlation distance $R_o\ [B_A(R_o) = 0]$ and f_m, which has the form

$$R_o = 0.44 \frac{v_n}{f_m} , \qquad (12.8)$$

is met satisfactorily, since according to the experimental data, $R_o = 1.5 \sqrt{\lambda L}$, which together with (12.7) leads to the formula

$$R_o = 0.48 \frac{v_n}{f_m} . \qquad (12.9)$$

Fig. 30 gives a more detailed verification of the similarity hypothesis expressed by Eq. (12.5). In Fig. 30 all the frequency spectra represented in Fig. 29 are reduced to the values $v_n = 1$ m/sec and $L = 1000$ m. As is clear from the figure, the spectra which are transformed in this way differ very little from one another. This confirms the fact that the function $U(f)$ depends only on the argument $f \sqrt{\lambda L} / v_n$, i.e.

$$\frac{fW(f)}{\int_0^\infty W(f)df} = F\left(\frac{f\sqrt{\lambda L}}{v_n}\right). \qquad (12.10)$$

A theoretical calculation of the function appearing in the right hand side of (12.10) was made above, by using the hypothesis of "frozen-in" turbulence. Fig. 31 gives a comparison of the theoretical curve and the experimental data obtained by averaging the graphs in Fig. 30 [j]. It is clear from the figure that the theoretical curve is "narrower" than

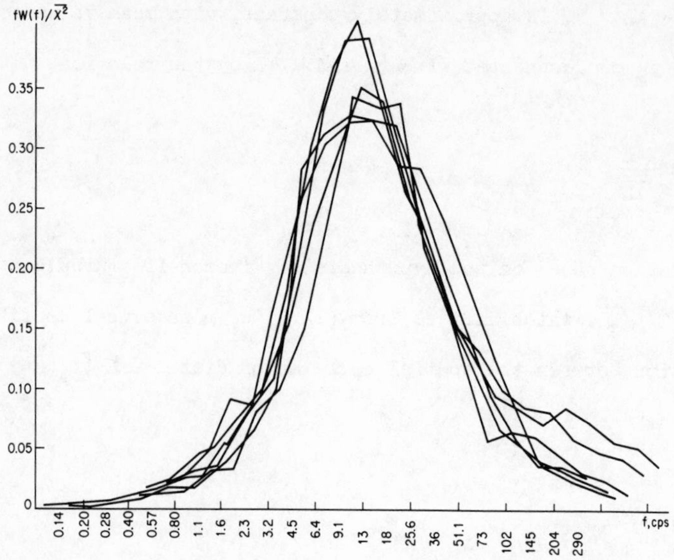

Fig. 30 Reduction of the frequency spectra to v_n = 1 m/sec and L = 1000 m.

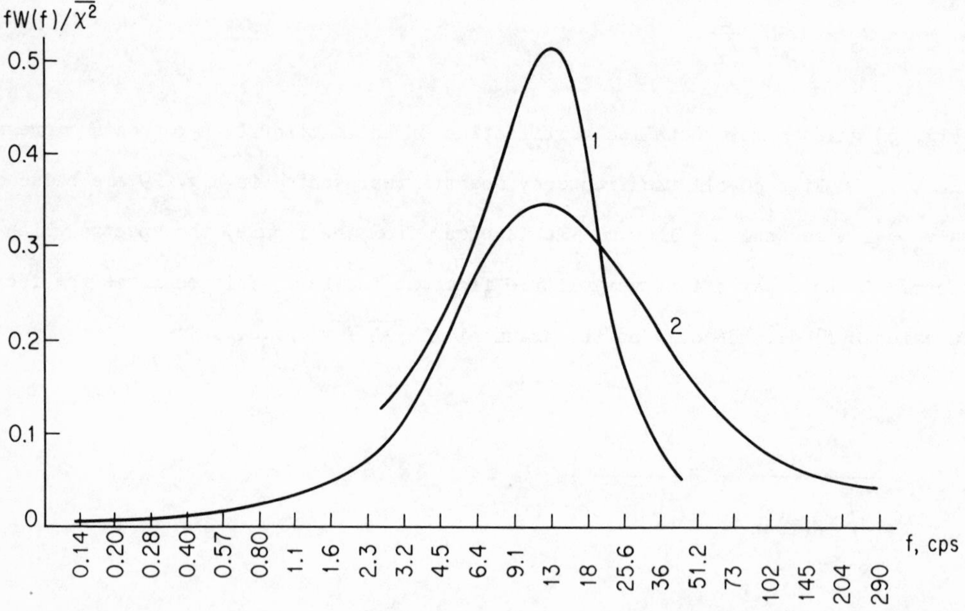

Fig. 31 Comparison of the empirical spectrum of fluctuations of light intensity with the theoretical spectrum (1, theoretical curve; 2, experimental curve).

the experimental curve; this is evidently related to the fact that it is assumed in the theory that the wind velocity is constant along the entire propagation path.

In conclusion, we state the basic results of the experiment:

1. The fluctuations of light intensity caused by atmospheric turbulence have a log normal distribution.

2. The dependence of $\sigma^2 = \overline{[\log(I/I_0)]^2}$ on L is found to be in satisfactory agreement with the theory of the phenomenon, which leads to the formula $\sigma^2 \propto L^{11/6}$.

3. Direct measurements confirm the theoretical conclusion that the correlation function of the fluctuations of light intensity depends on $\rho/\sqrt{\lambda L}$ and that the correlation distance is of order $\sqrt{\lambda L}$.

4. It is confirmed that the frequency spectrum of the fluctuations of light intensity depends on $f\sqrt{\lambda L}\,/\,v_n$, and good agreement is observed between the intervals of time correlation and space correlation.

Chapter 13

TWINKLING AND QUIVERING OF STELLAR IMAGES IN TELESCOPES

The first experiments concerned with the study of fluctuations of intensity and angle of arrival of light waves were carried out while investigating the twinkling and quivering of stellar images in telescopes. Recently, interest in this problem has increased; this is explained both by the requirements of observational astronomy and by the close relation which exists between these phenomena and certain features of radio propagation in the troposphere. Here we shall not give a detailed exposition of all the known facts, nor shall we present the numerous theories which describe the phenomena of twinkling and quivering of stellar images in telescopes; we confine ourselves merely to a short account of the basic facts and their interpretation.

When we make an observation in a telescope, we see the diffraction image of a star in the form of a luminous core and a series of concentric rings. However, it is hardly the case that such an image is seen all the time. Usually the stellar image does not remain fixed in the field of vision, but rather experiences irregular displacements in all possible directions, which are called "quivering". At the same time, some of the diffraction rings are missing or are smeared out. Under especially unfavorable observational conditions, we see a "dancing" irregular "patch", which in no way recalls the diffraction image of the star. Simultaneously, one also observes "twinkling" of the star, i.e. irregular changes in its brightness. The astronomical "seeing" (i.e. diffraction image) and the quivering of the image are intimately related (since both of these effects are produced by phase fluctuations of the wave). When the "seeing" is bad, one usually observes considerable "quivering" of the images.

A large number of experimental papers are devoted to the study of the phenomenon of quivering of images, a review of which is contained in the papers of Kolchinski [80,81]. This author arrives at the basic conclusion that the mean square fluctuation of the angle of arrival of the light from the star is directly proportional to the secant of the zenith distance θ of the star, i.e.

$$\overline{(\Delta\alpha)^2} = A^2 \sec\theta. \tag{13.1}$$

The quantity A is a few tenths of an angular second in order of magnitude, and depends on the meteorological conditions. Fig. 32 gives the results of observations of the quivering of stars, performed at the Central Astronomical Observatory of the Academy of Sciences of the USSR at Goloseyev [81]. The rms values of the fluctuations of the propagation direction of the wave is plotted along the vertical axis, while sec θ is plotted along the horizontal axis.

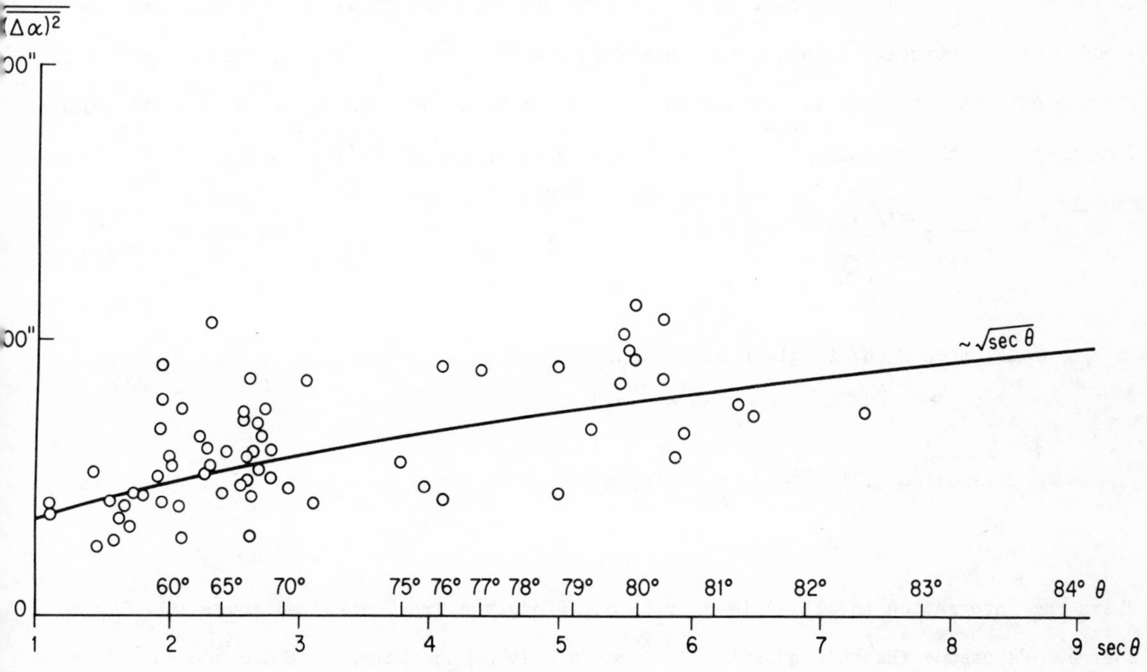

Fig. 32 Dependence of the amount of quivering of stellar images on the zenith distance.

The points in Fig. 32 have a large scatter, caused by the fact that the graph comprises results of observations made under different meteorological conditions. In order to show the dependence of the quantity $\overline{(\Delta\alpha)^2}$ on sec θ, we must average the quantities $\overline{(\Delta\alpha)^2}$ which belong to neighboring values of sec θ. One also obtains a similar result by constructing the regression line, whose equation has the form (with a logarithmic scale):

$$\log \overline{(\Delta\alpha)^2} = \log A^2 + 2p \log \sec \theta. \tag{13.2}$$

The quantities A^2 and p, found by the method of least squares, turn out to be equal to $A = 0.35''$ and $p = 0.47$. This value of p is in good agreement with Eq. (13.1).

The theoretical law (13.1) was first established by Krasilnikov [82]. Suppose that two interferometer slits are located at the points A and B at a distance b from each other. If the surface of the wave front is parallel to AB, then the phases of the oscillations at A and B are identical. Rotating the wave front by the angle $\Delta\alpha \ll 1$ produces a phase difference ΔS between the oscillations at A and B which is equal to $\Delta S = kb\,\Delta\alpha$. It follows from this that the quantity $\overline{(\Delta\alpha)^2}$ can be expressed in terms of $\overline{(\Delta S)^2} = D_S(b)$ by using the formula

$$\overline{(\Delta\alpha)^2} = \frac{D_S(b)}{k^2 b^2}. \tag{13.3}$$

If $b > \sqrt{\lambda L}$, then $D_S(b)$ is given by Eq. (8.22), and

$$\overline{(\Delta\alpha)^2} = 2.91\, b^{-1/3} \int_0^\infty C_n^2(\vec{r})dx, \tag{13.4}$$

where the integration in (13.4) is carried out along the "ray" directed toward the light source. We assume that the quantity C_n^2 depends only on the height z above the earth's surface. Setting $x = z \sec \theta$, we obtain from (13.4):

$$\overline{(\Delta\alpha)^2} = 2.91\, b^{-1/3} \sec \theta \int_0^\infty C_n^2(z)dz. \tag{13.5}$$

In telescopic observations of the quivering of stars, the role of the quantity b is played by the diameter D of the telescope. In general, when b is changed to D, the value of the numerical coefficient in (13.5) can change a little. However, the character of Eq. (13.5) remains the same. It follows from (13.5) that the quantity $\overline{(\Delta\alpha)^2}$ is proportional to sec θ, which agrees with (13.1). The size of $\overline{(\Delta\alpha)^2}$ decreases slowly as the diameter D of the telescope is increased.

It is interesting to note that $C_n^2(z)$ usually takes its largest values in the lower layers of the atmosphere, which lie near the earth's surface. Therefore, the largest contribution to the integral

$$\int_0^\infty C_n^2(z)dz$$

is made by the lower layers of the atmosphere, which also play the basic role in the phenomena of astronomical "seeing" and quivering of stellar images.

As remarked in [81], the quantity $\Delta\alpha$ has a Gaussian distribution. This conclusion is in good agreement with the fact mentioned in Chapter 12 to the effect that the quantity $\log (A/A_0)$ has a Gaussian distribution, since, as follows from general considerations, $\log (A/A_0)$ and S_1 (the fluctuations of logarithmic amplitude and phase of the wave) must obey the same distribution law.

We now turn to the problem of the twinkling of stars (fluctuations of the light intensity). In practice, extensive measurements of fluctuations of light intensity are made much more easily than measurements of the "quivering" of stellar images, so that there exist a large number of experimental papers on this problem [83-86,78]. By placing a photoelectric device in the focal plane of the telescope, the light flux can be transformed into an electrical voltage, which is extremely suitable for statistical analysis [84,86,75]. As a result of numerous observations, it has been established that the size of the fluctuations of the light flux passing through the diaphragm of the telescope, depends significantly on the dimensions of the diaphragm, the zenith distance of the light source and its angular dimensions, and the meteorological conditions. The dimensions of the diaphragm of the telescope have a very great influence both on the size of the fluctuations (see Fig. 33) and on the way they depend on the zenith distance.

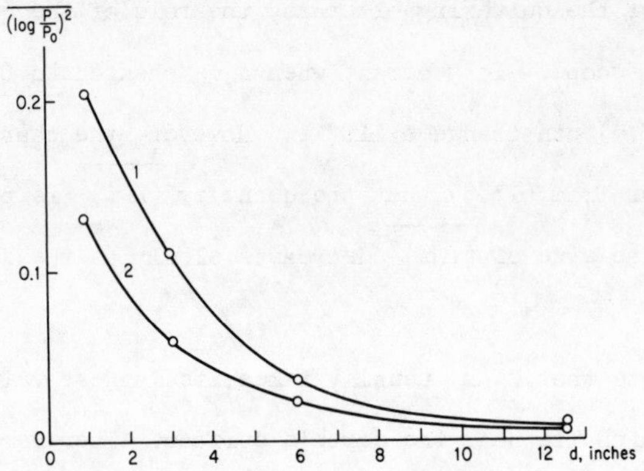

Fig. 33 Empirical dependence of the amount of twinkling on the diameter of the telescope diaphragm (1, winter; 2, summer) [a,84].

Figs. 34 and 35 show how two samples of the quantity $\sigma_P^2 = \overline{(P - \overline{P})^2} / \overline{P}^2$ (where P is the light flux through the telescope objective), obtained for different values of the diameter of the telescope diaphragm, depend on sec θ. The slope of the curves log σ_P = f(log sec θ) for small values of θ, as well as the behavior of the curve log σ_P = f(log sec θ) for large values of θ, depends strongly on the diameter of the diaphragm. Therefore, before proceeding to a further study of the experimental data and their interpretation, we investigate the theoretical role of the dimensions of the telescope diaphragm.

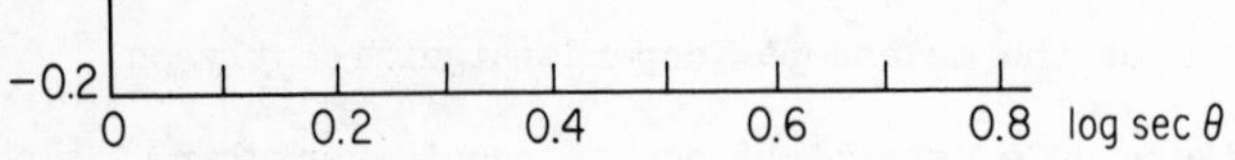

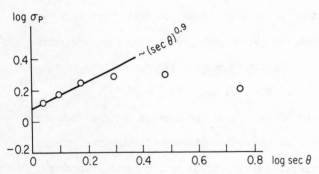

Fig. 34 Dependence of the amount of twinkling on the zenith distance when the telescope diaphragm has a diameter of three inches.

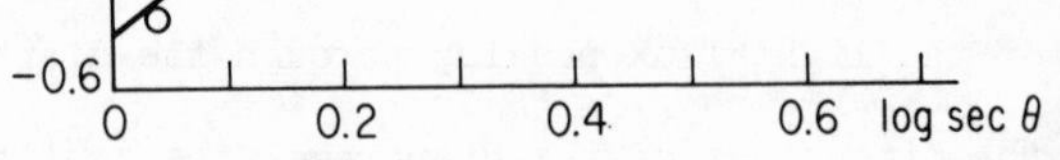

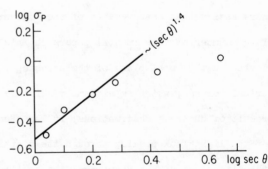

Fig. 35 Dependence of the amount of twinkling on the zenith distance when the telescope diaphragm has a diameter of 12.5 inches.

A photocell placed in the focal plane of the telescope responds to the entire light flux P through the telescope diaphragm. If $I(y,z)$ is the intensity of the light wave on the surface of the objective (the energy flow density), then

$$P = \iint_{\Sigma} I(y,z)\,dydz, \tag{13.6}$$

where Σ is the surface of the objective. The quantity I has a log normal probability distribution law (see Chapter 12). If $\sqrt{\Sigma} \lesssim \sqrt{\lambda L}$, i.e., if the diameter of the objective is less than the correlation distance of the fluctuations of the light intensity, and consequently if changes in the light flux through different parts of the objective take place simultaneously, then the quantity P also has a log normal distribution law. But if $\Sigma \gg \lambda L$, i.e., if a large number of uncorrelated inhomogeneities of the light field can be found within the limits of the objective, then by the central limit theorem, the quantity P has a normal distribution law. However, the telescopes used in practice usually have dimensions such that no more than 2 to 4 uncorrelated field inhomogeneities fit inside of Σ; for example, for D = 40 cm and $\sqrt{\lambda L} = 10$ cm (see below), $\frac{\Sigma}{\pi\lambda L} = 4$. In this case the distribution law of P is still very close to the log normal law. The experimental data of Butler [87], obtained with a fifteen inch telescope, confirm this conclusion. Thus, with a sufficiently high degree of accuracy, we can assume that P, just like I, has a log normal distribution. We now find the parameters of this distribution.

The quantity I can be represented in the form

$$I = I_0 \exp\left[2\log\frac{A}{A_0}\right] = I_0 \exp\left[2\chi(y,z)\right], \tag{13.7}$$

where $\chi(y,z) = \log\frac{A(y,z)}{A_0}$ is the logarithmic amplitude of the light wave, distributed according to the normal law. Thus we have

$$P = I_0 \iint_{\Sigma} e^{2\chi(y,z)}\,dydz. \tag{13.8}$$

To determine the important quantity $\overline{\left(\log \frac{P}{P_o}\right)^2}$, where $\log P_o \equiv \overline{\log P}$, it is sufficient to consider the first and second moments M_1 and M_2 of the quantity P. M_1 is defined by the equality

$$M_1 = \overline{P} = I_o \iint_{\Sigma} \overline{e^{2X(y,z)}} \, dydz. \tag{13.9}$$

But $\overline{e^{2X}} = e^{2\overline{X^2}}$, where $\overline{X^2} = \overline{\left(\log \frac{A}{A_o}\right)^2}$, which is valid for any normally distributed quantity X. Thus we have

$$M_1 = \overline{P} = I_o \Sigma \, e^{2\overline{X^2}}. \tag{13.10}$$

We now calculate M_2:

$$M_2 = \overline{P^2} = I_o^2 \iint_{\Sigma}\iint_{\Sigma} \overline{e^{2X(y,z)+2X(y',z')}} \, dydzdy'dz'. \tag{13.11}$$

If we assume that the two-dimensional distribution of the quantity X is also normal, then it is easy to show that

$$\overline{e^{2X(y,z)+2X(y',z')}} = e^{4\left[\overline{X^2}+B_A(\vec{r}-\vec{r}')\right]} \tag{13.12}$$

or

$$B_I(\vec{r} - \vec{r}') \equiv \overline{(I_1 - \overline{I}_1)(I_2 - \overline{I}_2)} = (\overline{I})^2\left[e^{4B_A(\vec{r}-\vec{r}')} - 1\right], \tag{13.13}$$

which is equivalent to (13.12); here $B_A(\vec{r} - \vec{r}')$ is the correlation function of the fluctuations of logarithmic amplitude, considered above. To derive (13.12), it is sufficient to consider the characteristic function of the two-dimensional normal distribution. Thus we have

$$M_2 = I_o^2 \, e^{4\overline{\chi^2}} \iint_{\Sigma} \iint_{\Sigma} e^{4B_A(\vec{r}_1-\vec{r}_2)} \, dy_1 dz_1 dy_2 dz_2 . \qquad (13.14)$$

If P has a log normal distribution, then the quantity $\overline{\left(\log \frac{P}{P_o}\right)^2}$ can be expressed in terms of M_1 and M_2 by using the formula

$$\overline{\left(\log \frac{P}{P_o}\right)^2} = \log \frac{M_2}{M_1^2}$$

and thus

$$\overline{\left(\log \frac{P}{P_o}\right)^2} = \log \left(\frac{1}{\Sigma^2} \iint_{\Sigma} \iint_{\Sigma} e^{4B_A(\vec{r}_1-\vec{r}_2)} \, d\sigma_1 d\sigma_2 \right) . \qquad (13.15)$$

To evaluate this expression, we introduce the spectral expansion of the correlation function of the intensity fluctuations of the wave:

$$B_I(\vec{r}_1 - \vec{r}_2) = \overline{\left[I(\vec{r}_1) - \overline{I}\right]\left[I(\vec{r}_2) - \overline{I}\right]} =$$

$$= \iint_{-\infty}^{\infty} F_I(\kappa_2,\kappa_3) e^{i\left[\kappa_2(y_1-y_2)+\kappa_3(z_1-z_2)\right]} \, d\kappa_2 d\kappa_3 . \qquad (13.16)$$

Since $I(\vec{r}_1) = I_o e^{2\chi(\vec{r}_1)}$, the quantity $e^{4B_A(\vec{r}_1-\vec{r}_2)}$ can be expressed in terms of $F_I(\kappa_2,\kappa_3)$ by using the formula

$$e^{4B_A(\vec{r}_1-\vec{r}_2)} = 1 + \frac{1}{(\overline{I})^2} \iint_{-\infty}^{\infty} F_I(\kappa_2,\kappa_3) e^{i\left[\kappa_2(y_1-y_2)+\kappa_3(z_1-z_2)\right]} \, d\kappa_2 d\kappa_3 . \qquad (13.17)$$

Then we have

$$\overline{\left(\log \frac{P}{P_o}\right)^2} = \log \left\{ 1 + \frac{1}{\Sigma^2(\overline{I})^2} \iint\limits_{-\infty}^{\infty} F_I(\kappa_2,\kappa_3)d\kappa_2 d\kappa_3 \times \right.$$

$$\left. \times \iiiint\limits_{\Sigma\ \ \Sigma} e^{i\left[\kappa_2(y_1-y_2)+\kappa_3(z_1-z_2)\right]} d\sigma_1 d\sigma_2 \right\} . \qquad (13.18)$$

We introduce the function

$$V_\Sigma(\kappa_2,\kappa_3) = \frac{1}{\Sigma} \int\limits_\Sigma e^{i(\kappa_2 y+\kappa_3 z)} dydz, \qquad (13.19)$$

which describes the Fraunhofer diffraction of the diaphragm Σ [b]. Then (13.18) takes the form

$$\overline{\left(\log \frac{P}{P_o}\right)^2} = \log \left\{ 1 + \frac{1}{(\overline{I})^2} \iint\limits_{-\infty}^{\infty} F_I(\kappa_2,\kappa_3)\left|V_\Sigma(\kappa_2,\kappa_3)\right|^2 d\kappa_2\, d\kappa_3 \right\} . \qquad (13.20)$$

As follows from Eq. (13.19), the function $V_\Sigma(\kappa_2,\kappa_3)$ is appreciably different from zero only for $\kappa \lesssim \frac{1}{D}$, where D is the dimension of the diaphragm Σ. Thus, the small-scale components of the field (with dimensions less than D) do not contribute to the fluctuations of P.

We consider the case where the telescope diaphragm is a circle of radius R. Then, as is easily seen

$$V_\Sigma = \frac{1}{\pi R^2} \int\limits_0^R \rho d\rho \int\limits_0^{2\pi} e^{i\kappa\rho \cos\varphi}\, d\varphi = \frac{2J_1(\kappa R)}{\kappa R}, \qquad (13.21)$$

where $\kappa = \sqrt{\kappa_2^2 + \kappa_3^2}$. Substituting this expression in Eq. (13.20), introducing the coordinates $\kappa_2 = \kappa \cos \varphi$, $\kappa_3 = \kappa \sin \varphi$ and integrating with respect to φ, we obtain the formula

$$\overline{\left(\log \frac{P}{P_o}\right)^2} = \log \left\{ 1 + \frac{2\pi}{(\bar{I})^2} \int_0^\infty F_I(\kappa) \left[\frac{2J_1(\kappa R)}{\kappa R}\right]^2 \kappa d\kappa \right\}. \qquad (13.22)$$

[It is assumed that $F_I(\kappa_2, \kappa_3) = F_I\left(\sqrt{\kappa_2^2 + \kappa_3^2}\right)$.] In Eq. (13.22) we can go over from the spectral density $F_I(\kappa)$ of the fluctuations to the correlation function $B_I(\rho)$ of the fluctuations. Inverting Eq. (13.16) and taking into account the isotropy of the fluctuations in the plane x = const, we obtain

$$F_I(\kappa) = \frac{1}{2\pi} \int_0^\infty B_I(\rho) J_o(\kappa\rho) \rho d\rho. \qquad (13.23)$$

We substitute this expression in (13.22) and change the order of integration:

$$\overline{\left(\log \frac{P}{P_o}\right)^2} = \log \left\{ 1 + \frac{4}{R^2(\bar{I})^2} \int_0^\infty B_I(\rho) \rho d\rho \int_0^\infty \frac{J_o(\kappa\rho) J_1^2(\kappa R)}{\kappa} d\kappa \right\}. \qquad (13.24)$$

The inner integral can be calculated [c] and turns out to be equal to

$$\begin{cases} \dfrac{1}{\pi} \left[\arccos \dfrac{\rho}{2R} - \dfrac{\rho}{2R} \sqrt{1 - \dfrac{\rho^2}{4R^2}} \right] & \text{for } \rho < 2R, \\ 0 & \text{for } \rho > 2R. \end{cases}$$

Consequently, we have

$$\overline{\left(\log \frac{P}{P_o}\right)^2} = \log \left\{ 1 + \frac{4}{\pi R^2 (\overline{I})^2} \int_0^{2R} B_I(\rho) \left[\text{arc cos} \frac{\rho}{2R} - \right.\right.$$

$$\left.\left. - \frac{\rho}{2R} \sqrt{1 - \frac{\rho^2}{4R^2}} \right] \rho d\rho \right\} =$$

$$= \log \left\{ 1 + \frac{16}{\pi (\overline{I})^2} \int_0^1 B_I(Dx) \left(\text{arc cos } x - x\sqrt{1 - x^2} \right) x dx \right\}, \quad (13.25)$$

where D = 2R. Noting that

$$\frac{16}{\pi} \int_0^1 \left(\text{arc cos } x - x \sqrt{1 - x^2} \right) x dx = 1,$$

we rewrite this formula in the form

$$\overline{\left(\log \frac{P}{P_o}\right)^2} = \log \left\{ \frac{16}{\pi} \int_0^1 \left[1 + \frac{B_I(Dx)}{(\overline{I})^2} \right] \left[\text{arc cos } x - x \sqrt{1 - x^2} \right] x dx \right\} . \quad (13.26)$$

But it follows from (13.13) that

$$1 + \frac{B_I(Dx)}{(\overline{I})^2} = e^{4B_A(Dx)} .$$

Thus we have [d]

$$\overline{\left(\log \frac{P}{P_o}\right)^2} = \log \left\{ \frac{16}{\pi} \int_0^1 e^{4B_A(Dx)} \left(\text{arc cos } x - x \sqrt{1 - x^2} \right) x dx \right\} . \quad (13.27)$$

Setting D = 0 here and recalling that $4B_A(0) = 4\overline{X^2} = \sigma^2$, we obtain $\overline{\left(\log \frac{P}{P_o}\right)^2} = \sigma^2$. For

$D > 0$, $\overline{\left(\log \frac{P}{P_0}\right)^2} < \sigma^2$. We introduce the quantity $G = \frac{1}{\sigma^2} \overline{\left(\log \frac{P}{P_0}\right)^2}$, which characterizes the decrease in twinkling due to the averaging action of the objective. Furthermore, setting

$$4B_A(\rho) = 4\overline{\chi^2}\, b_A(\rho) = \sigma^2\, b_A(\rho),$$

we obtain

$$G = \frac{1}{\sigma^2} \log \left\{ \frac{16}{\pi} \int_0^1 e^{\sigma^2 b_A(Dx)} \left(\text{arc cos } x - x\sqrt{1 - x^2}\right) x dx \right\}. \qquad (13.28)$$

For $b_A(\rho)$ we take the function represented in Fig. 13, which is applicable in the case where $\sqrt{\lambda L} \gg \ell_0$ and $C_n^2 = \text{const}$. Numerical integration of the expression (13.28) for $\sigma^2 = 4$ and $\sigma^2 \to 0$ leads to the results shown in Fig. 36. As was to be expected, the function G depends on the argument $D / \sqrt{\lambda L}$, i.e.

$$G = G\left(\frac{D}{\sqrt{\lambda L}}, \sigma\right).$$

We remark that

$$G\left(\frac{D}{\sqrt{\lambda L}}, \sigma\right) \propto \left(\frac{D}{\sqrt{\lambda L}}\right)^{-7/3}$$

or $D \gg \sqrt{\lambda L}$ and $\sigma \to 0$. As can be seen from the figure, G is small compared to unity when $\gg \sqrt{\lambda L}$. Thus, in the case where the diameter of the telescope diaphragm exceeds the orrelation distance $\sqrt{\lambda L}$ of the fluctuations, the fluctuations of the total light flux through he telescope diaphragm are weakened considerably. This is explained by the fact that for $> \sqrt{\lambda L}$, several field "inhomogeneities" with different signs can be found within the limits f the telescope diaphragm, and therefore they partially compensate one another.

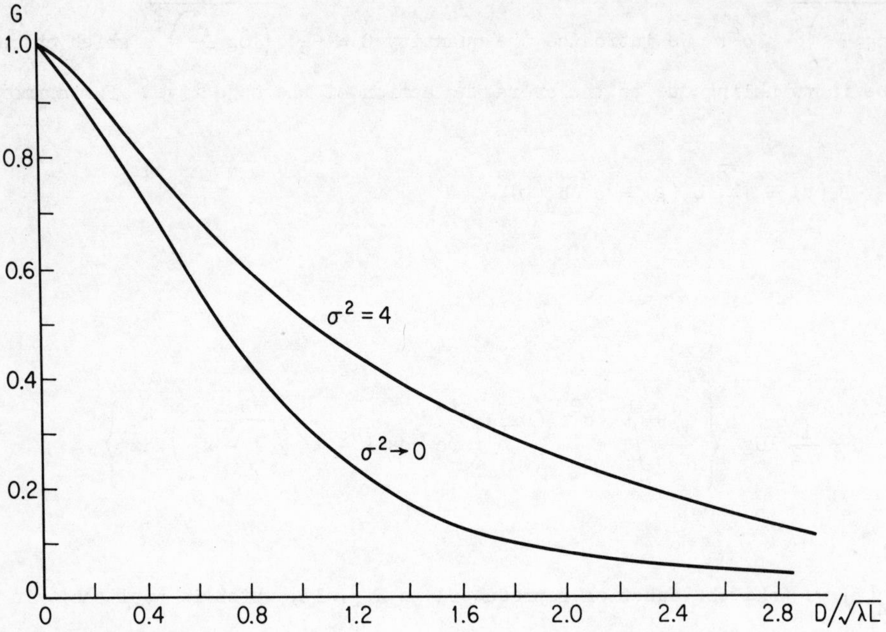

Fig. 36 The theoretical dependence of the relative decrease in the size of the total light flux through an objective on the diameter of the objective, under the condition $\ell_0 \ll \sqrt{\lambda L} \ll L_0$.

We now compare this dependence with the data observed by the Perkins Observatory [84]. Semi-annual averages of the frequency spectra of the fluctuations of the total light flux through the telescope diaphragm are given below (page 247), for different sizes of the diaphragm. Integrating these spectra, we can find the quantity $\sigma_P^2 = \overline{(P - \overline{P})^2} / \overline{P}^2$ as a function of the diameter of the diapragm [a]. The values of σ_P obtained in this way are given in Table 5.

TABLE 5

Diameter of the Diaphragm, inches	σ_P	
	Winter	Summer
1	0.476	0.373
3	0.346	0.250
6	0.189	0.160
12.5	0.098	0.080

As shown above, the quantity $\overline{[\log(P/P_0)]^2}$ is connected with σ_P^2 by the relation

$$\overline{\left(\log \frac{P}{P_0}\right)^2} = \log(1 + \sigma_P^2)$$

which is valid in the case where the quantity $\log(P/P_0)$ has a normal distribution law. We can use this formula to go over from the values of σ_P^2 just obtained to values of $\overline{[\log(P/P_0)]^2}$. As a result of these calculations, we obtain the following values (Table 6).

TABLE 6

Diameter of the Diaphragm, inches	$\overline{[\log(P/P_0)]^2}$	
	Winter	Summer
1	0.205	0.130
3	0.110	0.061
6	0.035	0.026
12.5	0.0096	0.0064

Choosing an appropriate value of the parameter $\sqrt{\lambda L}$, we can achieve very good agreement between the values of $\overline{[\log(P/P_0)]^2} = f(D)$ just obtained and the theoretical dependence. The data of Table 6 agree best with the curve in Fig. 36 (for $\sigma^2 \to 0$) when $\sqrt{\lambda L} = 3.6$ inches (winter measurements) and $\sqrt{\lambda L} = 3.2$ inches (summer measurements). In Fig. 37 we compare the quantities $\overline{[\log(P/P_0)]^2}$ (see Table 6) with the values of $G(D / \sqrt{\lambda L})$ calculated for these values of $\sqrt{\lambda L}$ and σ. Even small changes of the parameter $\sqrt{\lambda L}$ destroy the linear relation between $\overline{[\log(P/P_0)]^2}$ and $G(D / \sqrt{\lambda L})$. Thus, a comparison of the measured values of $\overline{[\log(P/P_0)]^2}$ and $G(D / \sqrt{\lambda L})$ allows us to determine the important parameter $\sqrt{\lambda L}$.

Direct measurements of the correlation distance of the fluctuations of light intensity made by Keller [98] by using two telescopes which could be moved apart, gave a value of $\sqrt{\lambda L}$ of the order of 3.5 inches.

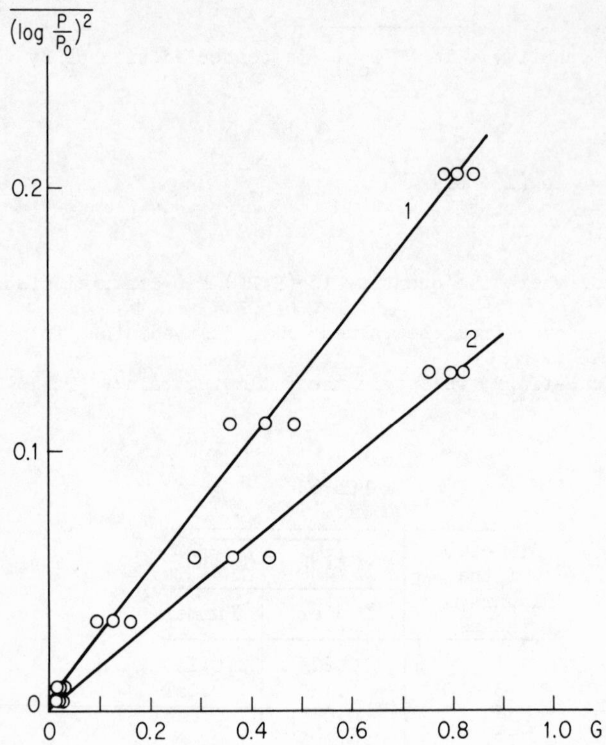

Fig. 37 Comparison of the data of Figs. 33 and 36 (1, winter; 2, summer). (To the left and right of the points joined by the straight line are points corresponding to the values of $\sqrt{\lambda L}$ changed by 1 cm. These points no longer lie on straight lines.)

We now turn to the dependence of the amount of twinkling on the star's zenith angle θ. It follows from Eq. (8.17) that

$$\sigma^2 = 4\overline{\chi^2} = 2.24\ k^{7/6} \int_0^\infty C_n^2(\vec{r})\ x^{5/6}\ dx, \tag{13.29}$$

where the integration in (13.29) is carried out along the ray directed toward the light source. Assuming that C_n^2 depends only on the height z above the earth's surface, we carry out the change of variables $x = z \sec \theta$ in (13.29), where θ is the star's zenith angle.

Then we obtain

$$\sigma^2 = \overline{\left(\log \frac{I}{I_o}\right)^2} = 2.24\, k^{7/6} (\sec\theta)^{11/6} \int_0^\infty C_n^2(z) z^{5/6} dz. \qquad (13.30)$$

Eq. (13.30) gives the mean square fluctuation of the light intensity. In order to obtain the mean square fluctuation of the light flux P through a telescope diaphragm of diameter D, we must multiply the right hand side of (13.20) by the function $G(D / \sqrt{\lambda L})$ which depends on the ratio $D / \sqrt{\lambda L}$. Since $L = H_o \sec\theta$, where H_o is the order of magnitude of the thickness of the atmospheric layer in which appreciable refractive index fluctuations occur, the function $G\left(D/\sqrt{\lambda L}\right)$ also depends on θ. Thus the formula

$$\overline{\left(\log \frac{P}{P_o}\right)^2} = \sigma^2 G\left(\frac{D}{\sqrt{\lambda L}}\right) = 2.24\, k^{7/6} (\sec\theta)^{11/6} G\left(\frac{D}{\sqrt{\lambda L}}\right) \int_0^\infty C_n^2(z) z^{5/6} dz$$

(13.31)

can lead to different types of dependence on $\sec\theta$ for different relations between D and $\sqrt{\lambda H_o}$. For example, in the case $D \gg \sqrt{\lambda H_o}$

$$G\left(\frac{D}{\sqrt{\lambda L}}\right) \propto \left(\frac{D}{\sqrt{\lambda L}}\right)^{-7/3} = D^{-7/3} (\lambda H_o)^{7/6} (\sec\theta)^{7/6}.$$

Substituting this expression in (13.31), we obtain

$$\overline{\left(\log \frac{P}{P_o}\right)^2} \propto D^{-7/3} H_o^{7/6} \sec^3\theta \int_0^\infty C_n^2(z) z^{5/6} dz. \qquad (13.32)$$

Thus, if we observe the dependence of the amount of twinkling on the zenith angle using a large diameter telescope ($D \gg \sqrt{\lambda H_o}$), we should obtain the dependence $\overline{[\log(P/P_o)]^2} \propto \sec^3\theta$.

As shown above, the quantity $\sqrt{\lambda H_o}$ is of the order of 3 to 4 inches, i.e. 8 to 10 cm. Therefore, when the diameter of the telescope diaphragm is of the order of 40 cm (15 inches), one can already expect the dependence $\sigma_P^2 \propto \sec^3\theta$ (for values of θ which are not very large, the relation $\sqrt{\lambda H_o} \sec\theta \ll D$ is still valid).

In Fig. 38 we show (in logarithmic units) the function $\sigma_P^2 = f(\sec\theta)$ obtained by Butler [89]. For $\theta < 60^\circ$, the experimental data are well approximated by the formula $\sigma \propto \sec^3\theta$. The Perkins Observatory [84] obtained the same kind of dependence, using a 12.5 inch diameter telescope (see Fig. 35).

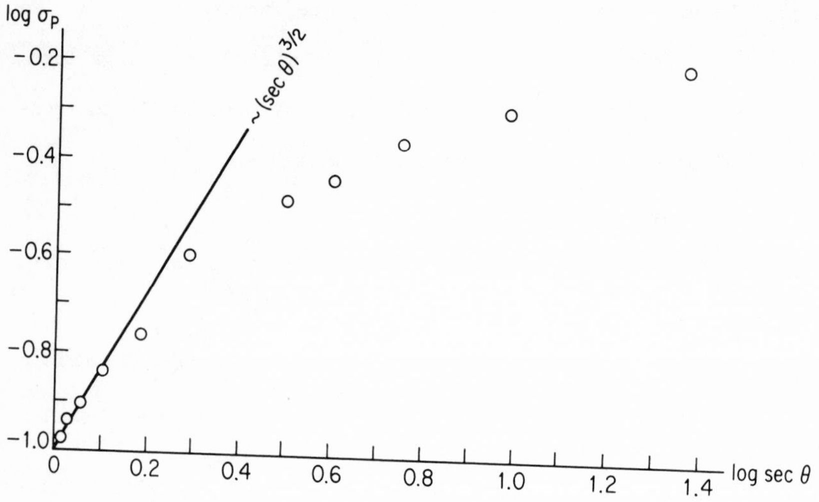

Fig. 38 Dependence of the amount of twinkling on the zenith distance, obtained by using a 15 inch diameter telescope.

For small values of $D \ll \sqrt{\lambda H_o}$ the function $G(D/\sqrt{\lambda L})$ changes inappreciably when $\sec\theta$ is changed. In this case, the dependence of $\overline{[\log(P/P_o)]^2}$ on $\sec\theta$ is determined by the factor $(\sec\theta)^{11/6}$. For intermediate values of the ratio $D/\sqrt{\lambda H_o}$, the function $\overline{[\log(P/P_o)]^2} = f(\sec\theta)$ can be approximated for small θ by the formula $\overline{[\log(P/P_o)]^2} = A(\sec\theta)^\alpha$, where $11/6 < \alpha < 3$. Fig. 34 shows the function $\sigma_P^2 = f(\sec\theta)$ obtained by the Perkins Observatory using a 3 inch diameter telescope; for small θ, σ_P^2 is satisfactorily approximated by the formula $\sigma_P^2 \propto (\sec\theta)^{1.8}$. This dependence is in good agreement with the value $\alpha = 11/6$. which ought to be expected for $D \ll \sqrt{\lambda H_o}$. According to the data of [84], $\alpha = 1.8$ for $D = 1$ inch, $\alpha = 2$ for $D = 3$ inches, $\alpha = 2.4$ for $D = 6$ inches and $\alpha = 3$ for $D = 12$ inches.

Fig. 39 shows in logarithmic units the function $\overline{[\log(P/P_o)]^2} = f(\sec\theta)$, obtained by Zhukova [88] using a 250 mm diameter telescope. The solid line indicates the theoretical curve calculated from Eq. (13.31) for $\sqrt{\lambda H_o} = 9$ cm.

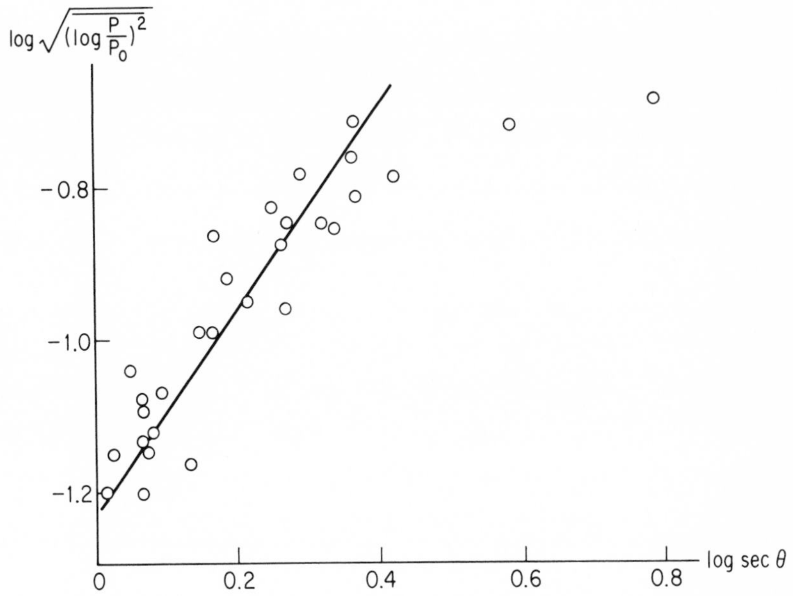

Fig. 39 The dependence of the quantity $\log\sqrt{\overline{[\log(P/P_o)]^2}}$ on the zenith distance, obtained by using a 250 mm diameter telescope.

Thus, for zenith angles which are not very large, the dependence of the amount of twinkling on the zenith distance, obtained as a result of observations, is well explained by Eq. (13.31). It should be noted that for large zenith angles, the quantity σ_P^2 depends strongly on azimuth, which greatly increases the scatter of the points in graphs of the type of Fig. 39 [e]. The agreement which we obtain between Eq. (13.31) and the function $\sigma_P^2 = f(\sec\theta)$ found as a result of observations with various values of D, assuming that the quantity $\sqrt{\lambda H_o} \sim 8$ to 10 cm, once again confirms this estimate for $\sqrt{\lambda H_o}$. Below, we shall obtain a few other estimates which also agree with the first estimate.

As follows from Eq. (13.31), the lower layers of the atmosphere, where the quantity C_n^2 is largest, do not have an important effect on the amount of twinkling, since the product $z^{5/6}C_n^2(z)$ is small for small z. Therefore, higher layers of the atmosphere, where the function $z^{5/6}C_n^2(z)$ takes larger values, play the chief role in the phenomenon of twinkling. Moreover, the height at which this function achieves its maximum can serve as a more precise definition of the quantity H_o.

We now consider the problem of the frequency spectrum of the fluctuations. Just as in the calculation of the size of the fluctuations, here we must also take into account the averaging action of the telescope objective. As we have already shown above, the small-scale components of the fluctuation field, with dimensions no greater than R (the radius of the telescope diaphragm) do not contribute appreciably to the quantity $\overline{[\log(P/P_o)]^2}$. Therefore, it can be stated that the high frequency components of the fluctuations of the light flux will also be considerably weakened. To calculate the frequency spectrum of the fluctuations of the total light flux through the telescope diaphragm, we must calculate the time autocorrelation function of the fluctuations of this quantity. As was already shown in Chapter 12, in considering the time behavior of the fluctuations, one may take into account only the motion of the refractive index inhomogeneities in the direction perpendicular to the ray (if the angle α between the direction of the ray and the wind velocity is not too small). As proved in deriving Eq. (12.2), the field at the point (L,y,z) at the time $t + \tau$ can be regarded as being the same as the field at the point $(L,y-v_y\tau,z-v_z\tau)$ at the time t. Using this argument, we can write a generalization of Eq. (13.6)

$$P(t) = \iint_{\Sigma} I(y',z')dy'dz'$$

in the form

$$P(t + \tau) = \iint_{\Sigma} I(y - v_y\tau, z - v_z\tau)dydz. \qquad (13.33)$$

Averaging these equations, subtracting them from the unaveraged equations and dividing by $\overline{P} = \overline{I}\,\Sigma$, we obtain

$$\frac{P(t) - \overline{P}}{\overline{P}} = \frac{1}{\Sigma} \iint_{\Sigma} \frac{I(y',z') - \overline{I}}{\overline{I}} dy'dz',$$

$$\frac{P(t + \tau) - \overline{P}}{\overline{P}} = \frac{1}{\Sigma} \iint_{\Sigma} \frac{I(y - v_y\tau, z - v_z\tau) - \overline{I}}{\overline{I}} dydz.$$

Multiplying these expressions together and averaging, we obtain the ratio of the time auto-correlation function of the fluctuations of the total light flux through the diaphragm of the objective to its mean value, i.e.

$$R_P(\tau) = \frac{1}{\Sigma^2(\overline{I})^2} \iint_{\Sigma}\iint_{\Sigma} B_I(\vec{r}_1 - \vec{r}_2 + \vec{v}_n\tau)d\sigma_1 d\sigma_2. \qquad (13.34)$$

We use the spectral expansion (13.16) and change the order of integration in the expression so obtained:

$$R_P(\tau) = \frac{1}{\Sigma^2(\overline{I})^2} \iint_{-\infty}^{\infty} F_I(\kappa_2,\kappa_3)d\kappa_2 d\kappa_3 \times$$

$$\times \iint_{\Sigma}\iint_{\Sigma} e^{i[\kappa_2(y_1-y_2+v_y\tau)+\kappa_3(z_1-z_2+v_z\tau)]} d\sigma_1 d\sigma_2.$$

Using the definition (13.19) of the function V_Σ, we obtain

$$R_P(\tau) = \frac{1}{(\overline{I})^2} \iint_{-\infty}^{\infty} F_I(\kappa_2,\kappa_3)|V_\Sigma(\kappa_2,\kappa_3)|^2 e^{i[\kappa_2 v_y+\kappa_3 v_z]\tau} d\kappa_2 d\kappa_3. \qquad (13.35)$$

We now find the time spectral density of the fluctuations, i.e.

$$W_P(f) = 4 \int_0^{\infty} \cos(2\pi f\tau) R_P(\tau)d\tau = 2 \int_{-\infty}^{\infty} e^{-2\pi i f\tau} R_P(\tau)d\tau.$$

Substituting the expression (13.35) into the right hand side of this formula and bearing in mind that

$$\int_{-\infty}^{\infty} e^{i\alpha\tau}d\tau = 2\pi\delta(\alpha),$$

we obtain

$$W_P(f) = \frac{4\pi}{(\bar{I})^2} \iint_{-\infty}^{\infty} F_I(\kappa_2,\kappa_3)|V_\Sigma(\kappa_2,\kappa_3)|^2 \times$$

$$\times\ \delta(2\pi f - \kappa_2 v_y - \kappa_3 v_z)d\kappa_2 d\kappa_3. \qquad (13.36)$$

We now consider the case where the diaphragm has the form of a circle of radius $R = D/2$. Using the expression (13.21) for V_Σ and bearing in mind that $F_I(\kappa_2,\kappa_3) = F_I\left(\sqrt{\kappa_2^2 + \kappa_3^2}\right)$, we introduce new variables $\kappa_2 = \kappa \cos\varphi$, $\kappa_3 = \kappa \sin\varphi$. Moreover, writing $v_y = v_n \cos\varphi_o$, $v_z = v_n \sin\varphi_o$, we obtain

$$W_P(f) = \frac{4\pi}{(\bar{I})^2} \int_0^{\infty} F_I \kappa) \left[\frac{2J_1(\kappa R)}{\kappa R}\right]^2 \kappa d\kappa \int_0^{2\pi} \delta\left[2\pi f - \kappa v_n\cos(\varphi - \varphi_o)\right]d\varphi .$$

Bearing in mind that

$$\int_0^{2\pi} \delta\left[2\pi f - \kappa v_n\cos(\varphi - \varphi_o)\right]d\varphi = \begin{cases} \dfrac{2}{\sqrt{\kappa^2 v_n^2 - 4\pi^2 f^2}} & \text{for } 4\pi^2 f^2 < \kappa^2 v_n^2 , \\ 0 & \text{for } 4\pi^2 f^2 > \kappa^2 v_n^2 , \end{cases}$$

we obtain the formula

$$W_P(f) = \frac{8\pi}{(\overline{I})^2} \int_{\frac{2\pi f}{v_n}}^{\infty} F_I(\kappa) \left[\frac{2J_1(\kappa R)}{\kappa R} \right]^2 \frac{\kappa d\kappa}{\sqrt{\kappa^2 v_n^2 - 4\pi^2 f^2}} . \tag{13.37}$$

By the change of variables $\sqrt{\kappa^2 v_n^2 - 4\pi^2 f^2} = \kappa' v_n$, this formula finally reduces to the form

$$W_P(f) = \frac{8\pi}{v_n (\overline{I})^2} \int_0^{\infty} F_I\left(\sqrt{\kappa^2 + \frac{4\pi^2 f^2}{v_n^2}}\right) \times$$

$$\times \left[\frac{2J_1 \; R\sqrt{\kappa^2 + 4\pi^2 f^2/v_n^2}}{R\sqrt{\kappa^2 + 4\pi^2 f^2/v_n^2}} \right]^2 d\kappa . \tag{13.38}$$

We consider the case where $F_I(\kappa)$ is given by Eq. (7.87), corresponding to the "two-thirds law" for the refractive index fluctuations [f]:

$$F_I(\kappa) \sim 4(\overline{I})^2 F_A(\kappa) = 4\pi(0.033)(\overline{I})^2 \, C_n^2 k^2 L \times$$

$$\times \left(1 - \frac{k}{\kappa^2 L} \sin \frac{\kappa^2 L}{k}\right) \kappa^{-11/3} . \tag{13.39}$$

Then we have

$$W_P(f) = \frac{10.4 k^2 L C_n^2}{v_n} \int_0^{\infty} \left[1 - \frac{k}{L(\kappa^2 + 4\pi^2 f^2/v_n^2)} \sin \frac{L(\kappa^2 + 4\pi^2 f^2/v_n^2)}{k} \right] \times$$

$$\times \left(\kappa^2 + \frac{4\pi^2 f^2}{v_n^2}\right)^{-11/6} \left[\frac{2J_1\left(R\sqrt{\kappa^2 + 4\pi^2 f^2/v_n^2}\right)}{R\sqrt{\kappa^2 + 4\pi^2 f^2/v_n^2}} \right]^2 d\kappa. \tag{13.40}$$

Instead of the function $W_P(f)$, it is more convenient to consider the function normalized with respect to σ^2, which characterizes the change in the frequency spectrum as a result of the averaging action of the objective. Dividing (13.40) by $\sigma^2 = 1.23C_n^2 k^{7/6} L^{11/6}$ and introducing the quantities

$$f_o = \frac{v_n}{2\pi}\sqrt{\frac{k}{L}}, \quad \Omega = f/f_o, \quad \rho = R\sqrt{\frac{k}{L}} \quad \text{and} \quad t = \kappa\sqrt{\frac{L}{k}},$$

we obtain

$$\frac{W_P}{\sigma^2} = 1.35\,\frac{1}{f_o}\int_0^\infty \left[1 - \frac{\sin(t^2 + \Omega^2)}{t^2 + \Omega^2}\right](t^2 + \Omega^2)^{-11/6} \times$$

$$\times \left[\frac{2J_1\left(\rho\sqrt{t^2 + \Omega^2}\right)}{\rho\sqrt{t^2 + \Omega^2}}\right]^2 dt\,. \tag{13.41}$$

It follows from this expression that the dimensionless quantity

$$\frac{fW_P(f)}{\sigma^2} = 1.35\Omega \int_0^\infty \left[1 - \frac{\sin(t^2 + \Omega^2)}{t^2 + \Omega^2}\right](t^2 + \Omega^2)^{-11/6} \times$$

$$\times \left[\frac{2J_1\left(\rho\sqrt{t^2 + \Omega^2}\right)}{\rho\sqrt{t^2 + \Omega^2}}\right]^2 dt \tag{13.42}$$

depends only on two dimensionless parameters: the parameter $\Omega = \sqrt{2\pi\lambda L}\, f/v_n$ considered in Chapter 12 and $\rho = \sqrt{2\pi/\lambda L}\, R$, the ratio of the radius of the diaphragm of the telescope to the correlation distance $\sqrt{\lambda L}$ of the intensity fluctuations, i.e.

$$\frac{fW_P(f)}{\sigma^2} = F(\Omega, \rho).$$

Since as $\rho \to 0$,

$$\frac{2J_1\left(\rho\sqrt{t^2+\Omega^2}\right)}{\rho\sqrt{t^2+\Omega^2}} \to 1,$$

the function $F(\Omega,0)$ coincides with the function (12.5) considered in Chapter 12.

In Fig. 40 we show, for various values of ρ, the function $f_o W_P(f)/\sigma^2$ obtained by numerical integration of Eq. (13.42). It is clear from the figure that when ρ is increased, the high frequency components drop out of the function $W_P(f)$; these components are related to the small scale components of the fluctuations of I, whose dimensions are less than R.

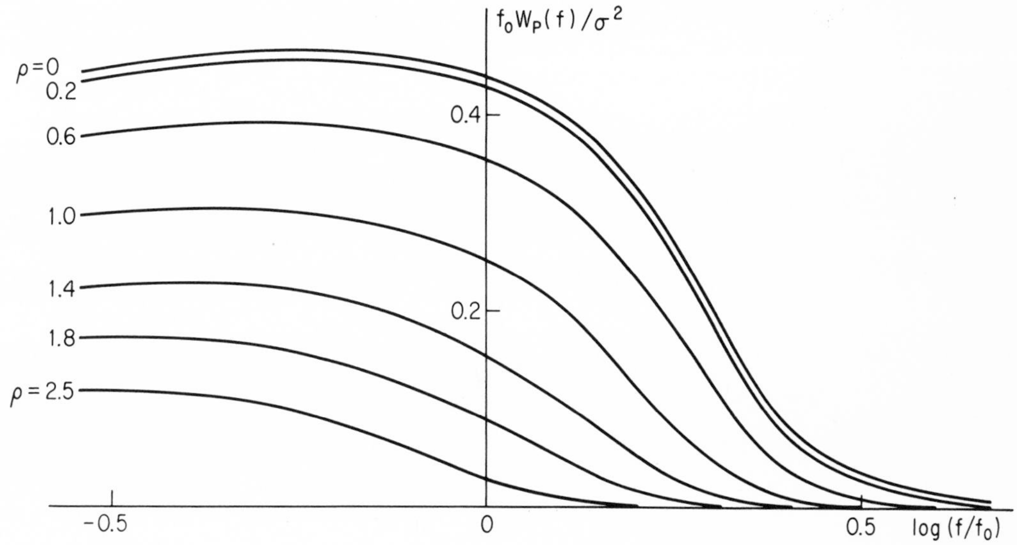

Fig. 40 Theoretical form of the frequency spectra of fluctuations of the logarithm of the total light flux through a telescope, as a function of the diameter of the telescope.

To compare the theoretical function $W_P(f)$ with experimental data, we have chosen the frequency spectra, obtained at the Perkins Observatory, of the intensity fluctuations of the light flux through a telescope with different diaphragm sizes (Figs. 41 to 44). As is clear from the figures, the experimental data agrees qualitatively with the functions $W_P(f)$ calculated above.

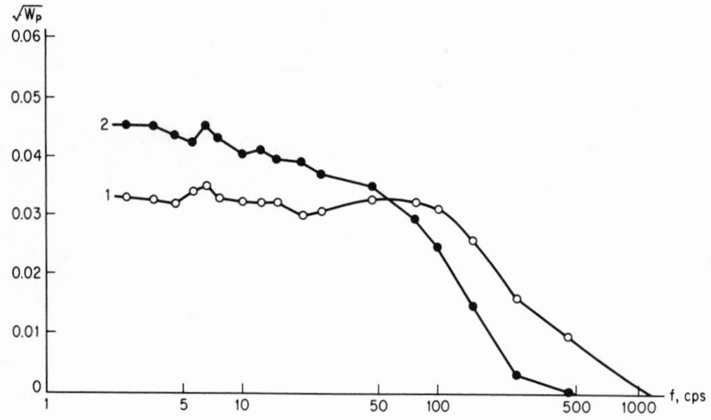

Fig. 41 Frequency spectrum of the fluctuations of total light flux through a telescope with a diaphragm of diameter 1 inch (1, winter; 2, summer).

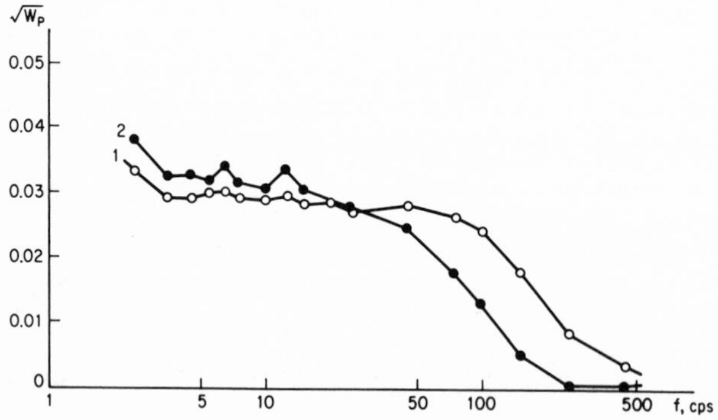

Fig. 42 Frequency spectrum of the fluctuations of total light flux through a telescope with a diaphragm of diameter 3 inches (1, winter; 2, summer).

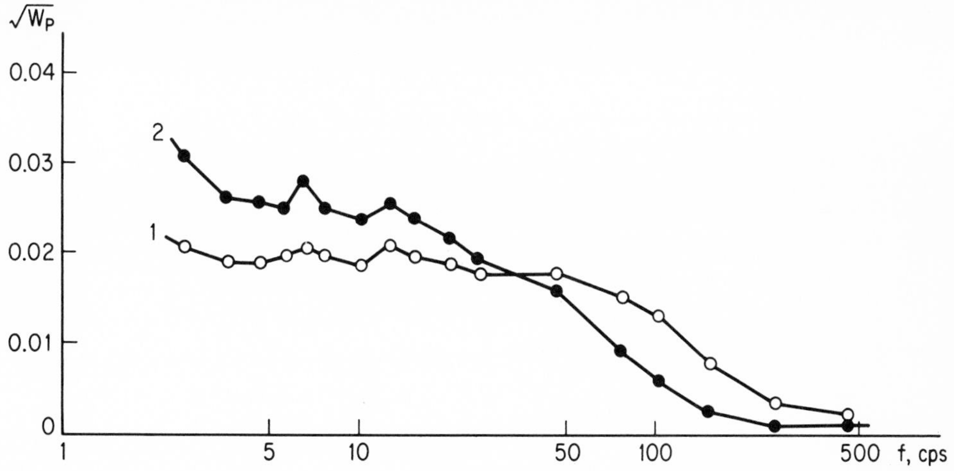

Fig. 43 Frequency spectrum of the fluctuations of total light flux through a telescope with a diaphragm of diameter 6 inches (1, winter; 2, summer).

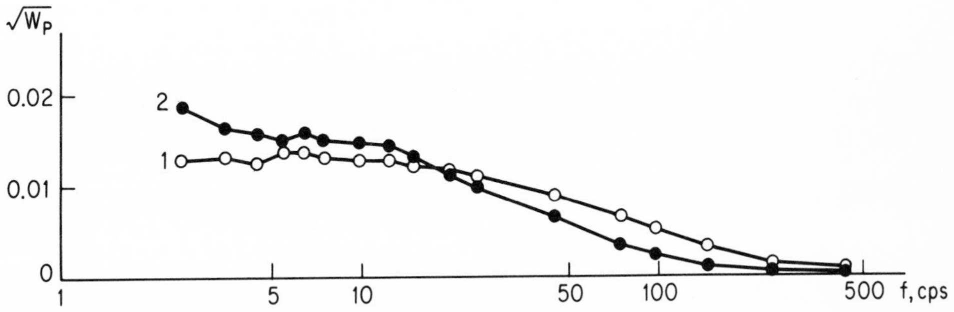

Fig. 44 Frequency spectrum of the fluctuations of total light flux through a telescope with a diaphragm of diameter 12.5 inches (1, winter; 2, summer).

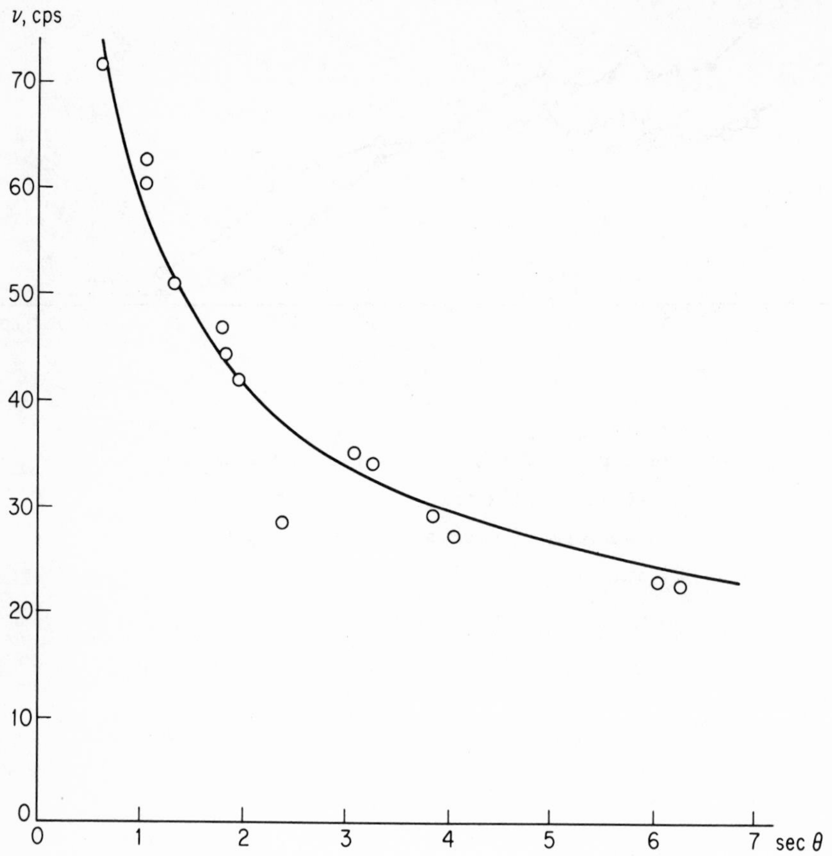

Fig. 45 Dependence of the quasifrequency of twinkling on the zenith distance.

It should be noted that the experimental data presented in Figs. 41 to 44 represent values of $W_P(f)$ which are averaged over a whole season and which pertain to different values of v_n, i.e. to different f_o. It is easy to see that when the functions $W_P(f)$ pertaining to different values of f_o are averaged, we obtain a spectrum which is wider in comparison to $W_P(f)$. Therefore, we ought not to expect quantitative agreement between the theoretical curve and average frequency spectra (of the type in Figs. 41 to 44). At the same time, the difference in wind speed is not reflected in the size of σ_P^2, which is the integral of $W_P(f)$.

In some papers, instead of detailed measurements of the frequency spectrum of fluctuations of light intensity, cruder estimates are made of the characteristic frequencies of twinkling. (For example, the average number of intersections of the function P(t) with its mean value or the average number of maxima of P(t) is determined.) Fig 45 shows the dependence obtained by Zhukova [88] for the average number (per second) ν of maxima of the function P(t) as a function of sec θ. The observations were made during the course of one night, when the wind velocity was 5 m/sec at the earth's surface and 36 m/sec at a height of 11 km. We can see a regular decrease of the quantity ν as a sec θ increases. The dependence $\nu = f(\sec\theta)$ shown in Fig. 45, which is well approximated by the curve $\nu = \text{const}\,(\sec\theta)^{-1/2}$ (the solid curve), can be simply explained from the point of view of the theory developed above. It can be shown (see [90]) that the number of maxima of the curve P(t) is determined by the smallest refractive index inhomogeneities. However, when the wind speed is appreciable and when the dimensions of these inhomogeneities are small, the "wiggles" which they produce in the curve P(t) have a very fine structure and cannot be registered by the recording device [g]. The number of strong maxima of the curve under consideration, which were actually calculated in [88], is determined by the dimensions and speed of motion of the "running shadows", which have dimensions of the order of $\sqrt{\lambda H_o \sec\theta}$ (i.e. the dimensions of the correlation distance of the intensity fluctuations). Therefore ν, the average rate of the maxima, is determined by the relation

$$\nu = \frac{\text{const}\; v_n}{\sqrt{\lambda H_o \sec\theta}}\,, \tag{13.43}$$

where v_n is the component of the wind velocity normal to the ray. It follows from Eq. (13.43) that the quantity ν is inversely proportional to $\sqrt{\sec\theta}$, which is in good agreement with the curve of Fig. 45 [h]. Thus, the curve in Fig. 45 is one of the direct corroborations of the fact that the quantity $\sqrt{\lambda L}$ is the correlation distance of the fluctuations of light intensity.

Starting from Eq. (13.43), we can once again estimate the quantity $\sqrt{\lambda H_o}$. Since the constant in (13.43) is of order unity, then taking $v_n = 20$ m/sec and $\nu = 70$ cps, we obtain $\sqrt{\lambda H_o} \sim \text{const} \times 30$ cm. This value of $\sqrt{\lambda H_o}$ agrees in order of magnitude with the estimate obtained previously.

We now briefly discuss the dependence of the amount of twinkling on the angular dimensions of the wave source. It is well known that the stars twinkle more than the planets. This fact can easily be explained with the help of the following simple considerations.

The various points of the surface of a planet are incoherent sources of light. As is well known [52], the intensity of the total field of incoherent sources is equal to the sum of the intensities of the separate sources. Denote by $i(\theta, \varphi)$ the density of the light flux in the direction (θ, φ). Then the intensity of the total field is

$$I = \int_{\Omega} i(\theta, \varphi) d\Omega, \tag{13.44}$$

where the integration extends over the solid angle subtended by the planet's disk. Averaging (13.44), we obtain

$$\overline{I} = \int_{\Omega} \overline{i(\theta, \varphi)}\, d\Omega. \tag{13.45}$$

It is natural to assume that $\overline{i}$ = const within the limits of the solid angle Ω. Then $\overline{I} = \overline{i}\, \Omega$, where the angular dimension of the planet is Ω. The fluctuations of the quantity I are given by the relation

$$I - \overline{I} = \int_{\Omega} \left[i(\theta, \varphi) - \overline{i} \right] d\Omega, \tag{13.46}$$

while the mean square intensity fluctuations are given by

$$\overline{(I - \overline{I})^2} = \int_\Omega\int_\Omega \overline{\left[i(\theta,\varphi) - \overline{i}\right]\left[i(\theta',\varphi') - \overline{i}\right]} d\Omega d\Omega'. \tag{13.47}$$

It is convenient to evaluate the size of the fluctuations by using the relative quantity

$$\frac{\overline{(I - \overline{I})^2}}{(\overline{I})^2} = \frac{1}{\Omega^2}\int_\Omega\int_\Omega \frac{\overline{i'(\theta_1,\varphi_1)i'(\theta_2,\varphi_2)}}{(\overline{i})^2} d\Omega_1 d\Omega_2, \tag{13.48}$$

where i' denotes the quantity $i - \overline{i}$. We introduce the correlation coefficient $b_i(\psi)$ of the fluctuations of the flux density i' for two directions (θ_1,φ_1) and (θ_2,φ_2) which make an angle ψ with each other:

$$b_i(\psi) = \frac{\overline{i'(\theta_1,\varphi_1)i'(\theta_2,\varphi_2)}}{\overline{(i')^2}}, \tag{13.49}$$

where $\cos\psi = \cos\theta_1 \cos\theta_2 + \sin\theta_1 \sin\theta_2 \cos(\varphi_1 - \varphi_2)$. Then we have

$$\frac{\overline{(I - \overline{I})^2}}{(\overline{I})^2} = \frac{\overline{i'^2}}{(\overline{i})^2}\frac{1}{\Omega^2}\int_\Omega\int_\Omega b_i(\psi) d\Omega_1 d\Omega_2. \tag{13.50}$$

It is obvious that

$$\frac{\overline{(I - \overline{I})^2}}{(\overline{I})^2} = \frac{\overline{i'^2}}{(\overline{i})^2}$$

for a point source. Therefore, the function

$$K_1(\Omega) = \frac{1}{\Omega^2} \iint\limits_{\Omega\ \Omega} b_1(\psi) d\Omega_1 d\Omega_2 \tag{13.51}$$

represents the relative decrease in twinkling of a planet of angular size Ω compared with a point source. In order to evaluate the function $K_1(\Omega)$, we can use the following argument.

Suppose that a point source of light is located at the observation point and that there is a circular objective with area $S = \Omega L^2$ at the boundary of the refracting atmosphere (L is the thickness of the refracting atmosphere). Then the dependence of the fluctuations of the total light flux through the objective on its dimensions is expressed by the same function $K_1(\Omega)$. On the other hand, this dependence is expressed by the function $G(D / \sqrt{\lambda L})$ calculated above (see Fig. 36).

Instead of the solid angle Ω, it is convenient to introduce the angle γ subtended by the planet's diameter. Then the diameter D of the imaginary objective will be equal to γL and the function $K_1(\Omega) = K(\lambda)$ takes the form

$$K(\gamma) = G\left(\mu \frac{\gamma L}{\sqrt{\lambda L}}\right) = G\left(\mu \sqrt{\frac{L}{\lambda}}\, \gamma\right), \tag{13.52}$$

where μ is a numerical coefficient of order unity [1]. As is well known, decrease in twinkling because of the finiteness of the angular dimensions of the light source is an effect which can already be observed for sources with angular dimensions of the order of $1'' = 0.5 \times 10^{-5}$ radians. This means that the argument of the function (13.52) is already of order unity for such a value of γ (see the curve in Fig. 36). Using this, we can make still another estimate of the quantity $\sqrt{\lambda H_0}$. From the relation $0.5 \times 10^{-5} \sqrt{H_0/\lambda} \sim 1$, we obtain $\sqrt{H_0/\lambda} \sim 2 \times 10^5$. Setting $\lambda = 0.5 \times 10^{-4}$ cm, we obtain $\sqrt{\lambda H_0} \sim 10$ cm, which is in good agreement with all previous estimates.

In conclusion, we make a numerical estimate of the parameter C_n^2 which characterizes the atmospheric refractive index fluctuations for visible light. In order to be able to estimate C_n^2 from data on the twinkling and quivering of stellar images in telescopes, it is necessary to specify somehow the profile of the quantity $C_n^2(z)$. According to some data on measurements of C_n^2 in the range of centimeter radio waves, this quantity falls off with height like z^{-2}. Therefore, we specify the profile of $C_n^2(z)$ in the form

$$C_n^2(z) = \frac{C_{n0}^2}{1 + \left(\frac{z}{H_o}\right)^2}. \tag{13.53}$$

Using Eqs. (8.27) and (8.28), we obtain

$$\overline{\left(\log \frac{P}{P_o}\right)^2} = 13.6\, k^{7/6} (\sec\theta)^{11/6}\, G\left(\frac{D}{\sqrt{\lambda H_o \sec\theta}}\right) C_{n0}^2\, H_o^{11/6}, \tag{13.54}$$

$$\overline{(\Delta\alpha)^2} = 4.6\, C_{n0}^2\, H_o\, b^{-1/3}. \tag{13.55}$$

According to experimental data, $\overline{[\log(P/P_o)]^2} = 0.205$ for $D \to 0$ and $\theta = 0$ (see Table 6). According to Kolchinski's data, at zenith $\sqrt{\overline{(\Delta\alpha)^2}} = 0.35'' = 1.7 \times 10^{-6}$ radians (this figure was obtained with a telescope of diameter $b = 40$ cm). Using the indicated data, and assuming moreover that $\lambda = 0.5$ microns, we can obtain $C_{n0} = 7 \times 10^{-9}$ cm$^{-1/3}$ from Eqs. (13.54) and (13.55), regarded as a system of equations in C_{n0}^2 and H_o.

It should be noted that the value of C_{n0} which is obtained is practically independent of how the profile of $C_n^2(z)$ is specified. For example, specifying $C_n^2(z) = C_{n0}^2 \exp(-z/H_o)$, we obtain $C_{n0} = 3.7 \times 10^{-9}$ cm$^{-1/3}$. Thus, the indicated estimate of the order of the quantity C_{n0} is reliable enough.

It is well known that the air's refractive index fluctuations in the range of visible light are mainly due to temperature fluctuations. C_n is connected with the characteristic C_T of the temperature fluctuations (C_T figures in the "two-thirds law" $\overline{(T_1 - T_2)^2} = C_T^2 r_{12}^{2/3}$ for the temperature field) by the relation

$$C_n = \frac{69 \times 10^{-6} p}{T^2} C_T, \tag{13.56}$$

where T is expressed in degrees K, C_T in degrees $cm^{-1/3}$ and p in millibars. Using this formula, we can estimate the quantity C_T. For z = 5 cm, for example, we obtain $C_T = 8 \times 10^{-3}$ degrees $cm^{-1/3}$ [j]. The estimates of C_n^2 which we obtain agree in order of magnitude with data based on measurements of the intensity of scattering of UHF waves, propagating beyond the horizon (see Chapter 4), where for heights of a few kilometers, one obtains a value of $C_T \sim 5$ to 10×10^{-3} degrees $cm^{-1/3}$. Of course, it should be noted that the estimates given are in the nature of a rough guide, which enables us to determine only orders of magnitude. Much better results could be achieved by analyzing measurements of the twinkling and quivering of stars together with simultaneous aerological measurements, like those which were made in the layer of the atmosphere near the earth. Such measurements would also enable us to evaluate more reliably the roles played by different layers of the atmosphere in the phenomena of twinkling and quivering of stars and other distant sources of radiation, and would enable us to solve a series of problems connected with long distance propagation of UHF radio waves in the troposphere.

By comparing the curves in Figs. 34, 35, 38 and 39 with each other, we can observe still another characteristic feature of the dependence $\overline{[\log(P/P_0)]^2} = f(\sec\theta)$. Beginning with values of $\theta \sim 60^\circ$, the power law growth of these functions slows down. In doing so, the curves $\overline{[\log(P/P_0)]^2} = f(\sec\theta)$ "saturate" for values of the diameter D of the telescope diaphragm which are large compared to $\sqrt{\lambda H_0}$, while for small D there even occurs a decrease in the twinkling of light as the zenith distance increases (Fig. 34). This circumstance, which is at first glance extraordinarily strange, was recently explained in the paper [99]. The issue involved here is that all the data given in Figs. 34, 35, 38 and 39 pertain to twinkling not of monochromatic but of polychromatic light. However, in point of fact, because of different atmospheric refraction for rays of different wavelengths, the rays of different colors arriving at the same observation point traverse different paths in the atmosphere. The distance between rays of different wavelengths increases as the zenith distance of the light source increases, and for $\theta \sim 60^\circ$ is of the order of 10 cm at the boundary of the refracting atmosphere. The fluctuations of light intensity are mainly produced by the atmospheric inhomogeneities with sizes of order $\sqrt{\lambda H_0}$, located within the paraboloid $\rho^2 = \lambda z \sec\theta$ surrounding the ray, which has a diameter of the order $\sqrt{\lambda H_0} \sim 10$ cm. Consequantly, if the distance between the rays exceeds $\sqrt{\lambda H_0}$ as a result of refractive differences, then the twinkling in different parts of the spectrum is uncorrelated. Therefore, for large θ, the total intensity of polychromatic light experiences smaller relative fluctuations than the intensity of monochromatic light. Moreover, if due to this "chromatic" effect, the twinkling of the polychromatic light decreases more rapidly than it increases due to growth of $L = H_0 \sec \theta$ (as is the case for small D, where, as θ increases, $\overline{[\log(P/P_0)]^2}$ grows comparatively slowly), then the total effect of the twinkling decreases as θ grows.

Detailed calculations given in [99] enable one to completely explain the character of the experimental curves in Figs. 34, 35, 38 and 39, both for large and for small values of θ.

APPENDIX*

Addendum to Chapter 5

Eqs. (5.1) and (5.3) of the text follow from more exact relations if one neglects terms involving the spatial derivatives of $\vec{u}'$ and T'. Treatments retaining such terms have been given by Lighthill [i] and Kraichnan [ii], for the case T' = 0, and by Batchelor [iii], for the general case. For T' = 0, these authors find

$$\Delta \rho' - \frac{1}{c^2}\frac{\partial^2 \rho'}{\partial t^2} = - 2\rho_o \left[\frac{\partial u_i'}{\partial x_j}\frac{\partial w_j}{\partial x_i} + u_i' \frac{\partial^2 w_j}{\partial x_i \partial x_j} \right] , \tag{A}$$

where ρ' and $\vec{w}$ are the density variation and particle velocity associated with a weak sound wave propagating in a medium of mean density ρ_o and turbulent velocity $\vec{u}'$. In contrast, one obtains from Eq. (5.3)

$$\Delta \rho' - \frac{1}{c^2}\frac{\partial^2 \rho'}{\partial t^2} = - 2\rho_o u_i' \frac{\partial^2 w_j}{\partial x_i \partial x_j} . \tag{B}$$

The part of the right side of Eq. (A) which is retained in Eq. (B) and the part which is neglected give contributions to the scattering in the first Born approximation which, in general, are of the same order of magnitude. This is because the scattering arises principally from interaction with eddy-structures of size comparable to the acoustic wave length. In particular, the angular dependence of the scattering is strongly affected. Eq. (A) implies a zero in scattered intensity at 90° which is lost in Eq. (B).

When the time dependence of $\vec{u}'$ is neglected, and when the turbulence is isotropic, one finds from Eq. (A) the differential cross-section

---

* See Translator's Preface.

$$d\sigma(\theta) = 2\pi k^4 V c^{-2} \left(\frac{\sin 2\theta}{4 \sin \frac{\theta}{2}} \right)^2 E(2k \sin \frac{\theta}{2}) d\Omega, \qquad (C)$$

which is to be contrasted with Eq. (5.23) of the text, for the case $\Phi_T = 0$. (Cf. [i], Eq. (25), and [ii], Eq. (5.14). The notation in Eq. (C) agrees with that in Eq. (5.23) of the text; E(k) is identical with $E(k)/4\pi k^2$ of [i] and with E(k)/2 of [ii].) When the time dependence of $\vec{u}'$ is taken into account [ii], there result deviations from Eq. (C) at very small scattering angles. A recent investigation of a time-dependent case has been given by Lyon [iv] (cf. also note [a] to Chapter 4).

There is an analogous change in the angular dependence of the scattering when the terms involving spatial derivatives of T', which are neglected in deriving Eq. (5.23) of the text, are reinstated. Under conditions which are plausible for atmospheric scattering, Batchelor [iii] finds that the angular dependence of $d\sigma(\theta)$ is given by $\cos^2\theta$, for the case $\vec{u}' = 0$, in contrast to Eq. (5.23).

It should be emphasized that all the corrections discussed above are negligible when the sound wave length is very small compared to scales in which there is appreciable turbulent excitation. In this case, however, the Born approximation no longer provides a valid description of the sound propagation.

REFERENCES

[i] M.J. Lighthill, Proc. Cambridge Phil. Soc., 49, 531-551 (1953).

[ii] R.H. Kraichnan, J. Acoust. Soc. Am., 25, 1096-1104 (1953); erratum, 28, 314 (1956).

[iii] G.K. Batchelor, Symposium on Naval Hydrodynamics (Editor, F.S. Sherman), Ch. XVI (Publication 515, National Academy of Sciences - National Research Council, Washington, 1957).

[iv] R.H. Lyon, J. Acoust. Soc. Am., 31, 1176-1182 (1959).

NOTES AND REMARKS*

Part I

Chapter 1

a (p.3) A detailed exposition of the topics discussed in this section can be found in the papers of Yaglom [1,4,5] and Obukhov [2,3].

b (p.3) Here and everywhere afterwards, the overbar denotes averaging over the whole set of realizations of the function f(t); in the applications, this averaging is very often replaced by time averaging or space averaging.

c (p.3) The asterisk denotes the complex conjugate. (T)

d (p.4) In addition to this definition of stationarity (stationarity in the wide sense), there is also another definition (stationarity in the narrow sense), namely, f(t) is called stationary if the distribution function (1.1) is invariant with respect to all shifts of the set of points $t_1, t_2, \ldots, t_N$ by the same amount τ. However, in practice, functions which are stationary in the wide sense are almost always stationary in the narrow sense as well, so that we need not distinguish between these two definitions. Below we shall need only the definition of stationarity in the wide sense; therefore, in the text of this book we shall always omit the explanatory phrase "in the wide sense".

e (p.4) In cases where $\overline{f(t)} \neq 0$, one can always introduce the new random function $F(t) = f(t) - \bar{f}$, for which $\overline{F(t)} = 0$.

f (p.5) $\delta(\cdot)$ denotes the Dirac delta function. (T)

g (p.5) Since $B_f(\tau) = B_f(-\tau)$, then $W(\omega) = W(-\omega)$, and the expansion (1.6) can also be written in the forms

$$B_f(\tau) = \int_{-\infty}^{\infty} \cos(\omega\tau)W(\omega)d\omega = 2\int_{0}^{\infty} \cos(\omega\tau)W(\omega)d\omega .$$

---

* See Translator's Preface.

h (p.9) We note that it can easily be shown that the mean value of f(t) must be a linear function of time (in the case of a function with stationary first increments). Thus, the assumption that f(t) is a function with stationary increments is valid only for time intervals during which the law of change of the mean value $\overline{f(t)}$ can be considered to be approximately linear. However, this leads to a much larger range of applicability than the assumption of stationarity, according to which the mean value cannot change at all. In general, in cases where the assumption that the first increments are stationary is not sufficiently accurate, we can go further and assume that the increments of some higher order are stationary [10]. In what follows, we shall assume that the first increments are stationary.

i (p.10) In fact, in beginning the study of a random process which we are not sure beforehand is stationary, it is more appropriate to construct its structure function than its correlation function. Furthermore, the practical construction of the structure function is always more reliable, since errors in the determination of the mean value $\overline{f(t)}$ do not affect the value of $D_f(\tau)$. In the case where the constructed structure function turns out to be constant for large τ, we can find $B_f(\tau)$ as well by using eq. (1.14').

j (pp.12,21) Of course, in all actual cases, the energy of the fluctuations is finite. From this it is clear that in cases where the function $W(\omega)$ becomes infinite at $\omega = 0$, the function does not have the physical meaning of energy.

k (p.13) Combine the formulas

$$K_\nu(z) = \frac{\pi}{2} \frac{1}{\sin \nu\pi} \left[I_{-\nu}(z) - I_\nu(z)\right],$$

$$I_\nu(z) = \sum_{m=0}^{\infty} \left(\frac{z}{2}\right)^{2m+\nu} \Big/ \left[m!\Gamma(m + \nu + 1)\right]$$

and

$$\Gamma(\nu)\Gamma(1 - \nu) = \frac{\pi}{\sin \nu\pi}$$

to obtain

$$K_\nu(z) = \frac{1}{2}\Gamma(\nu)(\frac{z}{2})^{-\nu} - \frac{1}{2\nu}\Gamma(1-\nu)(\frac{z}{2})^{\nu} + \dots, \quad (|\nu| < 1). \quad \text{(T)}$$

$\underline{\ell}$ (p.13) To calculate the integral

$$\int_0^\infty \omega^{-(p+1)}(1 - \cos \omega t)d\omega ,$$

one can start with the familiar expression for

$$\int_0^\infty \omega^\beta e^{-\alpha\omega} \cos \omega t \, d\omega , \quad (\beta > -1) ,$$

and then apply the principle of analytic continuation with respect to β. To obtain the final result, one has to pass to the limit $\alpha \to 0$.

$\underline{m}$ (p.16) Here $\delta(\vec{\kappa}_1 - \vec{\kappa}_2) \equiv \delta(\kappa_{1x} - \kappa_{2x})\delta(\kappa_{1y} - \kappa_{2y})\delta(\kappa_{1z} - \kappa_{2z})$ and $d\vec{\kappa} \equiv d\kappa_x d\kappa_y d\kappa_z$.

$\underline{n}$ (p.17) Equivalently, differentiating

$$V(\kappa) = \frac{1}{\pi}\int_0^\infty B_f(r) \cos \kappa r \, dr ,$$

we obtain

$$\frac{dV(\kappa)}{d\kappa} = -\frac{1}{\pi}\int_0^\infty r\, B_f(r) \sin \kappa r \, dr ,$$

so that (1.27) follows from (1.25). (T)

$\underline{o}$ (p.23)

$$\int_0^{2\pi} \cos(x \cos \theta)d\theta = 2\pi \, J_0(x),$$

where $J_0(x)$ is the Bessel function of the first kind of order zero. (T) p (p.26) Use the formula

$$\Gamma(2z) = \frac{1}{2\sqrt{\pi}} 2^{2z} \Gamma(z)\Gamma(z + \tfrac{1}{2}). \quad (T)$$

Chapter 2

a (p.31) The value of this constant must be found experimentally. In this regard see Part IV.

b (p.33) Some considerations pertaining to the behavior of D_{rr} and D_{tt} for large r are given at the end of Chapter 3.

c (p.38) If we assume that the eddies, even including infinitely large ones, are isotropic, then from the incompressibility condition and some supplementary hypotheses we can obtain the following expansion for $E(\kappa)$ for small κ [16]:

$$E(\kappa) = C\kappa^4 + O(\kappa^6).$$

However, since under actual conditions the large scale eddies are inhomogeneous and anisotropic, the applicability of this result to atmospheric turbulence is very doubtful.

d (p.38) In studying the structure functions D_{tt} and D_{rr} in wind tunnels, one does not usually succeed in obtaining large enough Reynolds numbers to make the interval (ℓ_0, L) large. [We recall that $\ell_0 \sim L/(Re)^{3/4}$.]

Chapter 3

a (p.40) The assumption that the temperature is passive is in general not true, since buoyancy forces are associated with the temperature inhomogeneities [20]. However, for a given dynamical regime of turbulence, which already takes into account the action of the mean temperature profile, the fluctuating part of the temperature can be considered to be a passive additive. Recently, Obukhov [94] investigated the departures from the "two-thirds law" for a temperature field, which are connected with its lack of passivity. As a result of an analysis of the influence of the buoyancy forces on the turbulent regime, he concludes in this paper that in regions small compared to the characteristic dimension L_k, the temperature fluctuations obey the same "two-thirds law" (see p. 46) as obeyed by passive additives. However, in the range of sizes (L_k, L_o), the "two-thirds law" is violated. The dimension L_k is defined by the relation $L_K = \epsilon^{5/4} \overline{N}^{-3/4} \beta^{-3/2}$ (where $\beta = g/T_o$, g is the acceleration due to gravity, T_o is the mean temperature, and the symbol $\overline{N}$ is explained on p. 44). In the free troposphere, L_k can be several times smaller than L_o. (The ratio L_o/L_k depends on the meteorological conditions and turns out to be equal to $L_o/L_k = (Ri)^{3/2}$, where R_i is the Richardson number; see note [e] to Chapter 10.)

b (p.41) To justify Eq. (3.4), one can give an argument similar to that made in deriving the formula $\vec{q}_m = - D \text{ grad } \overline{\vartheta}$, by just replacing the process of transport of the property ϑ due to molecular motion by the transport of ϑ due to the chaotic motion of small parcels of air.

c (p.42) We recall that we consider the motion of the fluid to be incompressible, i.e., we take div $\vec{v} = \partial v_i/\partial x_i = 0$, whence it follows that $\partial \overline{v}_i/\partial x_i = 0$ and $\partial v_i'/\partial x_i = 0$.

d (p.49) The relation (3.28) can be obtained from the Navier-Stokes equation in just the same way as the relation (3.11) was obtained from the diffusion equation. The relation (3.28) is valid in the case of stationary turbulence and actually represents a condition for the turbulence to be stationary.

e (p.51) For a more detailed account of the results of measurements of temperature fluctuations in the atmosphere, see Part IV.

f (p.52) We note that the constant $D_f^{(o)}(|\vec{r}_1 - \vec{r}_2|)$ is defined only for $|\vec{r}_1 - \vec{r}_2| \ll L_o$. To construct the spectral expansion (3.34), we must specify the function $D_f(|\vec{r}_1 - \vec{r}_2|)$ in some reasonable fashion for large values of $|\vec{r}_1 - \vec{r}_2|$. The function $\Phi_f(\vec{\kappa}, \frac{1}{2}(\vec{r}_1 + \vec{r}_2))$ which is obtained as a result has meaning only for $|\vec{\kappa}| \gg L_o^{-1}$, so that the way of specifying the function D_f does not influence the function Φ_f in the range $|\vec{\kappa}| \gg L_o^{-1}$. The situation is just the same in deriving Eq. (3.33).

g (p.53) This is true only approximately. Some details of the spectral distribution can in general depend on C_f^2. (For example, the quantity ℓ_o depends on the Reynolds number.) However, in the region $L_o^{-1} \ll \kappa \ll \ell_o^{-1}$, a universal spectral density $\Phi_f^{(o)}(\vec{\kappa})$ can still be defined. [An exact mathematical theory of random processes with smoothly varying mean haracteristics, has been given in [92] and in R.A. Silverman, "A matching theorem for locally tationary random processes", Comm. Pure Appl. Math., 12, 373 (1959). (T)]

h (p.54) Actually, as shown in the reference cited in note [g] above, in the case of a random process with smoothly varying mean characteristics, there is no need for using stochastic Fourier-Stieltjes integrals, since in general ordinary individual Fourier transforms of the sample functions of the process exist with probability one. (T)

i (p.55) This correlation between neighboring spectral components of the random field $f(\vec{r})$ is simply related to the space correlation properties of radiation scattered by $f(\vec{r})$, when the latter is a random refractive index field. In this connection, see R.A. Silverman, "Scattering of plane waves by locally homogeneous dielectric noise", Proc. Camb. Phil. Soc., 54, 530 (1958). (T)

Part II

Chapter 4

a (p.59) In Part IV, time changes of the refractive index field are taken into account for the case of line-of-sight propagation. For the case of radio scattering, time changes are taken into account in several papers, e.g., R.A. Silverman, "Fading of radio waves scattered by dielectric turbulence", J. Appl. Phys., 28, 506 (1957); erratum, ibid., 28, 922 (1957) and R.A. Silverman, "Remarks on the fading of scattered radio waves", IRE Trans. Antennas and Propagation, Vol. AP-6, 378 (1958). See also Appendix. (T)

b (p.60) Δ denotes the Laplace operator. (T)

c (p.61) Thus we neglect the fluctuations produced in the incident wave as a result of its propagation from the source of radiation to the scattering volume (see Part III).

d (p.61) It follows from (4.13) that

$$\frac{\overline{|\vec{E}_1|^2}}{\overline{|\vec{E}_0|^2}} \lesssim \frac{k^4\overline{n_1^2}}{4\pi^2 r^2} V L_0^3 ,$$

where L_0 is the outer scale of the turbulence. Thus it is not just the smallness of n_1 which justifies neglecting multiple scattering (i.e. the terms $\vec{E}_2 + \vec{E}_3 + \dots$); in fact, the random nature of the scattering medium also helps attenuate multiple scattering, for otherwise we would have V^2 instead of VL_0^3 in this estimate. For a detailed analysis of multiple scattering in a one-dimensional random medium, see I. Kay and R.A. Silverman, "Multiple scattering by a random stack of dielectric slabs", Nuovo Cimento, Vol. 9, Serie X, Supplemento No. 2, 626 (1958). (T)

e (p.64) In detail, $C_2 = iC_1 \vec{A}_o \cdot (\vec{k} - k\vec{m}) = ikC_1 \vec{A}_o \cdot \vec{m}$. (T)

f (p.64) The velocity of light is denoted by c. (T)

g (p.67) When the volume is a cube with side 2h, we have

$$F(\vec{\lambda}) = \frac{\sin \lambda_1 h}{\pi\lambda_1} \frac{\sin \lambda_2 h}{\pi\lambda_2} \frac{\sin \lambda_3 h}{\pi\lambda_3}$$

where $\vec{\lambda} = (\lambda_1, \lambda_2, \lambda_3)$. For $\vec{\lambda} = 0$, $F(0) = (h/\pi)^3$ for $\lambda_i = \pi/h$, $F(\vec{\lambda})$ vanishes, and for large λ, $F(\vec{\lambda})$ oscillates and falls off rapidly. As $h \to \infty$, $F(\vec{\lambda}) \to \delta(\vec{\lambda})$.

h (p.68) Rigorous conditions for the validity of approximations like $\tilde{\Phi}_n(\vec{\kappa}) \sim \Phi_n(\vec{\kappa})$ as $\kappa \to \infty$ are given in the one-dimensional case by H.S. Shapiro and R.A. Silverman, "Some spectral properties of weighted random processes", IRE Trans. Inform. Theory, Vol. 5, No. 3, 123 (1959). (T)

i (p.69) As is well known, an infinite sinusoidal diffraction grating produces diffraction of a plane monochromatic wave only at one angle θ (more accurately, at two equal angles $\pm\theta$), which satisfies a relation similar to (4.20). In the case of diffraction by a sinusoidal diffraction grating of finite dimensions L_o, each of the diffracted bundles has a spread $\Delta\theta \sim \lambda/L_o$. This means that finite dimensional sinusoidal diffraction gratings with neighboring periods can also participate in diffraction at the angle θ, since these lattices include the direction θ because of the spread of their diffracted bundles.

j (p.69) For example, for $\lambda = 10$ cm, $\theta = 0.033$ and H = 2 km, the size of ℓ is 3m ± 0.5 cm.

k (p.69) In the majority of applications, the condition (4.21) is met satisfactorily. Apparently, the size of L_o in the troposphere is of the order of 100 m.

ℓ (p.69) The structure of this kind of turbulence was described at the end of Chapter 3.

m (p.74) Actually, pressure fluctuations in a turbulent flow lead to much smaller refractive index fluctuations than temperature and humidity fluctuations. The corresponding estimates are easily carried out by using Eqs. (4.36) and (3.44). We do not consider here the second paper by the same authors [93], because of its incompatability with turbulence theo n (p.75) Incidentally, we note that Villars and Weisskopf were apparently unfamiliar with the papers of Obukhov [30] and Of Obukhov and Yaglom [13] on pressure fluctuations. Therefore, their way of deriving Eq. (4.39) is much more complicated than the way we give.

o (p.76) A similar expression for the effective scattering cross section of sound waves in a turbulent flow was obtained by Blokhintsev [32,33] in 1946.

p (p.77) A more detailed investigation shows that Eq. (4.47) is applicable only in the case where the quantity γ is small compared with θ. In the case where $\gamma > \theta$, the change of θ within the scattering volume begins to play an important role. In this case, the effective size of the scattering volume is determined by the angle θ rather than γ, and $V \sim D^3\theta^2$. [Taking this into account modifies the analysis of the experiment of Bullington et al. given in [31] and the conclusion drawn from it. (T)]

q (p.80) A more detailed description of the results of measurements of C_T will be given in Part IV.

Chapter 5

a (p.81) See Appendix. (T)

b (p.83) We assume, therefore, that $\vec{u}'(\vec{r})$ and $T'(\vec{r})$ do not depend on time. The actual changes of these quantities in time can be regarded as a change of the different realizations of the random fields.

c (p.84) At first glance, Eqs. (5.13) to (5.15) differ from the corresponding Eq. (4.12) for electromagnetic waves by the presence of the factor k^6 instead of k^4. However, this difference is only apparent, since in (4.12), A_0 represents the amplitude of the field E_0, whereas in (5.13), A_0 is the amplitude of the potential Π_0. However, the amplitude of the acoustic pressure or the acoustic velocity is proportional to kA_0, so that $k^6A_0^2 = k^4(kA_0)^2$.

d (p.84) In fact, in the case of isotropic turbulence, the quantity $\overline{\vec{u}'(\vec{r}_1)T'(\vec{r}_2)}$ can depend only on the vector $\vec{\rho} = \vec{r}_1 - \vec{r}_2$, i.e. has the form $A(\rho)\vec{\rho}$. Since $\mathrm{div}\,\vec{u} = 0$, then $\mathrm{div}(A(\rho)\vec{\rho}) = 3A + \rho A'(\rho) = 0$ also, whence $A = C/\rho^3$. Since for $\rho = 0$, $A(\rho)\vec{\rho}$ must be finite, it follows that $C = 0$, as was to be shown.

e (p.89) In Part IV we shall study this matter in more detail.

f (p.90)

$$E(\kappa) = \frac{1}{16\pi^3} \iiint\limits_{-\infty}^{\infty} \exp(-i\vec{\kappa}\cdot\vec{r})B_{ii}(\vec{r})dV =$$

$$= \frac{1}{4\pi^2\kappa} \int_0^{\infty} B_{ii}(r) r \sin \kappa r \, dr = \frac{1}{4\pi^2\kappa} \int_0^{\infty} r \sin \kappa r \left[B_{rr} + \frac{1}{r}\frac{d}{dr}(r^2 B_{rr})\right] dr =$$

$$= \frac{v_o^2}{12\pi^2\kappa} \left[\int_0^{\infty} e^{-r/\ell} r \sin \kappa r \, dr - \kappa \int_0^{\infty} e^{-r/\ell} r^2 \cos \kappa r \, dr\right] =$$

$$= \frac{2v_o^2\kappa^2\ell^5}{3\pi^2(1 + \kappa^2\ell^2)^3} . \quad (T)$$

g (p.90) This fact follows from the general expression for $E(\kappa)$ for small κ which is valid for homogeneous isotropic turbulence, i.e. $E(\kappa) = C\kappa^4 + \ldots$ (see note [c] to Chapter 2). However, this result is hardly applicable to atmospheric turbulence.

Chapter 6

a (p.93) Let $n = 1 + n_1$, where $|n_1| \ll 1$ and $\vec{E} = \vec{E}_o + \vec{E}_1$. Then

$$\Delta \vec{E}_o + k^2 \vec{E}_o = 0$$

and

$$\Delta \vec{E}_1 + k^2 \vec{E}_1 + 2k^2 n_1 \vec{E}_o + 2 \text{ grad } (\vec{E}_o \cdot \text{grad } n_1) = 0.$$

The last term of the equation is of order no greater than $k\vec{E}n_1/\ell_o$ and is always much less than the third term of the equation when $k\ell_o \gg 1$. Since the term 2 grad $(\vec{E}\cdot\text{grad} \log n)$ in Eq. (6.1) is related to the change of polarization as the wave propagates, this effect is small in the case $\lambda \ll \ell_o$.

b (p.94) See pages 60 - 61.

c (p.104) To avoid confusion, we agree that the differential of the variable which is integrated will be the first to appear after the integral sign.

d (p.112) We have used the formula

$$\int_0^\infty \left[1 - J_0(x)\right] x^{-p} dx = \pi \left\{ 2^p \left[\Gamma \frac{(p+1)}{2}\right]^2 \sin \frac{\pi(p-1)}{2} \right\}^{-1} \qquad (1 < p < 3),$$

which can be obtained from the familiar formula

$$\int_0^\infty J_0(ax) x^q dx = \frac{2^q}{a^{q+1}} \frac{\Gamma(\frac{1+q}{2})}{\Gamma(\frac{1-q}{2})} \qquad (-1 < q < \tfrac{1}{2})$$

by analytic continuation with respect to q.

e (p.112) A formula similar to (6.68) was first obtained by Krasilnikov [43,44]. However, in this work, instead of the "inner scale" of turbulence ℓ_0, he uses a "smoothing parameter" which is assumed to be proportional to the wavelength (without sufficient justification).

f (p.113) This is the condition for the applicability of the geometrical optics approximation; see section 6.7. (T)

g (p.118) We assume here that the "two-thirds law" is satisfied for the temperature T rather than for the potential temperature H; this is valid only in the layer of the atmosphere near the earth, where T and H are practically the same.

Chapter 7

a (p.124) This way of approximately solving the wave equation was proposed by Rytov [50] and was used by Obukhov [51] to solve the problem of amplitude and phase fluctuations.

b (p.126) The quantity $\varphi = \frac{1}{k}[\nabla S_1]$ is equal to the deviation of the direction of propagation of the perturbed wave from the initial direction. Thus, the condition (7.19) imposes a restriction on the size of the fluctuations of the propagation direction of the wave.

c (p.137) This assertion can be proved rigorously for monotone decreasing functions $\Phi_n(\kappa)$.

d (p.144) The quantity L_n is finite only when the function $B_n(r)$ decreases sufficiently rapidly as $r \to \infty$.

e (p.145) If we bear in mind that the spectral density of the correlation function of the amplitude fluctuations of the wave is small in the region $\kappa < 2\pi/\sqrt{\lambda L}$, then we can conclude that the correlation function $B_A(\rho)$ must undergo smooth oscillations of small size, with period of order $\sqrt{\lambda L}$. Because of these oscillations of the function $B_A(\rho)$, the relation (7.55) is also satisfied.

f (p.147) The function (7.73) was used in the paper of Obukhov [51] and in the related papers of Chernov [56,57] and other authors [58,61].

g (pp. 147,150) If we define, as usual, the inner scale ℓ_0 of the turbulence as

$$\ell_0 = \sqrt{-2B(0)/B''(0)},$$

and the outer scale L_n of the turbulence as

$$L_n = \frac{1}{B(0)} \int_0^\infty B(r)dr,$$

then, using (7.73), we obtain $\ell_0 = a$ and $L_n = \frac{1}{2}\sqrt{\pi}\, a$.

h (p.152) It is easy to show that

$$pA^{-p} \int_0^A (1 - \frac{\sin x}{x})x^{p-1}dx = 1 + O(A^{-p})$$

for $0 < p < 1$.

i (p.153) In calculating the integral, we used the formula

$$\int_0^\infty (1 - \frac{\sin x}{x})x^{\alpha-3}dx = \pi\left[2\Gamma(4 - \alpha) \sin \frac{\pi\alpha}{2}\right]^{-1} \qquad (0 < \alpha < 2),$$

which can be obtained from the well-known formula for

$$\int_0^\infty x^{\alpha-4} e^{-\beta x} \sin x \, dx \qquad (\alpha > 2)$$

by analytic continuation with respect to α and subsequent passage to the limit $\beta \to 0$.

[A more accurate value of the numerical constant in (7.94) is 0.307. (T)]

j (pp.153,155) By using (7.92) we can obtain asymptotic expansions of $b_A(\rho)$ for large and small values of the parameter $\rho/\sqrt{\lambda L}$. For $\ell_o \ll \rho \ll \sqrt{\lambda L}$, we have

$$b_A(\rho) \sim 1 - 2.37(k/L)^{5/6} \rho^{5/3}.$$

For $\rho \gg \sqrt{\lambda L}$, we have

$$b_A(\rho) \sim - 0.12(L/k)^{7/6} \rho^{-7/3} .$$

We recall that

$$b_A(\rho) \sim 1 - 2.80(k/L)^{5/6} \ell_o^{-1/3} \rho^2$$

for $\rho \ll \ell_o$.

k (p.153) We note that the quantity $\sqrt{\lambda L}$, for which the correlation function (7.92) has a negative minimum, corresponds to the average size of the "running shadows" which appear when one observes twinkling sources of light.

ℓ (p.160) As we have seen above, this condition is not necessary (see page 126).

Chapter 8

a (p.164) Strictly speaking, the function $\Phi_n(\vec{\kappa},\vec{r})$ can be defined uniquely only in the region $\kappa \gg 1/L_o$.

$\underline{b}$ (pp.168,170) As is well known, if the observation point is located near the surface of the lens, then the intensity of light at the point is just the same as in the absence of the lens.

$\underline{c}$ (p.169) We have

$$\overline{\chi^2} = 2^{1/6}\,\pi^2(0.033)k^{7/6}\int_0^\infty x^{-11/6}\sin^2 x\,dx.$$

To evaluate the integral, we use the formula

$$\int_0^\infty x^{-(p+1)}\sin^2 x\,dx = \frac{2^{p-2}\,\pi}{\sin\frac{\pi p}{2}\,\Gamma(p+1)} \qquad (0 < p < 2),$$

which is obtained from the formula

$$2\int_{-\infty}^{\infty}(1 - \cos\omega\tau)A|\omega|^{-(p+1)}d\omega = \frac{2A\pi}{\sin\frac{\pi p}{2}\,\Gamma(p+1)}\,\tau^p \qquad (0 < p < 2),$$

(see example b on page 13 and note $[\ell]$ to Chapter 1) by setting $\tau = 1$ and $\omega = 2x$. (T)

$\underline{d}$ (p.170) This remark can be illustrated by the following example. If a plane-parallel slab is placed on the ray path, then the phase shift produced by it does not depend on the coordinate of the slab.

Chapter 9

$\underline{a}$ (p.176) This equality acquires precise meaning after multiplying both sides by $f(\kappa_2,\kappa_3)$ and integrating with respect to κ_2 and κ_3.

$\underline{b}$ (p.177) Eq. (7.32) can be obtained from (9.13) if we carry out the integration in (9.13) on the segment from L - R to L and let L go to infinity, keeping R finite. This case corresponds to an infinitely remote source of spherical waves.

c (p.183) We note that the transition from Eq. (9.25) to (9.26) can only be carried out for a spherical wave. Therefore, the subsequent formulas do not go over to the corresponding formulas for a plane wave (see [b]).

d (p.184) In general, it can not be asserted that the integrand in Eq. (9.31) is the spectral density of the correlation function of the fluctuations of logarithmic amplitude.

e (p.185) This effect can be explained with the help of the following simple considerations. Suppose that along the path of the plane wave, at a distance L from the observation point, there is located a converging lens with a focal distance f which greatly exceeds L. It can easily be calculated that as a result, the diameter of the bundle bounded by the contour of the lens is reduced in the ratio $1:(1 + \frac{L}{f})$, as compared to the diameter of the same bundle without the lens. The compression of the bundle leads to an increase of light intensity in the ratio $1:(1 + \frac{L}{f})^2 \sim 1:(1 + \frac{2L}{f})$. Carrying out a similar calculation for the case where the source of light is located at the distance L + a from the observation point (i.e., at the distance a from the lens), where $a \ll f$, we find that the relative compression of the diameter of the bundle is equal to $1 + \frac{L}{f}\frac{a}{a + L}$. Since we always have $\frac{a}{a + L} < 1$, then the relative change of light intensity of a spherical wave is always less than the corresponding quantity for a plane wave. Thus, the amplitude fluctuations of a spherical wave must be less than the amplitude fluctuations of a plane wave.

Part IV

Chapter 10

a (p.190) Thus, fluctuations in the difference of velocities at two points which are a fixed distance r from each other, decrease when the pair of points is translated upwards. However, wind velocity fluctuations at one point do not depend on the height of the point and have the order of magnitude v_* (see [14]).

b (p.192) We note that this relation is non-linear, which makes working with the apparatus much more difficult.

c (p.192) Later (see p.203) we cite a value of the constant $\sqrt{C}$ obtained from measurements of amplitude fluctuations of sound waves. It is close to the value of 1.4 obtained by Townsend.

d (p.193) We give preference to this value of C, since it agrees better with numerous measurements of amplitude fluctuations of sound (see p. 203).

e (p.195) By a more refined argument, one can arrive at the conclusion that for stable stratification

$$\frac{C_T}{\kappa^{2/3} z^{-1/3} T_*} = f(Ri) ,$$

where Ri is the (dimensionless) Richardson number, which characterizes the extent to which the temperature stratification influences the turbulent regime. The Richardson number

$$Ri = \frac{g(\partial \overline{T}/\partial z)}{T(\partial \overline{u}/\partial z)^2}$$

depends both on the form of the temperature profile and on the form of the wind profile; here $g = 9.8$ m/sec^2.

f (p.196) The information cited above concerning temperature fluctuations in the lower troposphere is of a preliminary nature and needs further elaboration.

Chapter 11

a (pp.198,204) It can be shown that this condition is satisfied in the layer of the atmosphere near the earth if $\tau \ll \kappa z/v_*$. For z of the order of a few meters, the quantity $\kappa z/v_*$ is of the order of a few seconds.

b (p.201) See Eq. (7.94). (T)

c (p.201) Here $\overline{T}$ is written instead of T_0 (cf. Eq. (6.91)). (T)

d (p.201) This is the order of magnitude obtained if we set z = 8 m (the value given in [71]), $\overline{\Delta T} = 0$ in Eq. (11.4). (T)

Chapter 12

a (p. 209) Another justification of this conclusion can be given, based on the independence of the different spectral components of the turbulence. (However, note that the finite size of D leads to correlation between neighboring spectral components in the harmonic analysis of the integral

$$\iiint_D F(\vec{r}')n'(\vec{r}')dV'.$$

Thus, for the integral to be approximately normal, we must require that the volume in wave number space which contributes most to the integral contain many "substantially uncorrelated subvolumes". This is tantamount to the requirement that D itself contain many "substantially uncorrelated subvolumes". (T))

b (p.209) In Fig. 25 the function log x is marked off along the horizontal axis, while the function $\Phi^{-1}(x)$ is marked off along the vertical axis. Thus, the points in Fig. 25 are actually a plot of $\Phi^{-1}(F(I))$ vs. $\log(I/I_0)$. If a random variable has a normal distribution (with mean zero and variance one, say), then its empirical distribution function G(x), which is itself a random variable depending on the sample used, converges uniformly in probability to

$$\Phi(x) = (1/\sqrt{2\pi}) \int_{-\infty}^{x} \exp(-t^2/2)dt$$

as the sample size increases. Moreover, $\Phi^{-1}(\Phi(x)) = x$, so that $\Phi^{-1}(G(x))$ is approximately x. Similarly, if a positive random variable ξ has a log normal distribution, then its empirical distribution function F(x) converges (in the sense indicated) to the distribution function

$$(1/\sqrt{2\pi}) \int_{-\infty}^{\log x} \exp(-t^2/2)dt,$$

since $\text{Prob}(\xi < x) = \text{Prob}(\log \xi < \log x)$ and $\log \xi$ is normally distributed. Thus, $\Phi^{-1}(F(x))$ is approximately log x and if $\Phi^{-1}(F(x))$ is plotted against $\log(x/x_0)$, the resulting curve is approximately a straight line. (T) c (p.212) See pages 140, 153. (T)

d (p.214) We note that the theoretical curve of $R = f(\rho/\sqrt{\lambda L})$ has a zero for $\rho = 0.8\sqrt{\lambda L}$, while the experimental curve has a zero for $\rho = 1.5\sqrt{\lambda L}$. This discrepancy can evidently be explained by the fact that in the experiment described we had a geometrical bundle instead of a plane wave. It is easy to see that this ought to lead to an increase in the correlation distance.

e (p.215) As we convinced ourselves above, the chief contribution to the fluctuations of I are produced by the inhomogeneities of order $\sqrt{\lambda L}$ contained inside of the paraboloid $y^2 + z^2 = \lambda x$ with vertex at the point of observation. Displacement of an inhomogeneity along the axis of the paraboloid can appreciably affect the field I only in the case where as a result of the displacement, the ratio between the size of the inhomogeneity and the diameter of the paraboloid changes appreciably. It is easy to see that such a displacement is of order L. At the same time, a displacement of the inhomogeneity perpendicular to the axis of the paraboloid by an amount $\sqrt{\lambda L}$, which takes place in a time $\tau = \sqrt{\lambda L} / v_n$, also appreciably changes the field I. The longitudinal displacement in the time τ is equal to $\Delta x = \tau v_t = (v_t/v_n)\sqrt{\lambda L}$. If $\Delta x \ll L$, i.e. if $\alpha = v_n/v_t \gg \sqrt{\lambda/L}$, then the longitudinal displacement can be neglected.

f (p.216) We use the frequency f instead of ω and we make the expansion with respect to positive frequencies; this simplified comparison of the results of theory and experiment. The relation inverse to (1.23) has the form

$$R_A(\tau) = \int_0^\infty \cos(2\pi f\tau) W(f) df.$$

g (p.216) Cf. Eq. (1.51). (T)

h (p.218) The condition $\sqrt{\lambda L} \gg \ell_0$ has been used to set the upper limit of integration in (12.5) equal to ∞. (T)

i (p.218) The function $fW(f) / \overline{\chi^2}$ has a maximum for $f = 1.38 f_0 = 0.55 v_n / \sqrt{\lambda L}$.

j (p.221) The positions of the maxima of the theoretical and experimental curves in Fig. 31 have been deliberately made to coincide.

Chapter 13

a (p.228,236) The dependence of the amount of twinkling on the size of the diaphragm given in [84] has to be corrected, since this dependence was obtained by summing the amplitudes of the fluctuations at different frequencies instead of summing the squares of the amplitudes. Table 5 was constructed by using the integrals (given in [84], pp. 120-123) of the squares of the frequency spectra shown in Figs. 42 - 45. The date presented in Fig. 33 was constructed from Table 6.

b (p.232) In radiophysical applications V_Σ is expressed in terms of the function which describes the directivity pattern of the antenna.

c (p.233) For $\mathrm{Re}(\nu) > -\frac{1}{2}$, $\mathrm{Re}(\mu + \nu + 2) > \mathrm{Re}(\lambda + 1) > 0$, the formula

$$A = \int_0^\infty \frac{J_\mu(at)J_\nu(bt)J_\nu(ct)}{t^{\nu+\lambda}}\,dt = \frac{\left(\frac{bc}{2}\right)^\nu}{\sqrt{\pi}\,\Gamma\left(\nu+\frac{1}{2}\right)} \times$$

$$\times \int_0^\infty\int_0^\pi \frac{J_\mu(at)J_\nu(\tilde{\omega}t)\sin^{2\nu}\varphi}{\tilde{\omega}^\nu t^\lambda}\,d\varphi dt$$

is valid [53], where $\tilde{\omega} = \sqrt{b^2 + c^2 - 2bc\cos\varphi}$. Setting $\mu = 0$, $\nu = 1$, $\lambda = 0$, $b = c = R$, $a = \rho$, we obtain

$$A = \frac{R^2}{\pi} \int_0^\pi\int_0^\infty \frac{J_0(\kappa\rho)J_1\left(2\kappa R\sin\frac{\varphi}{2}\right)}{2R\sin\frac{\varphi}{2}} \sin^2\varphi\, d\varphi d\kappa.$$

But we have [53]

$$\int_0^{\infty} J_p(ux)J_{p-1}(vx)dx = \begin{cases} \dfrac{v^{p-1}}{u^p} & \text{for } v < u , \\ 0 & \text{for } v > u . \end{cases}$$

Consequently, $A = 0$ for $\rho > 2R$ and

$$A = \frac{1}{\pi} \int_{2 \text{ arc } \sin(\rho/2R)}^{\pi} \cos^2 \frac{\varphi}{2} d\varphi = \frac{1}{\pi} \left[\text{arc } \cos \frac{\rho}{2R} - \frac{\rho}{2R} \sqrt{1 - \frac{\rho^2}{4R^2}} \right]$$

for $\rho < 2R$.

d (p.234) We note that this formula could also have been obtained immediately from (13.15) by introducing the coordinates $J_1 = R \sin \psi$, $z_1 = R \cos \psi$, $J_1 - J_2 = \rho \cos \varphi$, $z_1 - z_2 = \rho \sin \varphi$, and integrating with respect to ψ, φ and R.

e (p.241) See also page 256.

f (p.245) The formula in question describes the spectrum of the fluctuations of light intensity only in the case of small fluctuations, when we neglect the difference between σ^2 and $\log (1 + \sigma^2)$.

g (p.251) The frequency of these "wiggles" is of the order of thousands of cycles per second, whereas their amplitude is negligible. Therefore they do not register when P(t) is recorded by using a relatively low frequency loop oscillograph.

h (p.252) The quantity v_n generally depends on θ also, i.e. $v_n = v\sqrt{1 - \sin^2\theta \cos^2\varphi}$, where φ is the angle between the azimuth of the star and the direction of the wind. However, the data of Fig. 45 apparently attests to the fact that at the time of the observations the quantity φ was close to 90°.

i (p.254) It should be noted that the function $G(D / \sqrt{\lambda L})$ calculated above was computed for the case of fluctuations of a plane wave, whereas in the case being considered we have a homocentric bundle of incoherent waves. This difference can slightly modify the function $G(D / \sqrt{\lambda L})$. We can take account approximately of such a modification by introducing into the argument of the function some constant factor μ of order unity.

j (p.256) The estimates of the size of the temperature fluctuations made in [91] were based on the erroneous idea that under atmospheric conditions both the case $\sqrt{\lambda H_0 \sec\theta} \ll \ell_0$ (for small θ) and the case $\sqrt{\lambda H_0 \sec\theta} \gg L_0$ (for large θ) can occur.

REFERENCES*

1. Yaglom, A.M., "Introduction to the theory of stationary random functions", Uspekhi Mat. Nauk, 7, 3 (1952). Translated into German as "Einführung in die Theorie Stationärer Zufallsfunktionen", Akademie-Verlag, Berlin (1959).

2. Obukhov, A.M., "Statistical description of continuous fields", Trudy Geofiz. Inst. Akad. Nauk SSSR, 24, 3 (1954). German translation in "Sammelband zur Statistischen Theorie der Turbulenz", Akademie-Verlag, Berlin (1958), p. 1.

3. Obukhov, A.M., "Probabilistic description of continuous fields", Ukr. Mat. Zh., 6, 37 (1954).

4. Yaglom, A.M., "Some classes of random fields in n-dimensional space, related to stationary random processes", Teor. Veroyatnost. i Primenen., 2, 242 (1957). To appear in the corresponding issue of Theory of Probability and its Applications, an English translation prepared and published by the Society for Industrial and Applied Mathematics, Philadelphia, Pa.

5. Yaglom, A.M., "Correlation theory of continuous processes and fields, with applications to the problem of statistical extrapolation of time series and to turbulence theory", Dissertation at the Geophysics Institute of the Academy of Sciences of the USSR, Moscow (1955).

6. Khinchin, A.Ya., "Correlation theory of stationary random processes", Uspekhi Mat. Nauk, No. 5 (1938).

7. Bershtein, I.L., "Amplitude and phase fluctuations of a vacuum-tube oscillator", Izv. Akad. Nauk SSSR, Ser. Fiz., 14, 2 (1950).

8. Kolmogorov, A.N., "The local structure of turbulence in incompressible viscous fluid for very large Reynolds' numbers", Doklady Akad. Nauk SSSR, 30, 301 (1941). German translation in "Sammelband zur Statistischen Theorie der Turbulenz", Akademie-Verlag, Berlin (1958), p. 71.

9. Kolmogorov, A.N., "Dissipation of energy in locally isotropic turbulence", Doklady Akad. Nauk SSSR, 32, 16 (1941). German translation in "Sammelband zur Statistischen Theorie der Turbulenz", Akademie-Verlag, Berlin (1958), p. 77.

10. Yaglom, A.M., "Correlation theory of processes with random stationary n'th increments", Mat. Sb., 37, 141 (1955); English translation in American Mathematical Society Translations, Series 2, Vol. 8, p. 87, Providence, R.I. (1958).

11. Obukhov, A.M., "On the distribution of energy in the spectrum of turbulent flow", Doklady Akad. Nauk SSSR, 32, 19 (1941).

12. Obukhov, A.M., "On the distribution of energy in the spectrum of turbulent flow", Izv. Akad. Nauk SSSR, Ser. Geograf. Geofiz., 5, 453 (1941). German translation in "Sammelband zur Statistischen Theorie der Turbulenz", Akademie-Verlag, Berlin (1958), p. 83.

13. Obukhov, A.M. and Yaglom, A.M., "The microstructure of turbulent flow", Prikl. Mat. Mekh., 15, 3 (1951). Translated into English as Tech. Memor. 1350, National Advisory Committee for Aeronautics, Washington (1953). German translation in "Sammelband zur Statistischen Theorie der Turbulenz", Akademie-Verlag, Berlin (1958), p. 97.

---

* See Translator's Preface.

14. Landau, L.D. and Lifshitz, E.M., "Fluid Mechanics", Addison-Wesley, Reading, Mass. (1959).

15. Loitsyanski, L.G., "Some basic laws of isotropic turbulent flow", Trudy Aero. Gidro. Inst., No. 440, Moscow (1939). Translated into English as Tech. Memo. No. 1079, Nat. Adv. Comm. Aero., Washington, D.C.

16. Batchelor, G.K., "The Theory of Homogeneous Turbulence", Cambridge Univ. Press (1953).

17. Obukhov, A.M., "Characteristics of the microstructure of the wind in the layer of the atmosphere near the earth", Izv. Akad. Nauk SSSR, Ser. Geofiz., No. 3, 49 (1951). German translation in "Sammelband zur Statistischen Theorie der Turbulenz", Akademie-Verlag, Berlin (1958), p. 173.

18. Obukhov, A.M., Pinus, N.Z. and Krechmer, S.I., "Results of experimental investigations of microturbulence in the free atmosphere", Trudy Tsent. Aerolog. Observ., No. 6, 174 (1951).

19. Kramer, M., "Turbulence measurements in flight", J. Aero. Sci., 20, 655 (1953).

20. Brunt, D., "Physical and Dynamical Meteorology", 2d ed., Cambridge Univ. Press (1939).

21. Obukhov, A.M., "Structure of the temperature field in a turbulent flow", Izv. Akad. Nauk SSSR, Ser. Geograf. Geofiz., 13, 58 (1949). German translation in "Sammelband zur Statistischen Theorie der Turbulenz", Akademie-Verlag, Berlin (1958), p. 127.

22. Yaglom, A.M., "On the local structure of the temperature field in a turbulent flow", Doklady Akad. Nauk SSSR, 69, 743 (1949). German translation in "Sammelband zur Statistischen Theorie der Turbulenz", Akademie-Verlag, Berlin (1948), p. 141.

23. Laikhtman, D.L., "A new method of determining the coefficient of turbulent viscosity in the boundary layer of the atmosphere", Trudy Glav. Geofiz. Observ., No. 37 (1952).

24. Laikhtman, D.L., "Some properties of the boundary layer of the atmosphere", Trudy Glav. Geofiz. Observ., No. 56 (1956).

25. Churinova, M.P., "Experimental determination of the turbulence coefficient from temperature and wind soundings", Trudy Glav. Geofiz. Observ., No. 63 (1956).

26. Matveyev, L.T., "Quantitative characteristics of turbulent exchange in the upper troposphere and lower stratosphere", Izv. Akad. Nauk SSSR, Ser. Geofiz., No. 7 (1958).

27. Booker, H.G. and Gordon, W.E., "A theory of radio scattering in the troposphere", Proc. Inst. Radio Engrs. 38, 401 (1950).

28. Krasilnikov, V.A., Dissertation, Moscow State University, Moscow (1952).

29. Villars, F. and Weisskopf, V.F., "The scattering of electromagnetic waves by turbulent atmospheric fluctuations", Phys. Rev., 94, 232 (1954).

30. Obukhov, A.M., "Pressure fluctuations in a turbulent flow", Doklady Akad. Nauk SSSR, 66, 17 (1949).

31. Silverman, R.A., "Turbulent mixing theory applied to radio scattering", J. Appl. Phys., 27, 699 (1956).

32. Blokhintsev, D.I., "Propagation of sound in a turbulent flow", Doklady Akad. Nauk SSSR, 46, 136 (1945).

33. Blokhintsev, D.I., "Acoustics of an inhomogeneous moving medium", Gostekhizdat, Moscow (1946).

34. Chisholm, J.H., Portmann, P.A., de Bettencourt, J.T. and Roche, J.F., "Investigations of angular scattering and multipath properties of tropospheric propagation of short radio waves beyond the horizon", Proc. Inst. Radio Engrs., 43, 1317 (1955).

35. Bullington, K., "Radio transmission beyond the horizon in the 40 to 4000 mc band", Proc. Inst. Radio Engrs., 41, 132 (1953).

36. Krechmer, S.I., "Investigations of microfluctuations of the temperature field in the atmosphere", Doklady Akad. Nauk SSSR, 84, 55 (1952).

37. Tatarski, V.I., "Microstructure of the temperature field in the layer of the atmosphere near the earth", Izv. Akad. Nauk SSSR, Ser. Geofiz., No. 6, 689 (1956).

38. Obukhov, A.M., "On the scattering of sound in a turbulent flow", Doklady Akad. Nauk SSSR, 30, 611 (1941).

39. Tatarski, V.I., "On the theory of propagation of sound waves in a turbulent flow", Zh. Eksp. Teor. Fiz., 25, 74 (1953).

40. Andreyev, N.N. and Rusakov, I.G., "Acoustics of a Moving Medium", Gostekhizdat, Moscow (1934).

41. Pekeris, C.L., "Note on the scattering of radiation in an inhomogeneous medium", Phys. Rev., 71, 268 (1947).

42. Krasilnikov, V.A., "On the propagation of sound in a turbulent atmosphere", Doklady Akad. Nauk SSSR, 47, 486 (1945).

43. Krasilnikov, V.A., "On amplitude fluctuations of sound propagating in a turbulent atmosphere", Doklady Akad. Nauk SSSR, 58, 1353 (1947).

44. Krasilnikov, V.A., "On the influence of refractive index fluctuations in the atmosphere on the propagation of ultrashort radio waves", Izv. Akad. Nauk SSSR, Ser. Geograf. Geofiz., 13, 33 (1949).

45. Bergmann, P.G., "Propagation of radiation in a medium with random inhomogeneities", Phys. Rev., 70, 486 (1946).

46. Tatarski, V.I., "On phase fluctuations of sound in a turbulent medium", Izv. Akad. Nauk SSSR, Ser. Geofiz., No. 3, 252 (1953).

47. Landau, L.D. and Lifshitz, E.M., "The Classical Theory of Fields", Addison-Wesley, Reading, Mass. (1959).

48. Tatarski, V.I., "On the criterion for the applicability of geometrical optics in problems of wave propagation in a medium with weak refractive index inhomogeneities", Zh. Eksp. Teor. Fiz., 25, 84 (1953).

49. Ellison, T.H., "The propagation of sound waves through a medium with very small variations in refractive index", J. Atmos. Terr. Phys., 2, 14 (1951).

50. Rytov, S.M., "Diffraction of light by ultrasonic waves", Izv. Akad. Nauk SSSR, Ser. Fiz., No. 2, 223 (1937).

51. Obukhov, A.M., "On the influence of weak atmospheric inhomogeneities on the propagation of sound and light", Izv. Akad. Nauk SSSR, Ser. Geofiz., No. 2, 155 (1953). German translation in "Sammelband zur Statistischen Theorie der Turbulenz", Akademie-Verlag, Berlin (1958). p. 157.

52. Gorelik, G.S., "Oscillations and Waves", Gostekhizdat, Moscow (1950).

53. Watson, G.N., "A Treatise on the Theory of Bessel Functions", 2d ed., Cambridge Univ. Press (1958).

54. Tatarski, V.I., "On amplitude and phase fluctuations of a wave propagating in a weakly inhomogeneous atmosphere", Doklady Akad. Nauk SSSR, 107, 245 (1956).

55. Chernov, L.A., "Correlation of amplitude and phase fluctuations of a wave propagating in a medium with random inhomogeneities", Akust. Zh., 1, 89 (1955).

56. Chernov, L.A., "Correlation properties of a wave in a medium with random inhomogeneities", Akust. Zh., 2, 211 (1956).

57. Chernov, L.A., "Correlation of field fluctuations", Akust. Zh., 3, 192 (1957).

58. Karavainikov, V.N., "Amplitude and phase fluctuations in a spherical wave", Akust. Zh., 3, 165 (1957).

59. Tatarski, V.I., "On the propagation of waves in a locally isotropic turbulent medium with smoothly varying characteristics", Doklady Akad. Nauk SSSR, 120, 289 (1958).

60. Tatarski, V.I., "Micro-inhomogeneities of the temperature field and fluctuation phenomena of waves propagating in the atmosphere", Dissertation, Akust. Inst. Akad. Nauk SSSR, Moscow (1957).

61. Li Sek-Zu, "On the propagation of sound in a medium with random inhomogeneities", Dissertation, Kim Il-Sung Institute, (?), Pyongyang, North Korea (1957).

62. Krechmer, S.I., "Experimental determination of the characteristics of temperature fluctuations in the atmosphere", Trudy Tsent. Aerolog. Observ., No. 16, 39 (1956).

63. Shiotani, M., "On the fluctuation of the temperature and turbulent structure near the ground", J. Meteorol. Soc. Japan, 33, 117 (1955).

64. Monin, A.S. and Obukhov, A.M., "Dimensionless characteristics of turbulence in the layer of the atmosphere near the earth", Doklady Akad. Nauk SSSR, 93, 257 (1953).

65. Monin, A.S. and Obukhov, A.M., "Basic laws of turbulent mixing in the layer of the atmosphere near the earth", Trudy Geofiz. Inst. Akad. Nauk SSSR, No. 24, 163 (1954). German translation in "Sammelband zur Statistischen Theorie der Turbulenz", Akademie-Verlag, Berlin (1958). p. 199.

66. Yaglom, A.M., "On taking account of the inertia of meteorological apparatus in making measurements in the turbulent atmosphere", Trudy Geofiz. Inst. Akad. Nauk SSSR, No. 24, 112 (1954).

67. Perepelkina, A.V., "Some results of investigations of turbulent fluctuations of the temperature and the vertical component of the wind velocity", Izv. Akad. Nauk SSSR, Ser. Geofiz., No. 6, 765 (1957).

68. Krechmer, S.I., "Methods for measuring microfluctuations of wind velocity and temperature in the atmosphere", Trudy Geofiz. Inst. Akad. Nauk SSSR, No. 24, 43 (1954).

69. Gödecke, K., "Messungen der atmosphärischen Turbulenz", Ann. d. Hydrographie, 10, 400 (1936).

70. Townsend, A.A., "Experimental evidence for the theory of local isotropy", Proc. Camb. Phil. Soc., 44, 560 (1948).

71. Krasilnikov, V.A. and Ivanov-Shyts, K.M., "Some experiments on the propagation of sound in the atmosphere", Doklady Akad. Nauk SSSR, 67, 639 (1949).

72. Krasilnikov, V.A., "On phase fluctuations of ultrasonic waves propagating in the layer of the atmosphere near the earth", Doklady Akad. Nauk SSSR, 88, 657 (1953).

73. Suchkov, B.A., "Amplitude fluctuations of sound in a turbulent medium", Akust. Zh., 4, 85 (1958).

74. Tatarski, V.I., Gurvich, A.S., Kallistratova, M.A. and Terenteva, L.V., "On the influence of meteorological conditions on the intensity of twinkling of light in the layer of the atmosphere near the earth", Astronom. Zh., 35, 123 (1958).

75. Gurvich, A.S., Tatarski, V.I. and Tsvang, L.R., "Experimental investigation of the statistical characteristics of the twinkling of a terrestrial light source", Doklady Akad. Nauk SSSR, 123, 655 (1958).

76. Bovsheverov, V.M., Gurvich, A.S., Tatarski, V.I. and Tsvang, L.R., "Apparatus for the statistical analysis of turbulence", in press.

77. Arley, N. and Buch, K.R., "Introduction to the Theory of Probability and Statistics", Wiley, New York (1950).

78. Ellison, M.A. and Seddon, H., "Some experiments on the scintillation of stars and planets", Monthly Notices Roy. Astron. Soc., 112, 73 (1952).

79. Van Isacker, J., "The analysis of stellar scintillation phenomena", Quart. J. Roy. Meteorol. Soc., 80, 251 (1954).

80. Kolchinski, I.G., "On the amplitude of quivering of stellar images in telescopes as a function of the zenith distance", Astron. Zh., 29, 350 (1952).

81. Kolchinski, I.G., "Some results of observations of quivering of stellar images at the site of the Central Astronomical Observatory of the Academy of Sciences of the USSR at Goloseyev", Astron. Zh., 34, 638 (1957).

82. Krasilnikov, V.A., "On fluctuations of the angle of arrival in the phenomenon of twinkling of stars", Doklady Akad. Nauk SSSR, 65, 291 (1949).

83. Butler, H.E., "Observations of stellar scintillation", Quart. J. Roy. Meteorol. Soc., 80, 241 (1954).

84. Protheroe, W.M., "Preliminary report on stellar scintillation", Contrib. Perkins Observ., Ser. 2, No. 4, 127 (1955).

85. Nettlebald, F., "Recordings of scintillations", Observatory, 71, 111 (1951).

86. Mikesell, A.H., Hoag, A.A. and Hall, J.S., "The scintillation of starlight", J. Opt. Soc. Am., 41, 689 (1951).

87. Butler, H.E., "Observations of stellar scintillation", Proc. Roy. Irish Acad. A, 54, 321 (1952).

88. Zhukova, L.N., "Recording of stellar scintillation by the photoelectric method", Izv. Glav. Astron. Observ. Akad. Nauk SSSR, 21, No. 162 (1958).

89. Megaw, E.C.S., "Interpretation of stellar scintillation", Quart. J. Roy. Meteorol. Soc., 80, 248 (1954).

90. Levin, B.R., "The Theory of Random Processes and its Application to Radio Engineering", Izdat. "Sov. Radio", Moscow (1957).

91. Yudalevich, F.F., "Some problems connected with the interpretation of the phenomenon of stellar scintillation", Doklady Akad. Nauk SSSR, 106, 441 (1956).

92. Silverman, R.A., "Locally stationary random processes", IRE Trans. Information Th., Vol. IT-3, No. 3, 182 (1957).

93. Villars, F. and Weisskopf, V.F., "On the scattering of radio waves by turbulent fluctuations of the atmosphere", Proc. Inst. Radio Engrs., 43, 1232 (1958).

94. Obukhov, A.M., "On the influence of buoyancy forces on the structure of the temperature field in a turbulent flow", Doklady Akad. Nauk SSSR, 125, 1246 (1959).

95. Crain, C.M., "Survey of airborne microwave refractometer measurements", Proc. Inst. Radio Engrs., 43, 1405 (1955).

96. Bolgiano, R., "The role of turbulent mixing in scatter propagation", IRE Trans. Anten. Prop., Vol. AP-6, No. 2, 161 (1958).

97. Kallistratova, M.A., "Experimental investigation of the scattering of sound in the turbulent atmosphere", Doklady Akad. Nauk SSSR, 125, 69 (1959).

98. Keller, G., "Relation between the structure of stellar shadow band patterns and stellar scintillation", J. Opt. Soc. Am., 45, 845 (1955).

99. Tatarski, V.I. and Zhukova, L.N., "On chromatic twinkling of stars", Doklady Akad. Nauk SSSR, 124, 567 (1959).

CATALOGUE OF DOVER BOOKS

ENGINEERING AND TECHNOLOGY

General and mathematical

ENGINEERING MATHEMATICS, Kenneth S. Miller. A text for graduate students of engineering to strengthen their mathematical background in differential equations, etc. Mathematical steps very explicitly indicated. Contents: Determinants and Matrices, Integrals, Linear Differential Equations, Fourier Series and Integrals, Laplace Transform, Network Theory, Random Function . . . all vital requisites for advanced modern engineering studies. Unabridged republication. Appendices: Borel Sets; Riemann-Stieltjes Integral; Fourier Series and Integrals. Index. References at Chapter Ends. xii + 417pp. 6 x 8½. S1121 Paperbound **$2.00**

MATHEMATICAL ENGINEERING ANALYSIS, Rufus Oldenburger. A book designed to assist the research engineer and scientist in making the transition from physical engineering situations to the corresponding mathematics. Scores of common practical situations found in all major fields of physics are supplied with their correct mathematical formulations—applications to automobile springs and shock absorbers, clocks, throttle torque of diesel engines, resistance networks, capacitors, transmission lines, microphones, neon tubes, gasoline engines, refrigeration cycles, etc. Each section reviews basic principles of underlying various fields: mechanics of rigid bodies, electricity and magnetism, heat, elasticity, fluid mechanics, and aerodynamics. Comprehensive and eminently useful. Index. 169 problems, answers. 200 photos and diagrams. xiv + 426pp. 5⅜ x 8½. S919 Paperbound **$2.50**

MATHEMATICS OF MODERN ENGINEERING, E. G. Keller and R. E. Doherty. Written for the Advanced Course in Engineering of the General Electric Corporation, deals with the engineering use of determinants, tensors, the Heaviside operational calculus, dyadics, the calculus of variations, etc. Presents underlying principles fully, but purpose is to teach engineers to deal with modern engineering problems, and emphasis is on the perennial engineering attack of set-up and solve. Indexes. Over 185 figures and tables. Hundreds of exercises, problems, and worked-out examples. References. Two volume set. Total of xxxiii + 623pp. 5⅜ x 8.
S734 Vol I Paperbound **$1.85**
S735 Vol II Paperbound **$1.85**
The set **$3.70**

MATHEMATICAL METHODS FOR SCIENTISTS AND ENGINEERS, L. P. Smith. For scientists and engineers, as well as advanced math students. Full investigation of methods and practical description of conditions under which each should be used. Elements of real functions, differential and integral calculus, space geometry, theory of residues, vector and tensor analysis, series of Bessel functions, etc. Each method illustrated by completely-worked-out examples, mostly from scientific literature. 368 graded unsolved problems. 100 diagrams. x + 453pp. 5⅝ x 8⅜. S220 Paperbound **$2.00**

THEORY OF FUNCTIONS AS APPLIED TO ENGINEERING PROBLEMS, edited by R. Rothe, F. Ollendorff, and K. Pohlhausen. A series of lectures given at the Berlin Institute of Technology that shows the specific applications of function theory in electrical and allied fields of engineering. Six lectures provide the elements of function theory in a simple and practical form, covering complex quantities and variables, integration in the complex plane, residue theorems, etc. Then 5 lectures show the exact uses of this powerful mathematical tool, with full discussions of problem methods. Index. Bibliography. 108 figures. x + 189pp. 5⅜ x 8.
S733 Paperbound **$1.35**

Aerodynamics and hydrodynamics

AIRPLANE STRUCTURAL ANALYSIS AND DESIGN, E. E. Sechler and L. G. Dunn. Systematic authoritative book which summarizes a large amount of theoretical and experimental work on structural analysis and design. Strong on classical subsonic material still basic to much aeronautic design . . . remains a highly useful source of information. Covers such areas as layout of the airplane, applied and design loads, stress-strain relationships for stable structures, truss and frame analysis, the problem of instability, the ultimate strength of stiffened flat sheet, analysis of cylindrical structures, wings and control surfaces, fuselage analysis, engine mounts, landing gears, etc. Originally published as part of the CALCIT Aeronautical Series. 256 Illustrations. 47 study problems. Indexes. xi + 420pp. 5⅜ x 8½.
S1043 Paperbound **$2.25**

FUNDAMENTALS OF HYDRO- AND AEROMECHANICS, L. Prandtl and O. G. Tietjens. The well-known standard work based upon Prandtl's lectures at Goettingen. Wherever possible hydrodynamics theory is referred to practical considerations in hydraulics, with the view of unifying theory and experience. Presentation is extremely clear and though primarily physical, mathematical proofs are rigorous and use vector analysis to a considerable extent. An Engineering Society Monograph, 1934. 186 figures. Index. xvi + 270pp. 5⅜ x 8.
S374 Paperbound **$1.85**

FLUID MECHANICS FOR HYDRAULIC ENGINEERS, H. Rouse. Standard work that gives a coherent picture of fluid mechanics from the point of view of the hydraulic engineer. Based on courses given to civil and mechanical engineering students at Columbia and the California Institute of Technology, this work covers every basic principle, method, equation, or theory of interest to the hydraulic engineer. Much of the material, diagrams, charts, etc., in this self-contained text are not duplicated elsewhere. Covers irrotational motion, conformal mapping, problems in laminar motion, fluid turbulence, flow around immersed bodies, transportation of sediment, general charcteristics of wave phenomena, gravity waves in open channels, etc. Index. Appendix of physical properties of common fluids. Frontispiece + 245 figures and photographs. xvi + 422pp. 5⅜ x 8. S729 Paperbound **$2.25**

WATERHAMMER ANALYSIS, John Parmakian. Valuable exposition of the graphical method of solving waterhammer problems by Assistant Chief Designing Engineer, U.S. Bureau of Reclamation. Discussions of rigid and elastic water column theory, velocity of waterhammer waves, theory of graphical waterhammer analysis for gate operation, closings, openings, rapid and slow movements, etc., waterhammer in pump discharge caused by power failure, waterhammer analysis for compound pipes, and numerous related problems. "With a concise and lucid style, clear printing, adequate bibliography and graphs for approximate solutions at the project stage, it fills a vacant place in waterhammer literature," WATER POWER. 43 problems. Bibliography. Index. 113 illustrations. xiv + 161pp. 5⅜ x 8½.
S1061 Paperbound **$1.65**

AERODYNAMIC THEORY: A GENERAL REVIEW OF PROGRESS, William F. Durand, editor-in-chief. A monumental joint effort by the world's leading authorities prepared under a grant of the Guggenheim Fund for the Promotion of Aeronautics. Intended to provide the student and aeronautic designer with the theoretical and experimental background of aeronautics. Never equalled for breadth, depth, reliability. Contains discussions of special mathematical topics not usually taught in the engineering or technical courses. Also: an extended two-part treatise on Fluid Mechanics, discussions of aerodynamics of perfect fluids, analyses of experiments with wind tunnels, applied airfoil theory, the non-lifting system of the airplane, the air propeller, hydrodynamics of boats and floats, the aerodynamics of cooling, etc. Contributing experts include Munk, Giacomelli, Prandtl, Toussaint, Von Karman, Klemperer, among others. Unabridged republication. 6 volumes bound as 3. Total of 1,012 figures, 12 plates. Total of 2,186pp. Bibliographies. Notes. Indices. 5⅜ x 8.
S328-S330 Paperbound The Set **$13.50**

APPLIED HYDRO- AND AEROMECHANICS, L. Prandtl and O. G. Tietjens. Presents, for the most part, methods which will be valuable to engineers. Covers flow in pipes, boundary layers, airfoil theory, entry conditions, turbulent flow in pipes, and the boundary layer, determining drag from measurements of pressure and velocity, etc. "Will be welcomed by all students of aerodynamics," NATURE. Unabridged, unaltered. An Engineering Society Monograph, 1934. Index. 226 figures, 28 photographic plates illustrating flow patterns. xvi + 311pp. 5⅜ x 8.
S375 Paperbound **$2.00**

SUPERSONIC AERODYNAMICS, E. R. C. Miles. Valuable theoretical introduction to the supersonic domain, with emphasis on mathematical tools and principles, for practicing aerodynamicists and advanced students in aeronautical engineering. Covers fundamental theory, divergence theorem and principles of circulation, compressible flow and Helmholtz laws, the Prandtl-Busemann graphic method for 2-dimensional flow, oblique shock waves, the Taylor-Maccoll method for cones in supersonic flow, the Chaplygin method for 2-dimensional flow, etc. Problems range from practical engineering problems to development of theoretical results. "Rendered outstanding by the unprecedented scope of its contents . . . has undoubtedly filled a vital gap," AERONAUTICAL ENGINEERING REVIEW. Index. 173 problems, answers. 106 diagrams. 7 tables. xii + 255pp. 5⅜ x 8. S214 Paperbound **$1.45**

HYDRAULIC TRANSIENTS, G. R. Rich. The best text in hydraulics ever printed in English . . . by one of America's foremost engineers (former Chief Design Engineer for T.V.A.). Provides a transition from the basic differential equations of hydraulic transient theory to the arithmetic intergration computation required by practicing engineers. Sections cover Water Hammer, Turbine Speed Regulation, Stability of Governing, Water-Hammer Pressures in Pump Discharge Lines, The Differential and Restricted Orifice Surge Tanks, The Normalized Surge Tank Charts of Calame and Gaden, Navigation Locks, Surges in Power Canals—Tidal Harmonics, etc. Revised and enlarged. Author's prefaces. Index. xiv + 409pp. 5⅜ x 8½.
S116 Paperbound **$2.50**

HYDRAULICS AND ITS APPLICATIONS, A. H. Gibson. Excellent comprehensive textbook for the student and thorough practical manual for the professional worker, a work of great stature in its area. Half the book is devoted to theory and half to applications and practical problems met in the field. Covers modes of motion of a fluid, critical velocity, viscous flow, eddy formation, Bernoulli's theorem, flow in converging passages, vortex motion, form of effluent streams, notches and weirs, skin friction, losses at valves and elbows, siphons, erosion of channels, jet propulsion, waves of oscillation, and over 100 similar topics. Final chapters (nearly 400 pages) cover more than 100 kinds of hydraulic machinery: Pelton wheel, speed regulators, the hydraulic ram, surge tanks, the scoop wheel, the Venturi meter, etc. A special chapter treats methods of testing theoretical hypotheses: scale models of rivers, tidal estuaries, siphon spillways, etc. 5th revised and enlarged (1952) edition. Index. Appendix. 427 photographs and diagrams. 95 examples, answers. xv + 813pp. 6 x 9.
S791 Clothbound **$8.00**

FLUID MECHANICS THROUGH WORKED EXAMPLES, D. R. L. Smith and J. Houghton. Advanced text covering principles and applications to practical situations. Each chapter begins with concise summaries of fundamental ideas. 163 fully worked out examples applying principles outlined in the text. 275 other problems, with answers. Contents: The Pressure of Liquids on Surfaces; Floating Bodies; Flow Under Constant Head in Pipes; Circulation; Vorticity; The Potential Function; Laminar Flow and Lubrication; Impact of Jets; Hydraulic Turbines; Centrifugal and Reciprocating Pumps; Compressible Fluids; and many other items. Total of 438 examples. 250 line illustrations. 340pp. Index. 6 x 8⅞. S981 Clothbound **$6.00**

THEORY OF SHIP MOTIONS, S. N. Blagoveshchensky. The only detailed text in English in a rapidly developing branch of engineering and physics, it is the work of one of the world's foremost authorities—Blagoveshchensky of Leningrad Shipbuilding Institute. A senior-level treatment written primarily for engineering students, but also of great importance to naval architects, designers, contractors, researchers in hydrodynamics, and other students. No mathematics beyond ordinary differential equations is required for understanding the text. Translated by T. & L. Strelkoff, under editorship of Louis Landweber, Iowa Institute of Hydraulic Research, under auspices of Office of Naval Research. Bibliography. Index. 231 diagrams and illustrations. Total of 649pp. 5⅜ x 8½. Vol. I: S234 Paperbound **$2.00**
Vol. II: S235 Paperbound **$2.00**

THEORY OF FLIGHT, Richard von Mises. Remains almost unsurpassed as balanced, well-written account of fundamental fluid dynamics, and situations in which air compressibility effects are unimportant. Stressing equally theory and practice, avoiding formidable mathematical structure, it conveys a full understanding of physical phenomena and mathematical concepts. Contains perhaps the best introduction to general theory of stability. "Outstanding," Scientific, Medical, and Technical Books. New introduction by K. H. Hohenemser. Bibliographical, historical notes. Index. 408 illustrations. xvi + 620pp. 5⅜ x 8⅜. S541 Paperbound **$3.50**

THEORY OF WING SECTIONS, I. H. Abbott, A. E. von Doenhoff. Concise compilation of subsonic aerodynamic characteristics of modern NASA wing sections, with description of their geometry, associated theory. Primarily reference work for engineers, students, it gives methods, data for using wing-section data to predict characteristics. Particularly valuable: chapters on thin wings, airfoils; complete summary of NACA's experimental observations, system of construction families of airfoils. 350pp. of tables on Basic Thickness Forms, Mean Lines, Airfoil Ordinates, Aerodynamic Characteristics of Wing Sections. Index. Bibliography. 191 illustrations. Appendix. 705pp. 5⅜ x 8. S558 Paperbound **$3.25**

WEIGHT-STRENGTH ANALYSIS OF AIRCRAFT STRUCTURES, F. R. Shanley. Scientifically sound methods of analyzing and predicting the structural weight of aircraft and missiles. Deals directly with forces and the distances over which they must be transmitted, making it possible to develop methods by which the minimum structural weight can be determined for any material and conditions of loading. Weight equations for wing and fuselage structures. Includes author's original papers on inelastic buckling and creep buckling. "Particularly successful in presenting his analytical methods for investigating various optimum design principles," AERONAUTICAL ENGINEERING REVIEW. Enlarged bibliography. Index. 199 figures. xiv + 404pp. 5⅜ x 8⅜. S660 Paperbound **$2.50**

Electricity

TWO-DIMENSIONAL FIELDS IN ELECTRICAL ENGINEERING, L. V. Bewley. A useful selection of typical engineering problems of interest to practicing electrical engineers. Introduces senior students to the methods and procedures of mathematical physics. Discusses theory of functions of a complex variable, two-dimensional fields of flow, general theorems of mathematical physics and their applications, conformal mapping or transformation, method of images, freehand flux plotting, etc. New preface by the authrr. Appendix by W. F. Kiltner. Index. Bibliography at chapter ends. xiv + 204pp. 5⅜ x 8½. S1118 Paperbound **$1.50**

FLUX LINKAGES AND ELECTROMAGNETIC INDUCTION, L. V. Bewley. A brief, clear book which shows proper uses and corrects misconceptions of Faraday's law of eleotromagnetic induction in specific problems. Contents: Circuits, Turns, and Flux Linkages; Substitution of Circuits; Electromagnetic Induction; General Criteria for Electromagnetic Induction; Applications and Paradoxes; Theorem of Constant Flux Linkages. New Section: Rectangular Coil in a Varying Uniform Medium. Valuable supplement to class texts for engineering students. Corrected, enlarged edition. New preface. Bibliography in notes. 49 figures. xi + 106pp. 5⅜ x 8. S1103 Paperbound **$1.25**

INDUCTANCE CALCULATIONS: WORKING FORMULAS AND TABLES, Frederick W. Grover. An invaluable book to everyone in electrical engineering. Provides simple single formulas to cover all the more important cases of inductance. The approach involves only those parameters that naturally enter into each situation, while extensive tables are given to permit easy interpolations. Will save the engineer and student countless hours and enable them to obtain accurate answers with minimal effort. Corrected republication of 1946 edition. 58 tables. 97 completely worked out examples. 66 figures. xiv + 286pp. 5⅜ x 8½.
S974 Paperbound **$1.85**

GASEOUS CONDUCTORS: THEORY AND ENGINEERING APPLICATIONS, J. D. Cobine. An indispensable text and reference to gaseous conduction phenomena, with the engineering viewpoint prevailing throughout. Studies the kinetic theory of gases, ionization, emission phenomena; gas breakdown, spark characteristics, glow, and discharges; engineering applications in circuit interrupters, rectifiers, light sources, etc. Separate detailed treatment of high pressure arcs (Suits); low pressure arcs (Langmuir and Tonks). Much more. "Well organized, clear, straightforward," Tonks, Review of Scientific Instruments. Index. Bibliography. 83 practice problems. 7 appendices. Over 600 figures. 58 tables. xx + 606pp. 5⅜ x 8. S442 Paperbound **$3.25**

INTRODUCTION TO THE STATISTICAL DYNAMICS OF AUTOMATIC CONTROL SYSTEMS, V. V. Solodovnikov. First English publication of text-reference covering important branch of automatic control systems—random signals; in its original edition, this was the first comprehensive treatment. Examines frequency characteristics, transfer functions, stationary random processes, determination of minimum mean-squared error, of transfer function for a finite period of observation, much more. Translation edited by J. B. Thomas, L. A. Zadeh. Index. Bibliography. Appendix. xxii + 308pp. 5⅜ x 8. S420 Paperbound **$2.35**

TENSORS FOR CIRCUITS, Gabriel Kron. A boldly original method of analyzing engineering problems, at center of sharp discussion since first introduced, now definitely proved useful in such areas as electrical and structural networks on automatic computers. Encompasses a great variety of specific problems by means of a relatively few symbolic equations. "Power and flexibility . . . becoming more widely recognized," Nature. Formerly "A Short Course in Tensor Analysis." New introduction by B. Hoffmann. Index. Over 800 diagrams. xix + 250pp. 5⅜ x 8. S534 Paperbound **$2.00**

SELECTED PAPERS ON SEMICONDUCTOR MICROWAVE ELECTRONICS, edited by Sumner N. Levine and Richard R. Kurzrok. An invaluable collection of important papers dealing with one of the most remarkable devolopments in solid-state electronics—the use of the **p-n** junction to achieve amplification and frequency conversion of microwave frequencies. Contents: General Survey (3 introductory papers by W. E. Danielson, R. N. Hall, and M. Tenzer); General Theory of Nonlinear Elements (3 articles by A. van der Ziel, H. E. Rowe, and Manley and Rowe); Device Fabrication and Characterization (3 pieces by Bakanowski, Cranna, and Uhlir, by McCotter, Walker and Fortini, and by S. T. Eng); Parametric Amplifiers and Frequency Multipliers (13 articles by Uhlir, Heffner and Wade, Matthaei, P. K. Tien, van der Ziel, Engelbrecht, Currie and Gould, Uenohara, Leeson and Weinreb, and others); and Tunnel Diodes (4 papers by L. Esaki, H. S. Sommers, Jr., M. E. Hines, and Yariv and Cook). Introduction. 295 Figures. xiii + 286pp. 6½ x 9¼. S1126 Paperbound **$2.50**

THE PRINCIPLES OF ELECTROMAGNETISM APPLIED TO ELECTRICAL MACHINES, B. Hague. A concise, but complete, summary of the basic principles of the magnetic field and its applications, with particular reference to the kind of phenomena which occur in electrical machines. Part I: General Theory—magnetic field of a current, electromagnetic field passing from air to iron, mechanical forces on linear conductors, etc. Part II: Application of theory to the solution of electromechanical problems—the magnetic field and mechanical forces in non-salient pole machinery, the field within slots and between salient poles, and the work of Rogowski, Roth, and Strutt. Formery titled "Electromagnetic Problems in Electrical Engineering." 2 appendices. Index. Bibliography in notes. 115 figures. xiv + 359pp. 5⅜ x 8½. S246 Paperbound **$2.25**

Mechanical engineering

DESIGN AND USE OF INSTRUMENTS AND ACCURATE MECHANISM, T. N. Whitehead. For the instrument designer, engineer; how to combine necessary mathematical abstractions with independent observation of actual facts. Partial contents: instruments & their parts, theory of errors, systematic errors, probability, short period errors, erratic errors, design precision, kinematic, semikinematic design, stiffness, planning of an instrument, human factor, etc. Index. 85 photos, diagrams. xii + 288pp. 5⅜ x 8. S270 Paperbound **$2.00**

A TREATISE ON GYROSTATICS AND ROTATIONAL MOTION: THEORY AND APPLICATIONS, Andrew Gray. Most detailed, thorough book in English, generally considered definitive study. Many problems of all sorts in full detail, or step-by-step summary. Classical problems of Bour, Lottner, etc.; later ones of great physical interest. Vibrating systems of gyrostats, earth as a top, calculation of path of axis of a top by elliptic integrals, motion of unsymmetrical top, much more. Index. 160 illus. 550pp. 5⅜ x 8. S589 Paperbound **$2.75**

MECHANICS OF THE GYROSCOPE, THE DYNAMICS OF ROTATION, R. F. Deimel, Professor of Mechanical Engineering at Stevens Institute of Technology. Elementary general treatment of dynamics of rotation, with special application of gyroscopic phenomena. No knowledge of vectors needed. Velocity of a moving curve, acceleration to a point, general equations of motion, gyroscopic horizon, free gyro, motion of discs, the damped gyro, 103 similar topics. Exercises. 75 figures. 208pp. 5⅜ x 8. S66 Paperbound **$1.75**

STRENGTH OF MATERIALS, J. P. Den Hartog. Distinguished text prepared for M.I.T. course, ideal as introduction, refresher, reference, or self-study text. Full clear treatment of elementary material (tension, torsion, bending, compound stresses, deflection of beams, etc.), plus much advanced material on engineering methods of great practical value: full treatment of the Mohr circle, lucid elementary discussions of the theory of the center of shear and the "Myosotis" method of calculating beam deflections, reinforced concrete, plastic deformations, photoelasticity, etc. In all sections, both general principles and concrete applications are given. Index. 186 figures (160 others in problem section). 350 problems, all with answers. List of formulas. viii + 323pp. 5⅜ x 8. S755 Paperbound **$2.00**

PHOTOELASTICITY: PRINCIPLES AND METHODS, H. T. Jessop, F. C. Harris. For the engineer, for specific problems of stress analysis. Latest time-saving methods of checking calculations in 2-dimensional design problems, new techniques for stresses in 3 dimensions, and lucid description of optical systems used in practical photoelasticity. Useful suggestions and hints based on on-the-job experience included. Partial contents: strained and stress-strain relations, circular disc under thrust along diameter, rectangular block with square hole under vertical thrust, simply supported rectangular beam under central concentrated load, etc. Theory held to minimum, no advanced mathematical training needed. Index. 164 illustrations. viii + 184pp. 6⅛ x 9¼. S720 Paperbound **$2.00**

APPLIED ELASTICITY, J. Prescott. Provides the engineer with the theory of elasticity usually lacking in books on strength of materials, yet concentrates on those portions useful for immediate application. Develops every important type of elasticity problem from theoretical principles. Covers analysis of stress, relations between stress and strain, the empirical basis of elasticity, thin rods under tension or thrust, Saint Venant's theory, transverse oscillations of thin rods, stability of thin plates, cylinders with thin walls, vibrations of rotating disks, elastic bodies in contact, etc. "Excellent and important contribution to the subject, not merely in the old matter which he has presented in new and refreshing form, but also in the many original investigations here published for the first time," NATURE. Index. 3 Appendixes. vi + 672pp. 5⅜ x 8. S726 Paperbound **$3.25**

APPLIED MECHANICS FOR ENGINEERS, Sir Charles Inglis, F.R.S. A representative survey of the many and varied engineering questions which can be answered by statics and dynamics. The author, one of first and foremost adherents of "structural dynamics," presents distinctive illustrative examples and clear, concise statement of principles—directing the discussion at methodology and specific problems. Covers fundamental principles of rigid-body statics, graphic solutions of static problems, theory of taut wires, stresses in frameworks, particle dynamics, kinematics, simple harmonic motion and harmonic analysis, two-dimensional rigid dynamics, etc. 437 illustrations. xii + 404pp. 5⅜ x 8½. S1119 Paperbound **$2.50**

THEORY OF MACHINES THROUGH WORKED EXAMPLES, G. H. Ryder. Practical mechanical engineering textbook for graduates and advanced undergraduates, as well as a good reference work for practicing engineers. Partial contents: Mechanisms, Velocity and Acceleration (including discussion of Klein's Construction for Piston Acceleration), Cams, Geometry of Gears, Clutches and Bearings, Belt and Rope Drives, Brakes, Inertia Forces and Couples, General Dynamical Problems, Gyroscopes, Linear and Angular Vibrations, Torsional Vibrations, Transverse Vibrations and Whirling Speeds (Chapters on vibrations considerably enlarged from previous editions). Over 300 problems, many fully worked out. Index. 195 line illustrations. Revised and enlarged edition. viii + 280pp. 5⅝ x 8¾. S980 Clothbound **$5.00**

THE KINEMATICS OF MACHINERY: OUTLINES OF A THEORY OF MACHINES, Franz Reuleaux. The classic work in the kinematics of machinery. The present thinking about the subject has all been shaped in great measure by the fundamental principles stated here by Reuleaux almost 90 years ago. While some details have naturally been superseded, his basic viewpoint has endured; hence, the book is still an excellent text for basic courses in kinematics and a standard reference work for active workers in the field. Covers such topics as: the nature of the machine problem, phoronomic propositions, pairs of elements, incomplete kinematic chains, kinematic notation and analysis, analyses of chamber-crank trains, chamber-wheel trains, constructive elements of machinery, complete machines, etc., with main focus on controlled movement in mechanisms. Unabridged republication of original edition, translated by Alexander B. Kennedy. New introduction for this edition by E. S. Ferguson. Index. 451 illustrations. xxiv + 622pp. 5⅜ x 8½. S1124 Paperbound **$3.00**

ANALYTICAL MECHANICS OF GEARS, Earle Buckingham. Provides a solid foundation upon which logical design practices and design data can be constructed. Originally arising out of investigations of the ASME Special Research Committee on Worm Gears and the Strength of Gears, the book covers conjugate gear-tooth action, the nature of the contact, and resulting gear-tooth profiles of: spur, internal, helical, spiral, worm, bevel, and hypoid or skew bevel gears. Also: frictional heat of operation and its dissipation, friction losses, etc., dynamic loads in operation, and related matters. Familiarity with this book is still regarded as a necessary prerequisite to work in modern gear manufacturing. 263 figures. 103 tables. Index. x + 546pp. 5⅜ x 8½. S1073 Paperbound **$2.75**

Optical design, lighting

THE SCIENTIFIC BASIS OF ILLUMINATING ENGINEERING, Parry Moon, Professor of Electrical Engineering, M.I.T. Basic, comprehensive study. Complete coverage of the fundamental theoretical principles together with the elements of design, vision, and color with which the lighting engineer must be familiar. Valuable as a text as well as a reference source to the practicing engineer. Partial contents: Spectroradiometric Curve, Luminous Flux, Radiation from Gaseous-Conduction Sources, Radiation from Incandescent Sources, Incandescent Lamps, Measurement of Light, Illumination from Point Sources and Surface Sources, Elements of Lighting Design. 7 Appendices. Unabridged and corrected republication, with additions. New preface containing conversion tables of radiometric and photometric concepts. Index. 707-item bibliography. 92-item bibliography of author's articles. 183 problems. xxiii + 608pp. 5⅜ x 8½. S242 Paperbound **$3.25**

OPTICS AND OPTICAL INSTRUMENTS: AN INTRODUCTION WITH SPECIAL REFERENCE TO PRACTICAL APPLICATIONS, B. K. Johnson. An invaluable guide to basic practical applications of optical principles, which shows how to set up inexpensive working models of each of the four main types of optical instruments—telescopes, microscopes, photographic lenses, optical projecting systems. Explains in detail the most important experiments for determining their accuracy, resolving power, angular field of view, amounts of aberration, all other necessary facts about the instruments. Formerly "Practical Optics." Index. 234 diagrams. Appendix. 224pp. 5⅜ x 8. S642 Paperbound **$1.75**

APPLIED OPTICS AND OPTICAL DESIGN, A. E. Conrady. With publication of vol. 2, standard work for designers in optics is now complete for first time. Only work of its kind in English; only detailed work for practical designer and self-taught. Requires, for bulk of work, no math above trig. Step-by-step exposition, from fundamental concepts of geometrical, physical optics, to systematic study, design, of almost all types of optical systems. Vol. 1: all ordinary ray-tracing methods; primary aberrations; necessary higher aberration for design of telescopes, low-power microscopes, photographic equipment. Vol. 2: (Completed from author's notes by R. Kingslake, Dir. Optical Design, Eastman Kodak.) Special attention to high-power microscope, anastigmatic photographic objectives. "An indispensable work," J., Optical Soc. of Amer. "As a practical guide this book has no rival," Transactions, Optical Soc. Index. Bibliography. 193 diagrams. 852pp. 6⅛ x 9¼. Vol. 1 S366 Paperbound **$3.50**
Vol. 2 S612 Paperbound **$2.95**

Miscellaneous

THE MEASUREMENT OF POWER SPECTRA FROM THE POINT OF VIEW OF COMMUNICATIONS ENGINEERING, R. B. Blackman, J. W. Tukey. This pathfinding work, reprinted from the "Bell System Technical Journal," explains various ways of getting practically useful answers in the measurement of power spectra, using results from both transmission theory and the theory of statistical estimation. Treats: Autocovariance Functions and Power Spectra; Direct Analog Computation; Distortion, Noise, Heterodyne Filtering and Pre-whitening; Aliasing; Rejection Filtering and Separation; Smoothing and Decimation Procedures; Very Low Frequencies; Transversal Filtering; much more. An appendix reviews fundamental Fourier techniques. Index of notation. Glossary of terms. 24 figures. XII tables. Bibliography. General index. 192pp. 5⅜ x 8. S507 Paperbound **$1.85**

CALCULUS REFRESHER FOR TECHNICAL MEN, A. Albert Klaf. This book is unique in English as a refresher for engineers, technicians, students who either wish to brush up their calculus or to clear up uncertainties. It is not an ordinary text, but an examination of most important aspects of integral and differential calculus in terms of the 756 questions most likely to occur to the technical reader. The first part of this book covers simple differential calculus, with constants, variables, functions, increments, derivatives, differentiation, logarithms, curvature of curves, and similar topics. The second part covers fundamental ideas of integration, inspection, substitution, transformation, reduction, areas and volumes, mean value, successive and partial integration, double and triple integration. Practical aspects are stressed rather than theoretical. A 50-page section illustrates the application of calculus to specific problems of civil and nautical engineering, electricity, stress and strain, elasticity, industrial engineering, and similar fields.—756 questions answered. 566 problems, mostly answered. 36 pages of useful constants, formulae for ready reference. Index. v + 431pp. 5⅜ x 8. T370 Paperbound **$2.00**

METHODS IN EXTERIOR BALLISTICS, Forest Ray Moulton. Probably the best introduction to the mathematics of projectile motion. The ballistics theories propounded were coordinated with extensive proving ground and wind tunnel experiments conducted by the author and others for the U.S. Army. Broad in scope and clear in exposition, it gives the beginnings of the theory used for modern-day projectile, long-range missile, and satellite motion. Six main divisions: Differential Equations of Translatory Motion of a projectile; Gravity and the Resistance Function; Numerical Solution of Differential Equations; Theory of Differential Variations; Validity of Method of Numerical Integration; and Motion of a Rotating Projectile. Formerly titled: "New Methods in Exterior Ballistics." Index. 38 diagrams. viii + 259pp. 5⅜ x 8½. S232 Paperbound **$1.75**

LOUD SPEAKERS: THEORY, PERFORMANCE, TESTING AND DESIGN, N. W. McLachlan. Most comprehensive coverage of theory, practice of loud speaker design, testing; classic reference, study manual in field. First 12 chapters deal with theory, for readers mainly concerned with math. aspects; last 7 chapters will interest reader concerned with testing, design. Partial contents: principles of sound propagation, fluid pressure on vibrators, theory of moving-coil principle, transients, driving mechanisms, response curves, design of horn type moving coil speakers, electrostatic speakers, much more. Appendix. Bibliography. Index. 165 illustrations, charts. 411pp. 5⅜ x 8. S588 Paperbound **$2.25**

MICROWAVE TRANSMISSION, J. C. Slater. First text dealing exclusively with microwaves, brings together points of view of field, circuit theory, for graduate student in physics, electrical engineering, microwave technician. Offers valuable point of view not in most later studies. Uses Maxwell's equations to study electromagnetic field, important in this area. Partial contents: infinite line with distributed parameters, impedance of terminated line, plane waves, reflections, wave guides, coaxial line, composite transmission lines, impedance matching, etc. Introduction. Index. 76 illus. 319pp. 5⅜ x 8. S564 Paperbound **$1.50**

MICROWAVE TRANSMISSION DESIGN DATA, T. Moreno. Originally classified, now rewritten and enlarged (14 new chapters) for public release under auspices of Sperry Corp. Material of immediate value or reference use to radio engineers, systems designers, applied physicists, etc. Ordinary transmission line theory; attenuation; capacity; parameters of coaxial lines; higher modes; flexible cables; obstacles, discontinuities, and injunctions; tunable wave guide impedance transformers; effects of temperature and humidity; much more. "Enough theoretical discussion is included to allow use of data without previous background," Electronics. 324 circuit diagrams, figures, etc. Tables of dielectrics, flexible cable, etc., data. Index. ix + 248pp. 5⅜ x 8. S459 Paperbound **$1.65**

RAYLEIGH'S PRINCIPLE AND ITS APPLICATIONS TO ENGINEERING, G. Temple & W. Bickley. Rayleigh's principle developed to provide upper and lower estimates of true value of fundamental period of a vibrating system, or condition of stability of elastic systems. Illustrative examples; rigorous proofs in special chapters. Partial contents: Energy method of discussing vibrations, stability. Perturbation theory, whirling of uniform shafts. Criteria of elastic stability. Application of energy method. Vibrating systems. Proof, accuracy, successive approximations, application of Rayleigh's principle. Synthetic theorems. Numerical, graphical methods. Equilibrium configurations, Ritz's method. Bibliography. Index. 22 figures. ix + 156pp. 5⅜ x 8. S307 Paperbound **$1.85**

ELASTICITY, PLASTICITY AND STRUCTURE OF MATTER, R. Houwink. Standard treatise on rheological aspects of different technically important solids such as crystals, resins, textiles, rubber, clay, many others. Investigates general laws for deformations; determines divergences from these laws for certain substances. Covers general physical and mathematical aspects of plasticity, elasticity, viscosity. Detailed examination of deformations, internal structure of matter in relation to elastic and plastic behavior, formation of solid matter from a fluid, conditions for elastic and plastic behavior of matter. Treats glass, asphalt, gutta percha, balata, proteins, baker's dough, lacquers, sulphur, others. 2nd revised, enlarged edition. Extensive revised bibliography in over 500 footnotes. Index. Table of symbols. 214 figures. xviii + 368pp. 6 x 9¼. S385 Paperbound **$2.45**

THE SCHWARZ-CHRISTOFFEL TRANSFORMATION AND ITS APPLICATIONS: A SIMPLE EXPOSITION, Miles Walker. An important book for engineers showing how this valuable tool can be employed in practical situations. Very careful, clear presentation covering numerous concrete engineering problems. Includes a thorough account of conjugate functions for engineers—useful for the beginner and for review. Applications to such problems as: Stream-lines round a corner, electric conductor in air-gap, dynamo slots, magnetized poles, much more. Formerly "Conjugate Functions for Engineers." Preface. 92 figures, several tables. Index. ix + 116pp. 5⅜ x 8½. S1149 Paperbound **$1.25**

THE LAWS OF THOUGHT, George Boole. This book founded symbolic logic some hundred years ago. It is the 1st significant attempt to apply logic to all aspects of human endeavour. Partial contents: derivation of laws, signs & laws, interpretations, eliminations, conditions of a perfect method, analysis, Aristotelian logic, probability, and similar topics. xviii + 424pp. 5⅜ x 8. S28 Paperbound **$2.00**

SCIENCE AND METHOD, Henri Poincaré. Procedure of scientific discovery, methodology, experiment, idea-germination—the intellectual processes by which discoveries come into being. Most significant and most interesting aspects of development, application of ideas. Chapters cover selection of facts, chance, mathematical reasoning, mathematics, and logic; Whitehead, Russell, Cantor; the new mechanics, etc. 288pp. 5⅜ x 8. S222 Paperbound **$1.35**

FAMOUS BRIDGES OF THE WORLD, D. B. Steinman. An up-to-the-minute revised edition of a book that explains the fascinating drama of how the world's great bridges came to be built. The author, designer of the famed Mackinac bridge, discusses bridges from all periods and all parts of the world, explaining their various types of construction, and describing the problems their builders faced. Although primarily for youngsters, this cannot fail to interest readers of all ages. 48 illustrations in the text. 23 photographs. 99pp. 6⅛ x 9¼. T161 Paperbound **$1.00**

PHYSICS

General physics

FOUNDATIONS OF PHYSICS, R. B. Lindsay & H. Margenau. Excellent bridge between semi-popular works & technical treatises. A discussion of methods of physical description, construction of theory; valuable for physicist with elementary calculus who is interested in ideas that give meaning to data, tools of modern physics. Contents include symbolism, mathematical equations; space & time foundations of mechanics; probability; physics & continua; electron theory; special & general relativity; quantum mechanics; causality. "Thorough and yet not overdetailed. Unreservedly recommended," NATURE (London). Unabridged, corrected edition. List of recommended readings. 35 illustrations. xi + 537pp. 5⅜ x 8.
S377 Paperbound **$3.00**

FUNDAMENTAL FORMULAS OF PHYSICS, ed. by D. H. Menzel. Highly useful, fully inexpensive reference and study text, ranging from simple to highly sophisticated operations. Mathematics integrated into text—each chapter stands as short textbook of field represented. Vol. 1: Statistics, Physical Constants, Special Theory of Relativity, Hydrodynamics, Aerodynamics, Boundary Value Problems in Math. Physics; Viscosity, Electromagnetic Theory, etc. Vol. 2: Sound, Acoustics, Geometrical Optics, Electron Optics, High-Energy Phenomena, Magnetism, Biophysics, much more. Index. Total of 800pp. 5⅜ x 8. Vol. 1 S595 Paperbound **$2.25**
Vol. 2 S596 Paperbound **$2.25**

MATHEMATICAL PHYSICS, D. H. Menzel. Thorough one-volume treatment of the mathematical techniques vital for classic mechanics, electromagnetic theory, quantum theory, and relativity. Written by the Harvard Professor of Astrophysics for junior, senior, and graduate courses, it gives clear explanations of all those aspects of function theory, vectors, matrices, dyadics, tensors, partial differential equations, etc., necessary for the understanding of the various physical theories. Electron theory, relativity, and other topics seldom presented appear here in considerable detail. Scores of definitions, conversion factors, dimensional constants, etc. "More detailed than normal for an advanced text . . . excellent set of sections on Dyadics, Matrices, and Tensors," JOURNAL OF THE FRANKLIN INSTITUTE. Index. 193 problems, with answers. x + 412pp. 5⅜ x 8. S56 Paperbound **$2.00**

THE SCIENTIFIC PAPERS OF J. WILLARD GIBBS. All the published papers of America's outstanding theoretical scientist (except for "Statistical Mechanics" and "Vector Analysis"). Vol I (thermodynamics) contains one of the most brilliant of all 19th-century scientific papers—the 300-page "On the Equilibrium of Heterogeneous Substances," which founded the science of physical chemistry, and clearly stated a number of highly important natural laws for the first time; 8 other papers complete the first volume. Vol II includes 2 papers on dynamics, 8 on vector analysis and multiple algebra, 5 on the electromagnetic theory of light, and 6 miscellaneous papers. Biographical sketch by H. A. Bumstead. Total of xxxvi + 718pp. 5⅝ x 8⅜.
S721 Vol I Paperbound **$2.50**
S722 Vol II Paperbound **$2.00**
The set **$4.50**

BASIC THEORIES OF PHYSICS, Peter Gabriel Bergmann. Two-volume set which presents a critical examination of important topics in the major subdivisions of classical and modern physics. The first volume is concerned with classical mechanics and electrodynamics: mechanics of mass points, analytical mechanics, matter in bulk, electrostatics and magnetostatics, electromagnetic interaction, the field waves, special relativity, and waves. The second volume (Heat and Quanta) contains discussions of the kinetic hypothesis, physics and statistics, stationary ensembles, laws of thermodynamics, early quantum theories, atomic spectra, probability waves, quantization in wave mechanics, approximation methods, and abstract quantum theory. A valuable supplement to any thorough course or text.
Heat and Quanta: Index. 8 figures. x + 300pp. 5⅜ x 8½. S968 Paperbound **$2.00**
Mechanics and Electrodynamics: Index. 14 figures. vii + 280pp. 5⅜ x 8½.
S969 Paperbound **$1.85**

THEORETICAL PHYSICS, A. S. Kompaneyets. One of the very few thorough studies of the subject in this price range. Provides advanced students with a comprehensive theoretical background. Especially strong on recent experimentation and developments in quantum theory. Contents: Mechanics (Generalized Coordinates, Lagrange's Equation, Collision of Particles, etc.), Electrodynamics (Vector Analysis, Maxwell's equations, Transmission of Signals, Theory of Relativity, etc.), Quantum Mechanics (the Inadequacy of Classical Mechanics, the Wave Equation, Motion in a Central Field, Quantum Theory of Radiation, Quantum Theories of Dispersion and Scattering, etc.), and Statistical Physics (Equilibrium Distribution of Molecules in an Ideal Gas, Boltzmann statistics, Bose and Fermi Distribution, Thermodynamic Quantities, etc.). Revised to 1961. Translated by George Yankovsky, authorized by Kompaneyets. 137 exercises. 56 figures. 529pp. 5⅜ x 8½. S972 Paperbound **$2.50**

ANALYTICAL AND CANONICAL FORMALISM IN PHYSICS, André Mercier. A survey, in one volume, of the variational principles (the key principles—in mathematical form—from which the basic laws of any one branch of physics can be derived) of the several branches of physical theory, together with an examination of the relationships among them. Contents: the Lagrangian Formalism, Lagrangian Densities, Canonical Formalism, Canonical Form of Electrodynamics, Hamiltonian Densities, Transformations, and Canonical Form with Vanishing Jacobian Determinant. Numerous examples and exercises. For advanced students, teachers, etc. 6 figures. Index. viii + 222pp. 5⅜ x 8½. S1077 Paperbound **$1.75**

PHYSICS, HISTORIES AND CLASSICS

A HISTORY OF PHYSICS: IN ITS ELEMENTARY BRANCHES (THROUGH 1925), INCLUDING THE EVOLUTION OF PHYSICAL LABORATORIES, Florian Cajori. Revised and enlarged edition. The only first-rate brief history of physics. Still the best entry for a student or teacher into the antecedents of modern theories of physics. A clear, non-mathematical, handy reference work which traces in critical fashion the developments of ideas, theories, techniques, and apparatus from the Greeks to the 1920's. Within each period he analyzes the basic topics of mechanics, light, electricity and magnetism, sound, atomic theory and structure of matter, radioactivity, etc. A chapter on modern research: Curie, Kelvin, Planck's quantum theory, thermodynamics, Fitzgerald and Lorentz, special and general relativity, J. J. Thomson's model of an atom, Bohr's discoveries and later results, wave mechanics, and many other matters. Much bibliographic detail in footnotes. Index. 16 figures. xv + 424pp. 5⅜ x 8. T970 Paperbound **$2.00**

A HISTORY OF THE MATHEMATICAL THEORIES OF ATTRACTION AND THE FIGURE OF THE EARTH: FROM THE TIME OF NEWTON TO THAT OF LAPLACE, I. Todhunter. A technical and detailed review of the theories concerning the shape of the earth and its gravitational pull, from the earliest investigations in the seventeenth century up to the middle of the nineteenth. Some of the greatest mathematicians and scientists in history applied themselves to these questions: Newton ("Principia Mathematica"), Huygens, Maupertuis, Simpson, d'Alembert, etc. Others discussed are Poisson, Gauss, Plana, Lagrange, Boit, and many more. Particular emphasis is placed on the theories of Laplace and Legendre, several chapters being devoted to Laplace's "Mécanique Céleste" and his memoirs, and several others to the memoirs of Legendre. Important to historians of science and mathematics and to the specialist who desires background information in the field. 2 volumes bound as 1. Index. xxxvi + 984pp. 5⅜ x 8.
S148 Clothbound **$7.50**

OPTICKS, Sir Isaac Newton. In its discussions of light, reflection, color, refraction, theories of wave and corpuscular theories of light, this work is packed with scores of insights and discoveries. In its precise and practical discussion of construction of optical apparatus, contemporary understandings of phenomena it is truly fascinating to modern physicists, astronomers, mathematicians. Foreword by Albert Einstein. Preface by I. B. Cohen of Harvard University. 7 pages of portraits, facsimile pages, letters, etc. cxvi + 414pp. 5⅜ x 8.
S205 Paperbound **$2.25**

TREATISE ON LIGHT, Christiaan Huygens. The famous original formulation of the wave theory of light, this readable book is one of the two decisive and definitive works in the field of light (Newton's "Optics" is the other). A scientific giant whose researches ranged over mathematics, astronomy, and physics, Huygens, in this historic work, covers such topics as rays propagated in straight lines, reflection and refraction, the spreading and velocity of light, the nature of opaque bodies, the non-spherical nature of light in the atmosphere, properties of Iceland Crystal, and other related matters. Unabridged republication of original (1912) English edition. Translated and introduced by Silvanus P. Thompson. 52 illustrations. xii + 129pp. 5⅜ x 8. S179 Paperbound **$1.50**

FARADAY'S EXPERIMENTAL RESEARCHES IN ELECTRICITY. Faraday's historic series of papers containing the fruits of years of original experimentation in electrical theory and electrochemistry. Covers his findings in a variety of areas: Induction of electric currents, Evolution of electricity from magnetism, New electrical state or condition of matter, Explication of Arago's magnetic phenomena, New law of electric conduction, Electro-chemical decomposition, Electricity of the Voltaic Pile, Static Induction, Nature of the electric force or forces, Nature of electric current, The character and direction of the electric force of the Gymnotus, Magneto-electric spark, The magnetization of light and the illumination of magnetic lines of force, The possible relation of gravity to electricity, Sub-terraneous electrotelegraph wires, Some points of magnetic philosophy, The diamagnetic conditions of flame and gases, and many other matters. Complete and unabridged republication. 3 vols. bound as 2. Originally reprinted from the Philosophical Transactions of 1831-8. Indices. Illustrations. Total of 1463pp. 5⅜ x 8. S783-4, Clothbound **$17.50** (tentative)

REFLECTIONS ON THE MOTIVE POWER OF FIRE, Sadi Carnot, and other papers on the 2nd law of thermodynamics by E. Clapeyron and R. Clausius. Carnot's "Reflections" laid the groundwork of modern thermodynamics. Its non-technical, mostly verbal statements examine the relations between heat and the work done by heat in engines, establishing conditions for the economical working of these engines. The papers by Clapeyron and Clausius here reprinted added further refinements to Carnot's work, and led to its final acceptance by physicists. Selections from posthumous manuscripts of Carnot are also included. All papers in English. New introduction by E. Mendoza. 12 illustrations. xxii + 152pp. 5⅜ x 8.
S661 Paperbound **$1.50**

DIALOGUES CONCERNING TWO NEW SCIENCES, Galileo Galilei. This classic of experimental science, mechanics, engineering, is as enjoyable as it is important. A great historical document giving insights into one of the world's most original thinkers, it is based on 30 years' experimentation. It offers a lively exposition of dynamics, elasticity, sound, ballistics, strength of materials, the scientific method. "Superior to everything else of mine," Galileo. Trans. by H. Crew, A. Salvio. 126 diagrams. Index. xxi + 288pp. 5⅜ x 8.
S99 Paperbound **$1.75**

TREATISE ON ELECTRICITY AND MAGNETISM, James Clerk Maxwell. For more than 80 years a seemingly inexhaustible source of leads for physicists, mathematicians, engineers. Total of 1082pp. on such topics as Measurement of Quantities, Electrostatics, Elementary Mathematical Theory of Electricity, Electrical Work and Energy in a System of Conductors, General Theorems, Theory of Electrical Images, Electrolysis, Conduction, Polarization, Dielectrics, Resistance, etc. "The greatest mathematical physicist since Newton," Sir James Jeans. 3rd edition. 107 figures, 21 plates. 1082pp. 5⅜ x 8. S636-7, 2 volume set, paperbound **$4.00**

A HISTORY OF THE THEORY OF ELASTICITY AND THE STRENGTH OF MATERIALS, I. Todhunter and K. Pearson. For over 60 years a basic reference, unsurpassed in scope or authority. Both a history of the mathematical theory of elasticity from Galileo, Hooke, and Mariotte to Saint Venant, Kirchhoff, Clebsch, and Lord Kelvin and a detailed presentation of every important mathematical contribution during this period. Presents proofs of thousands of theorems and laws, summarizes every relevant treatise, many unavailable elsewhere. Practically a book apiece is devoted to modern founders: Saint Venant, Lamé, Boussinesq, Rankine, Lord Kelvin, F. Neumann, Kirchhoff, Clebsch. Hundreds of pages of technical and physical treatises on specific applications of elasticity to particular materials. Indispensable for the mathematician, physicist, or engineer working with elasticity. Unabridged, corrected reprint of original 3-volume 1886-1893 edition. Three volume set. Two indexes. Appendix to Vol. I. Total of 2344pp. 5⅜ x 8⅜. S914–916 The set, Clothbound **$15.00**

DE MAGNETE, William Gilbert. This classic work on magnetism founded a new science. Gilbert was the first to use the word "electricity", to recognize mass as distinct from weight, to discover the effect of heat on magnetic bodies; invent an electroscope, differentiate between static electricity and magnetism, conceive of the earth as a magnet. Written by the first great experimental scientist, this lively work is valuable not only as an historical landmark, but as the delightfully easy to follow record of a perpetually searching, ingenious mind. Translated by P. F. Mottelay. 25-page biographical memoir. 90 figures. lix +368pp. 5⅜ x 8. S470 Paperbound **$2.00**

ASTRONOMY

THE INTERNAL CONSTITUTION OF THE STARS, Sir A. S. Eddington. Influence of this has been enormous; first detailed exposition of theory of radiative equilibrium for stellar interiors, of all available evidence for existence of diffuse matter in interstellar space. Studies quantum theory, polytropic gas spheres, mass-luminosity relations, variable stars, etc. Discussions of equations paralleled with informal exposition of intimate relationship of astrophysics with great discoveries in atomic physics, radiation. Introduction. Appendix. Index. 421pp. 5⅜ x 8. S563 Paperbound **$2.75**

PLANETARY THEORY, E. W. Brown and C. A. Shook. Provides a clear presentation of basic methods for calculating planetary orbits for today's astronomer. Begins with a careful exposition of specialized mathematical topics essential for handling perturbation theory and then goes on to indicate how most of the previous methods reduce ultimately to two general calculation methods: obtaining expressions either for the coordinates of planetary positions or for the elements which determine the perturbed paths. An example of each is given and worked in detail. Corrected edition. Preface. Appendix. Index. xii + 302pp. 5⅜ x 8½. S1133 Paperbound **$2.25**

CANON OF ECLIPSES (CANON DER FINSTERNISSE), Prof. Theodor Ritter von Oppolzer. Since its original publication in 1887, this has been the standard reference and the most extensive single volume of data on the calculation of solar and lunar eclipses, past and future. A comprehensive introduction gives a full explanation of the use of the tables for the calculations of the exact dates of eclipses, etc. Data furnished for the calculation of 8,000 solar and 5,200 lunar eclipses, going back as far as 1200 B.C. and giving predictions up to the year 2161. Information is also given for partial and ring eclipses. All calculations based on Universal (Greenwich) Time. An unsurpassed reference work for astronomers, scientists engaged in space research and developments, historians, etc. Unabridged republication, with corrections. Preface to this edition by Donald Menzel and Owen Gingerich of the Harvard College Observatory. Translated by Owen Gingerich. 160 charts. lxx + 538pp. 8⅜ x 11¼. S114 Clothbound **$10.00**

THEORY OF THE MOTION OF THE HEAVENLY BODIES MOVING ABOUT THE SUN IN CONIC SECTIONS, Karl Friedrich Gauss. A landmark of theoretical astronomy by the great German scientist. Still authoritative and invaluable to the practicing astronomer. Part I develops the relations between the quantities on which the motion about the sun of the heavenly bodies depends—relations pertaining simply to position in the orbit, simply to position in space, between several places in orbit, and between several places in space. The calculation methods of Part II based on the groundwork of Part I include: determination of an orbit from 3 complete observations, from 4 observations (of which only two are complete), determination of an orbit satisfying as nearly as possible any number of observations whatever, and determination of orbits, taking into account the perturbations. Translation of "Theoria Motus" and with an appendix by C. H. Davis. Unabridged republication. Appendices and tables. 13 figures. xviii + 376pp. 6½ x 9¼. S1056 Paperbound **$2.95**

A COMPENDIUM OF SPHERICAL ASTRONOMY, S. Newcomb. Long a standard collection of basic methods and formulas most useful to the working astronomer, and clear full text for students. Includes the most important common approximations; 40 pages on the method of least squares; general theory of spherical coordinates; parallax; aberration; astronomical refraction; theory of precession; proper motion of the stars; methods of deriving positions of stars; and much more. Index. 9 Appendices of tables, formulas, etc. 36 figures. xviii + 444pp. 5⅜ x 8.
S690 Paperbound **$2.25**

PRINCIPLES OF STELLAR DYNAMICS, S. Chandrasekhar. A leading astrophysicist here presents the theory of stellar dynamics as a branch of classical dynamics, clarifying the fundamental issues and the underlying motivations of the theory. He analyzes the effects of stellar encounters in terms of the classical 2-body problem, and investigates problems centering about Liouville's theorem and the solutions of the equations of continuity. This edition also includes 4 important papers by the author published since "Stellar Dynamics," and equally indispensable for all workers in the field: "New Methods in Stellar Dynamics" and "Dynamical Friction," Parts I, II, and III. Index. 3 Appendixes. Bibliography. 50 illustrations. x + 313pp. 5⅜ x8.
S659 Paperbound **$2.25**

AN INTRODUCTION TO THE STUDY OF STELLAR STRUCTURE, Subrahmanyan Chandrasekhar. Outstanding treatise on stellar dynamics by one of world's greatest astrophysicists. Uses classical & modern math methods to examine relationship between loss of energy, the mass, and radius of stars in a steady state. Discusses thermodynamic laws from Carathéodory's axiomatic standpoint; adiabatic, polytropic laws; work of Ritter, Emden, Kelvin, others; Stroemgren envelopes as starter for theory of gaseous stars; Gibbs statistical mechanics (quantum); degenerate stellar configuration & theory of white dwarfs, etc. "Highest level of scientific merit," BULLETIN, AMER. MATH. SOC. Bibliography. Appendixes. Index. 33 figures. 509pp. 5⅜ x 8.
S413 Paperbound **$2.75**

STATISTICAL ASTRONOMY, Robert J. Trumpler and Harold F. Weaver, University of California. Standard introduction to the principles and techniques of statistical astronomy, a field of rapidly growing importance in this space age. An extensive section, "Elements of Statistical Theory," provides the astronomer with the tools for solving problems ot descriptive astronomy, observational errors, constitution of extra-galactic nebulae, etc. Procedures used in statistical astronomy are related to basic mathematical principles of statistics such as unvariate distribution, integral equations, general theory of samples, etc. Other sections deal with: Statistical Description of the Galactic System; Stellar Motions in the Vicinity of the Sun; Luminosity—Spectral Type Distribution; Space Distribution of Stars; and Galactic Rotation. List of symbols. Appendix (10 tables). 2 Indexes. Extensive bibliography. 31 tables. 97 figures. xxi + 644pp. 5⅜ x 8½.
S301 Paperbound **$3.00**

AN INTRODUCTORY TREATISE ON DYNAMICAL ASTRONOMY, H. C. Plummer. Unusually wide connected and concise coverage of nearly every significant branch of dynamical astronomy, stressing basic principles throughout: determination of orbits, planetary theory, lunar theory, precession and nutation, and many of their applications. Hundreds of formulas and theorems worked out completely, important methods thoroughly explained. Covers motion under a central attraction, orbits of double stars and spectroscopic binaries, the libration of the moon, and much more. Index. 8 diagrams. xxi + 343pp. 5⅝ x 8⅜.
S689 Paperbound **$2.35**

AN INTRODUCTORY TREATISE ON THE LUNAR THEORY, E. W. Brown. Indispensable for all scientists and engineers interested in orbital calculation, satellites, or navigation of space. Only work in English to explain in detail 5 major mathematical approaches to the problem of 3 bodies, those of Laplace, de Pontécoulant, Hansen, Delaunay, and Hill. Covers expressions for mutual attraction, equations of motion, forms of solution, variations of the elements in disturbed motion, the constants and their interpretations, planetary and other disturbing influences, etc. Index. Bibliography. Tables. xvi + 292pp. 5⅝ x 8⅜.
S666 Paperbound **$2.00**

SPHERICAL AND PRACTICAL ASTRONOMY, W. Chauvenet. First book in English to apply mathematical techniques to astronomical problems is still standard work. Covers almost entire field, rigorously, with over 300 examples worked out. Vol. 1, spherical astronomy, applications to nautical astronomy; determination of hour angles, parallactic angle for known stars; interpolation; parallax; laws of refraction; predicting eclipses; precession, nutation of fixed stars; etc. Vol. 2, theory, use, of instruments; telescope; measurement of arcs, angles in general; electro-chronograph; sextant, reflecting circles; zenith telescope; etc. 100-page appendix of detailed proof of Gauss' method of least squares. 5th revised edition. Index. 15 plates, 20 tables. 1340pp. 5⅜ x 8.
Vol. 1 S618 Paperbound **$2.75**
Vol. 2 S619 Paperbound **$2.75**
The set **$5.50**

RADIATIVE TRANSFER, S. Chandrasekhar. Definitive work in field provides foundation for analysis of stellar atmospheres, planetary illumination, sky radiation; to physicists, a study of problems analogous to those in theory of diffusion of neutrons. Partial contents: equation of transfer, isotropic scattering, H-functions, diffuse reflection and transmission, Rayleigh scattering, X, Y functions, radiative equilibrium of stellar atmospheres. Extensive bibliography. 3 appendices. 35 tables. 35 figures. 407pp. 5⅝ x 8⅜.
S599 Paperbound **$2.25**

History and classics

STAR NAMES AND THEIR MEANINGS, Richard Hinckley Allen. An unusual book documenting the various attributions of names to the individual stars over the centuries. Here is a treasure-house of information on a topic not normally delved into even by professional astronomers; provides a fascinating background to the stars in folk-lore, literary references, ancient writings, star catalogs and maps over the centuries. Constellation-by-constellation analysis covers hundreds of stars and other asterisms, including the Pleiades, Hyades, Andromedan Nebula, etc. Introduction. Indices. List of authors and authorities. xx + 563pp. 5⅜ x 8½. T1079 Paperbound **$2.35**

A HISTORY OF ASTRONOMY FROM THALES TO KEPLER, J. L. E. Dreyer. (Formerly A HISTORY OF PLANETARY SYSTEMS FROM THALES TO KEPLER.) This is the only work in English to give the complete history of man's cosmological views from prehistoric times to Kepler and Newton. Partial contents: Near Eastern astronomical systems, Early Greeks, Homocentric Spheres of Eudoxus, Epicycles, Ptolemaic system, medieval cosmology, Copernicus, Kepler, etc. Revised, foreword by W. H. Stahl. New bibliography. xvii + 430pp. 5⅜ x 8. S79 Paperbound **$2.25**

A SHORT HISTORY OF ASTRONOMY, A. Berry. Popular standard work for over 50 years, this thorough and accurate volume covers the science from primitive times to the end of the 19th century. After the Greeks and the Middle Ages, individual chapters analyze Copernicus, Brahe, Galileo, Kepler, and Newton, and the mixed reception of their discoveries. Post-Newtonian achievements are then discussed in unusual detail: Halley, Bradley, Lagrange, Laplace, Herschel, Bessel, etc. 2 Indexes. 104 illustrations, 9 portraits. xxxi + 440pp. 5⅜ x 8. T210 Paperbound **$2.00**

THREE COPERNICAN TREATISES, translated with notes by Edward Rosen. 3 papers available nowhere else in English: "The Commentariolus" and "Letter against Werner" of Copernicus; the "Narratio prima" of Rheticus. The "Commentariolus" is Copernicus's most lucid exposition of his system. The "Letter against Werner" throws light on development of Copernicus's thought. The "Narratio prima" is earliest printed presentation of the new astronomy. "Educational and enjoyable," Astrophysical Journal. Corrected edition. Biographical introduction. 877-item bibliography of virtually every book, article, on Copernicus published 1939-1958. Index. 19 illustrations. 218pp. 5⅜ x 8. S585 Paperbound **$2.00**

Prices subject to change without notice.

Dover publishes books on art, music, philosophy, literature, languages, history, social sciences, psychology, handcrafts, orientalia, puzzles and entertainments, chess, pets and gardens, books explaining science, intermediate and higher mathematics, mathematical physics, engineering, biological sciences, earth sciences, classics of science, etc. Write to:

Dept. catrr.
Dover Publications, Inc.
180 Varick Street, N.Y. 14, N.Y.